PEARSON CUSTOM LIBRARY

The Atmosphere and Maritime Weather

PEARSON

Cover Art: Courtesy of Photodisc/Getty Images, Photoubrary.com, Robert Harding World Imagery, Getty Images/Photodisc.

Attention bookstores: For permission to return any unsold stock, contact us at *pe-uscustomreturns@pearson.com*.

Pearson Learning Solutions, 501 Boylston Street, Suite 900, Boston, MA 02116
A Pearson Education Company
www.pearsoned.com

Printed in the United States of America
15 16

ISBN 10: 0-558-61898-7
ISBN 13: 978-0-558-61898-8

Table of Contents

Introduction to the Atmosphere

Weather clearly influences our lives a great deal. The United States has a great variety of weather. (Shutterstock)

Weather influences our everyday activities, our jobs, and our health and comfort. Many of us pay little attention to the weather unless we are inconvenienced by it or when it adds to our enjoyment of outdoor activities (Figure 1). Nevertheless, there are few other aspects of our physical environment that affect our lives more than the phenomena we collectively call the weather.

The United States occupies an area that stretches from the tropics to the Arctic Circle. It has thousands of miles of coastline and extensive regions that are far from the influence of the ocean. Some landscapes are mountainous, and others are dominated by plains. It is a place where Pacific storms strike the West Coast, while the East is sometimes influenced by events in the Atlantic and the Gulf of Mexico. For those in the center of the country, it is common to experience weather events triggered when frigid southward-bound Canadian air masses clash with northward-moving tropical ones.

Stories about weather are a routine part of the daily news. Articles and items about the effects of heat, cold, floods, drought, fog, snow, ice, and strong winds are commonplace. Globally, storms of all kinds are frequently front-page news. For example, in January 2008, severe winter weather in China, the worst in 50 years, affected millions of people (Figure 2a). A few months later, Cyclone Nargis brought death and destruction to China's neighbor, Myanmar (Figure 2b).* Mean-

*In Asia, the term *cyclone* is used instead of the term *hurricane*. The country of Myanmar is also known as Burma.

while, the United States was experiencing its usual variety of newsworthy weather events. On February 5 and 6, 2008, devastating tornadoes hit portions of the South and lower Ohio Valley. It was the deadliest outbreak in 23 years—more than 80 tornadoes took 59 lives (Figure 2c). June 2008 saw record-breaking floods in many parts of the Midwest. Then, as summer came to a close, hurricane season heated up. Millions of people were evacuated from vulnerable areas along the Gulf Coast with the approach of Hurricane Gustav, and two weeks later, Hurricane Ike. Damages were in the tens of billions of dollars.

Memorable weather events occur everywhere on our planet. The United States likely has the greatest variety of weather of any country in the world. Severe weather events such as tornadoes, flash floods, and intense thunderstorms, as well as hurricanes and blizzards, are collectively more frequent and more damaging in the United States than in any other nation. Beyond its direct impact on the lives of individuals, the weather has a strong effect on the world economy, by influencing agriculture, energy use, water resources, transportation, and industry.

FIGURE 1   Few aspects of our physical environment influence our daily lives more than the weather. (Photo by Shutterstock)

FIGURE 2 Weather events are frequently front-page news. (a) Workers repairing high voltage towers in China's Hunan Province in February 2008. Severe winter weather, the worst in 50 years, paralyzed parts of the country. Frigid temperatures, coupled with heavy snow and ice affected more than 78 million people, and was blamed for 60 fatalities. The adverse winter conditions destroyed about 107,000 homes, and damaged 400,000 others. Highways, railways, and airports were paralyzed, stranding hundreds of thousands of travelers. (Imaginechina/AP Images) (b) Cyclone Nargis devastated the low-lying delta region of Myanmar (Burma) in May 2008. More than 100 thousand people died and nearly 2 million were left homeless. (AP Photo) (c) Damage near Lafayette. Tennessee from one of the dozens of tornadoes that struck the South on February 5–6, 2008. It was the deadliest tornado outbreak in the United States in 23 years. (Frederick Breedon/AP Photo)

(a)

(b)

(c)

Weather clearly influences our lives a great deal. Yet it is also important to realize that people influence the atmosphere and its behavior as well (Figure 3). There are, and will continue to be, significant political and scientific decisions to make involving these impacts. Answers to questions regarding air pollution and its control and the effects of various emissions on global climate and the atmosphere's ozone layer are important examples. So there is a need for increased awareness and understanding of our atmosphere and its behavior.

Meteorology, Weather, and Climate

 Introduction to the Atmosphere
▶ **Weather and Climate**

Meteorology is the scientific study of the atmosphere and the phenomena that we usually refer to as *weather*. Along with geology, oceanography, and astronomy, meteorology is considered one of the *Earth sciences*—the sciences that seek to understand our planet. It is important to point out that there are not strict boundaries among the Earth sciences; there are many situations in which these sciences overlap. Moreover, all of the Earth sciences involve an understanding and application of knowledge and principles from physics, chemistry, and biology. You will see many examples of this fact in your study of meteorology.

FIGURE 3 Smoke bellows from a coal-fired electrical generating plant in New Delhi, India, in June 2008. Humans have a significant influence of the atmosphere and its behavior. (AP Photo/Gurindes Osan)

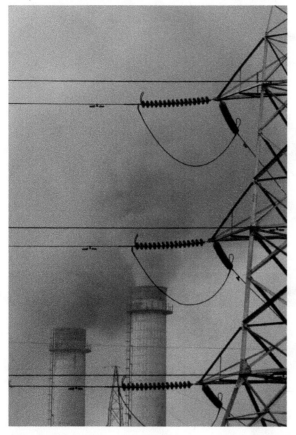

Acted on by the combined effects of Earth's motions and energy from the Sun, our planet's formless and invisible envelope of air reacts by producing an infinite variety of weather, which in turn creates the basic pattern of global climates. Although not identical, weather and climate have much in common.

Weather is constantly changing, sometimes from hour to hour and at other times from day to day. It is a term that refers to the state of the atmosphere at a given time and place. Whereas changes in the weather are continuous and sometimes seemingly erratic, it is nevertheless possible to arrive at a generalization of these variations. Such a description of aggregate weather conditions is termed **climate.** It is based on observations that have been accumulated over many decades. Climate is often defined simply as "average weather," but this is an inadequate definition. In order to accurately portray the character of an area, variations and extremes must also be included, as well as the probabilities that such departures will take place. For example, it is not only necessary for farmers to know the average rainfall during the growing season, but it is also important to know the frequency of extremely wet and extremely dry years. Thus, climate is the sum of all statistical weather information that helps describe a place or region.

Maps similar to the one in Figure 4 are familiar to everyone who checks the weather report in the morning newspaper or on a local television station. In addition to showing predicted high temperatures for the day, this map shows other basic weather information about cloud cover, precipitation, and fronts.

Suppose you were planning a vacation trip to an unfamiliar place. You would probably want to know what kind of weather to expect. Such information would help as you selected clothes to pack and could influence decisions regarding activities you might engage in during your stay. Unfortunately, weather forecasts that go beyond a few days are not very dependable. Thus, it would not be possible to get a reliable weather report about the conditions you are likely to encounter during your vacation.

Instead, you might ask someone who is familiar with the area about what kind of weather to expect. "Are thunderstorms common?" "Does it get cold at night?" "Are the

Students Sometimes Ask . . .

Does meteorology have anything to do with meteors?

Yes, there is a connection. Most people use the word "meteor" when referring to solid particles (meteoroids) that enter Earth's atmosphere from space and "burn up" due to friction ("shooting stars"). The term "meteorology" was coined in 340 BC when the Greek philosopher Aristotle wrote a book entitled *Meteorlogica,* which included explanations of atmospheric and astronomical phenomena. In Aristotle's day *anything* that fell from or was seen in the sky was called a meteor. Today we distinguish between particles of ice or water in the atmosphere (called *hydrometeors*) and extraterrestrial objects called meteoroids or "meteors."

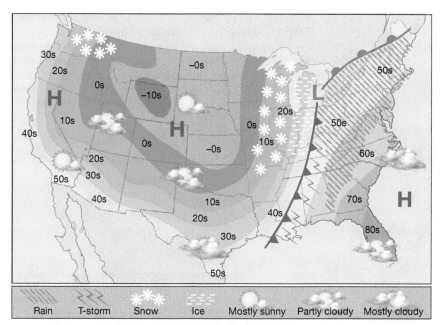

| Rain | T-storm | Snow | Ice | Mostly sunny | Partly cloudy | Mostly cloudy |

FIGURE 4 A typical newspaper weather map for a day in late December. The color bands show the high temperatures forecast for the day.

afternoons sunny?" What you are seeking is information about the climate, the conditions that are typical for that place. Another useful source of such information is the great variety of climate tables, maps, and graphs that are available. For example, the map in Figure 5 shows the average percentage of possible sunshine in the United States for the month of November, whereas the graph in Figure 6 shows average daily high and low temperatures for each month, as well as extremes, for New York City.

Such information could, no doubt, help as you planned your trip. But it is important to realize that *climate data cannot predict the weather*. Although the place may usually (climatically) be warm, sunny, and dry during the time of your planned vacation, you may actually experience cool, overcast, and rainy weather. There is a well-known saying that summarizes this idea: "Climate is what you expect, but weather is what you get."

The nature of both weather and climate is expressed in terms of the same basic **elements**, those quantities or properties that are measured regularly. The most important are (1) the temperature of the air, (2) the humidity of the air, (3) the type and amount of cloudiness, (4) the type and amount of precipitation, (5) the pressure exerted by the air, and (6) the speed and direction of the wind. These elements constitute the variables by which weather patterns and climate types are depicted. Although you will study these elements separately at first, keep in mind that they are very much interrelated. A

change in one of the elements often produces changes in the others.

Atmospheric Hazards: Assault by the Elements

Natural hazards are a part of living on Earth. Every day they adversely affect literally millions of people worldwide and are responsible for staggering damages. Some, such as earthquakes and volcanic eruptions, are geological. But a greater number are related to the atmosphere.

Occurrences of severe weather have a fascination that ordinary weather phenomena cannot provide. A spectacular lightning display generated by a severe thunderstorm can elicit both awe and fear (Figure 7). Of course, hurricanes and tornadoes attract a great deal of much deserved attention. A single tornado outbreak or hurricane can cause billions of dollars in property damage, much human suffering, and many deaths. For example, the four hurricanes that struck the United States in August and September 2004 collectively caused more than $40 billion in damages and 152 deaths. These figures were surpassed in 2005 when Hurricane Katrina struck. Estimates for this single storm are staggering. Although imprecise, the final accounting exceeds $130 billion, with more than 1800 deaths.

FIGURE 5 Mean percentage of possible sunshine for November. Southern Arizona is clearly the sunniest area. By contrast, parts of the Pacific Northwest receive a much smaller percentage of the possible sunshine. Climate maps such as this one are based on many years of data.

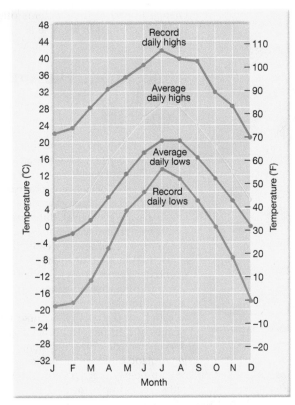

FIGURE 6 Graph showing daily temperature data for New York City. In addition to the average daily maximum and minimum temperatures for each month, extremes are also shown. As this graph shows, there can be significant departures from the average.

lars)! Table 1 lists the 25 "billion-dollar weather disasters" that occurred during the span 2002 through 2007. As you can see, although hurricanes, tornadoes, and floods stand out, cold, drought, heat waves, and hail also figure prominently.

Every day our planet experiences an incredible assault by the atmosphere, so it is important to develop an awareness and understanding of these significant weather events.

FIGURE 7 Many people have incorrect perceptions of weather dangers and are unaware of the relative differences of weather threats to human life. For example, they are awed by the threat of hurricanes and tornadoes and plan accordingly on how to respond (e.g. "Tornado Awareness Week" each spring), but they fail to realize that lightning or winter storms can be greater threats. (KEITH KENT/Peter Arnold)

In a typical year the United States experiences thousands of violent thunderstorms, hundreds of floods and tornadoes, and several hurricanes. According to the National Weather Service, during the 20-year span 1988–2007, tornadoes took an average of 54 lives each year, whereas hurricanes were responsible for 66 deaths. Surprisingly (to many), lightning was responsible for about as many deaths as tornadoes and flash floods were even deadlier. During the 1988–2007 period, lightning annually claimed 53 lives, and floods were responsible for an average of 81 fatalities each year.

Of course, there are other atmospheric hazards that adversely affect us. Some are storm-related, such as blizzards, hail, and freezing rain. Others are not the direct result of a storm. Heat waves, cold waves, and drought are important examples. In some years the loss of human life due to excessive heat or bitter cold exceeds that caused by all other weather events combined. Moreover, although severe storms and floods usually generate more attention, droughts can be just as devastating and carry an even bigger price tag.

Between 1980 and 2007 the United States experienced 78 weather-related disasters in which overall damages and costs reached or exceeded $1 billion (Figure 8). The combined costs of these events exceeded $600 billion (normalized to 2007 dol-

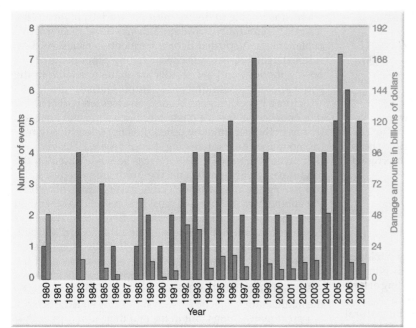

FIGURE 8 Between 1980 and 2007 the United States experienced 78 weather-related disasters in which overall damages and costs reached or exceeded $1 billion. This bar graph shows the number of events that occurred each year and the damage amounts in billions of dollars (normalized to 2007 dollars). The total losses for the 78 events exceeded $600 billion! (After NOAA)

TABLE 1 Billion-Dollar Weather Events 2002–2007*			
Event	**Date**	**Damage/Costs†**	**Fatalities**
Drought-Great Plains and East	Entire year 2007	$5 billion	Unknown
Western Wildfires (drought and high winds)	Summer-Fall 2007	$1 billion	12
Severe Freeze in East and Midwest	April 2007	$2 billion	0
Severe Storms and Tornadoes in East and South	April 2007	$1.5 billion	9
California Freeze	January 2007	$1.4 billion	1
Wildfires-Western states and Florida	Entire year 2006	$1 billion	28
Widespread Drought	Spring-Summer 2006	$6.2 billion	unknown
Northeast Floods	June 2006	$1 billion	20
Midwest/Southeast Tornadoes	April 2006	$1.5 billion	10
Midwest/Ohio Valley Tornadoes	April 2006	$1.1 billion	27
Severe Storms/Tornadoes in South/Southern Great Plains	March 2006	$1 billion	10
Hurricane Wilma	October 2005	$17.1 billion	35
Hurricane Rita	September 2005	$17.1 billion	19
Hurricane Katrina	August 2005	$134 billion	1833
Hurricane Dennis	July 2005	$2.1 billion	15
Midwest Drought	Spring-Summer 2005	$1.1 billion	0
Hurricane Jeanne	September 2004	$7.7 billion	28
Hurricane Ivan	September 2004	$15.4 billion	57
Hurricane Frances	September 2004	$9.9 billion	48
Hurricane Charley	August 2004	$16.5 billion	35
Southern California Wildfires (drought and winds)	October–November 2003	$2.8 billion	22
Hurricane Isabel	September 2003	$5.6 billion	55
Severe Storms and Tornadoes in Midwest and South	May 2003	$3.4 billion	51
Severe Storms and Hail in Midwest and South	April 2003	$1.6 billion	3
Drought in 30 states	Spring-Fall 2002	$10 billion	0
Western Fire Season (drought and winds)	Summer 2002	$2 billion	21

†To allow for more accurate comparison, dollar amounts are normalized to 2007.
*Source: National Climatic Data Center/NOAA.

The Nature of Scientific Inquiry

As members of a modern society, we are constantly reminded of the benefits derived from science. But what exactly is the nature of scientific inquiry? Developing an understanding of how science is done and how scientists work is important

All science is based on the assumption that the natural world behaves in a consistent and predictable manner that is comprehensible through careful, systematic study. The overall goal of science is to discover the underlying patterns in nature and then to use this knowledge to make predictions about what should or should not be expected, given certain facts or circumstances. For example, by understanding the processes and conditions that produce certain cloud types, meteorologists are often able to predict the approximate time and place of their formation.

The development of new scientific knowledge involves some basic logical processes that are universally accepted. To determine what is occurring in the natural world, scientists collect scientific *facts* through observation and measurement. Because some error is inevitable, the accuracy of a particular measurement or observation is always open to question. Nevertheless, these data are essential to science and serve as the springboard for the development of scientific theories.

Hypothesis

Once facts have been gathered and principles have been formulated to describe a natural phenomenon, investigators try to explain how or why things happen in the manner observed. They often do this by constructing a tentative (or untested) explanation, which is called a scientific **hypothesis** or **model**. (The term *model*, although often used synonymously with hypothesis, is a less precise term because it is sometimes used to describe a scientific theory as well.) It is best if an investigator can formulate more than one hypothesis to explain a given set of observations. If an individual

scientist is unable to devise multiple models, others in the scientific community will almost always develop alternative explanations. A spirited debate frequently ensues. As a result, extensive research is conducted by proponents of opposing models, and the results are made available to the wider scientific community in scientific journals.

Before a hypothesis can become an accepted part of scientific knowledge, it must pass objective testing and analysis. (If a hypothesis cannot be tested, it is not scientifically useful, no matter how interesting it might seem.) The verification process requires that *predictions* be made based on the model being considered and the predictions be tested by comparing them against objective observations of nature. Put another way, hypotheses must fit observations other than those used to formulate them in the first place. Those hypotheses that fail rigorous testing are ultimately discarded. The history of science is littered with discarded hypotheses. One of the best known is the Earth-centered model of the universe—a proposal that was supported by the apparent daily motion of the Sun, Moon, and stars around Earth. As the mathematician Jacob Bronowski so ably stated, "Science is a great many things, but in the end they all return to this: Science is the acceptance of what works and the rejection of what does not."

Theory

When a hypothesis has survived extensive scrutiny and when competing models have been eliminated, a hypothesis may be elevated to the status of a scientific **theory.** In everyday language we may say, "That's only a theory." But a scientific theory is a well-tested and widely accepted view that the scientific community agrees best explains certain observable facts.

Scientific theories, like scientific hypotheses, are accepted only provisionally. It is always possible that a theory that has withstood previous testing may eventually be modified or completely disproved. As theories survive more testing, they are regarded with higher levels of confidence. Theories that have withstood extensive testing, such as the theory of plate tectonics and the theory of evolution, are held with a very high degree of confidence. Theories of this stature that are comprehensive in scope have a special status. They are called **paradigms** because they explain a large number of interrelated aspects of the natural world.

Scientific Methods

The processes just described, in which scientists gather facts through observations and formulate scientific hypotheses and theories, is called the *scientific method.* Contrary to popular belief, the scientific method is not a standard recipe that scientists apply in a routine manner to unravel the secrets of our natural world. Rather, it is an endeavor that involves creativity and insight. Rutherford and Ahlgren put it this way: "Inventing hypotheses or theories to imagine how the world works and then figuring out how they can be put to the test of reality is as creative as writing poetry, composing music, or designing skyscrapers."*

There is no fixed path that scientists always follow that leads unerringly to scientific knowledge. Nevertheless, many scientific investigations involve the following steps: (1) collection of scientific facts (data) through observation and measurement (Figure 9); (2) development of one or more working hypotheses or models to explain these facts; (3) development of observations and experiments to test the hypotheses; and (4) the acceptance, modification, or rejection of the hypotheses based on extensive testing.

Other scientific discoveries may result from purely theoretical ideas that stand up to extensive examination. Some researchers use high-speed computers to simulate what is happening in the "real" world. These models are useful when dealing with natural processes that occur on very long time scales, or take place in extreme or inaccessible locations. Still

*F. James Rutherford and Andrew Ahlgren, *Science for All Americans* (New York: Oxford University Press, 1990), p. 7.

FIGURE 9 Gathering data is a basic part of the scientific method. This Automated Surface Observing System (ASOS) installation is one of nearly 900 in use for data gathering as part of the U.S. primary surface observing network. (Source: Bobbe Christopherson)

Students Sometimes Ask . . .

In class you compared a hypothesis to a theory. How is each one different from a scientific law?

A *scientific law* is a basic principle that describes a particular behavior of nature that is generally narrow in scope and can be stated briefly—often as a simple mathematical equation. Because scientific laws have been shown time and time again to be consistent with observations and measurements, they are rarely discarded. Laws may, however, require modifications to fit new findings. For example, Newton's laws of motion are still useful for everyday applications (NASA uses them to calculate satellite trajectories), but they do not work at velocities approaching the speed of light. For these circumstances, they have been supplanted by Einstein's theory of relativity.

other scientific advancements have been made when a totally unexpected happening occurred during an experiment. These serendipitous discoveries are more than pure luck; for as Louis Pasteur stated, "In the field of observation, chance favors only the prepared mind."

Scientific knowledge is acquired through several avenues, so it might be best to describe the nature of scientific inquiry as the *methods* of science rather than *the* scientific method. In addition, it should always be remembered that even the most compelling scientific theories are still simplified explanations of the natural world.

Observing the Atmosphere

Scientific study of the atmosphere began in the seventeenth century as instruments were developed to measure different elements. The instruments provided data that helped observers begin to gain an understanding of atmospheric processes. In 1593 Galileo invented an early version of the thermometer (Figure 10), and in 1643 Torricelli built the first barometer (for measuring air pressure). By 1661 Robert Boyle discovered the basic relationship between pressure and volume in a gas. During the eighteenth century, instruments were improved and standardized, and extensive data collection began. The acquisition of such data was fundamental to the study of physical processes and the development of explanations about atmospheric phenomena.

High-Altitude Observations

It became obvious to those studying the atmosphere that gathering data from only ground-level sites significantly limited understanding. In the late 1700s the only data for conditions at high altitudes came from observations made in the mountains. In 1752 Benjamin Franklin, using a kite, made his famous discovery that lightning is an electrical discharge. Not

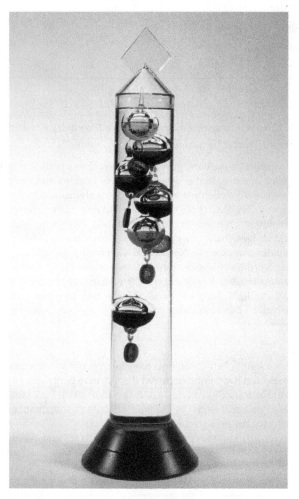

FIGURE 10 This thermometer is based on an instrument called a *thermoscope* that was invented by Galileo in the late 1500s. Today such devices, which are fairly accurate, are used mostly for decoration. The instrument is made of a sealed glass cylinder containing a clear liquid and a series of glass bulbs of different densities that can "float" up and down. (Frank Labua, Pearson Education)

atmosphere (Figure 11b). Radiosondes are sent aloft twice daily from an extensive network of stations worldwide. The data that they supply are essential for making accurate weather forecasts.

Other important means for exploring the atmosphere include rockets and airplanes. After World War II, rockets revolutionized the study of the upper atmosphere. Prior to this time, knowledge of the atmosphere beyond about 30 kilometers (20 miles) came almost exclusively from indirect ground-based measurements. Airplanes also play a significant role in atmospheric studies. High-flying aircraft are capable of reaching portions of the stratosphere. Others are designed to measure such relatively small-scale yet complex phenomena as cloud systems or to fly directly into hurricanes to monitor their current state of development (Figure 12).

Weather Radar and Satellites

Among the methods of studying the atmosphere that are best known to the general public and most useful to atmospheric scientists are weather radar and satellites. Today, when we watch a television weather report, we expect to see satellite images that show moving cloud patterns and radar displays that depict the intensity and regional extent of precipitation (Figure 13). Recent technological advances greatly enhance the value of weather radar for the purpose of storm detection, warning, and research. Meteorological satellites give us a perspective of the atmosphere that is unique and invaluable. For example, they provide images that allow us to study the distribution of clouds and the circulation patterns that they reveal. Moreover, they let us see the structure and determine the speed of weather systems over the oceans and other regions where observations are scanty or nonexistent. One obvious benefit is that storms can be detected early and tracked with great precision.

In addition to enabling us to monitor storms from space, instruments aboard modern satellites permit us to measure and monitor many variables including winds, solar radiation, temperatures, precipitation, and changes in atmostpheric

many years later, kites were being used to observe temperatures above the surface. In the late eighteenth century, manned balloons were used in an attempt to investigate the composition and properties of the "upper" atmosphere. Although several manned ascents were attempted over the years, they were dangerous undertakings. Unmanned balloons, on the other hand, could rise to higher altitudes, but there was no assurance that the instruments carried aloft would be recovered. Notwithstanding the difficulties and dangers, considerable data were gathered on the nature of the air above.

Today balloons continue to play a significant role in the systematic investigation of the atmosphere. Giant balloons are launched regularly, primarily for research purposes (Figure 11a). Such balloons can stay aloft for extended periods and represent an important means of carrying monitoring instruments into the region of the atmosphere known as the stratosphere.

Since the late 1920s balloons have carried aloft **radiosondes.** These lightweight packages of instruments are fitted with radio transmitters that send back data on temperature, pressure, and relative humidity in the lower portions of the

(a)

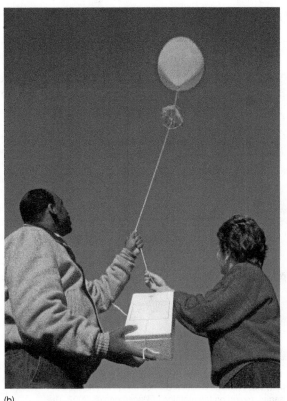

(b)

FIGURE 11 Exploring the atmosphere using balloons. (a) Giant balloons such as this one are filled with helium and carry instrument packages high into the atmosphere. (Source: University Corporation for Atmospheric Research/National Center for Atmospheric Research/National Science Foundation) (b) A lightweight package of instruments, the radiosonde, is carried aloft by a small weather balloon. (Photo by Mark Burnett/Photo Researchers, Inc.)

composition. Box 1 briefly describes one of these modern research satellites, the *Tropical Rainfall Measuring Mission (TRMM)*. Moreover, data relating to phenomena such as wind patterns over the oceans, the extent of sea ice and glaciers, ocean currents, vegetative cover, and many other variables are gathered from space.

Earth's Spheres

A view such as the one in Figure 14a provided the *Apollo 8* astronauts as well as the rest of humanity with a unique perspective of our home. Seen from space, Earth is breathtaking in its beauty and startling in its solitude. Such an image

FIGURE 12 Aircraft reconnaissance is one important source of information about hurricanes. Specially instrumented aircraft can fly directly into a storm and accurately measure details regarding its current state of development. (Photo by National Hurricane Center/NOAA)

FIGURE 13 Radar images show the distribution and intensity of precipitation. This National Weather Service image shows the St. Louis, Missouri, region on the morning of December 18, 2002. The unusual spring-like weather included heavy rain, severe thunderstorms, and a tornado watch. (National Weather Service)

reminds us that our home is, after all, a planet—small, self-contained, and in some ways even fragile.

As we look closely at our planet from space, it becomes apparent that Earth is much more than rock and soil. In fact, the most conspicuous features in Figure 14a are not continents but swirling clouds suspended above the surface of the vast global ocean. These features emphasize the importance of water on our planet.

The closer view of Earth from space shown in Figure 14b helps us appreciate why the physical environment is traditionally divided into three major parts: the solid Earth, the water portion of our planet, and Earth's gaseous envelope.

It should be emphasized that our environment is highly integrated and is not dominated by rock, water, or air alone. It is instead characterized by continuous interactions as air comes in contact with rock, rock with water, and water with air. Moreover, the biosphere, the totality of life forms on our planet, extends into each of the three physical realms and is an equally integral part of the planet.

The interactions among Earth's four spheres are incalculable. Figure 15 provides us with one easy-to-visualize example. The shoreline is an obvious meeting place for rock, water, and air. In this scene, ocean waves that were created by the

FIGURE 14 (a) View that greeted the *Apollo 8* astronauts as their spacecraft emerged from behind the Moon. (NASA Headquarters) (b) Africa and Arabia are prominent in this image of Earth taken from *Apollo 17*. The tan cloud-free zones over the land coincide with major desert regions. The band of clouds across central Africa is associated with a much wetter climate that in places sustains tropical rain forests. The dark blue of the oceans and the swirling cloud patterns remind us of the importance of the oceans and the atmosphere. Antarctica, a continent covered by glacial ice, is visible at the South Pole. (Courtesy of NASA/Science Source/Photo Researchers, Inc.)

(a)

(b)

FIGURE 15 The shoreline is one obvious example of an *interface*—a common boundary where different parts of a system interact. In this scene, ocean waves (*hydrosphere*) that were created by the force of moving air (*atmosphere*) break against a rocky shore (*geosphere*). (Photo by Insuratelu Gabriela Gianina/Shutterstock)

drag of air moving across the water are breaking against the rocky shore. The force of the water can be powerful, and the erosional work that is accomplished can be great.

On a human scale Earth is huge. Its surface area occupies 500,000,000 square kilometers (193 million square miles). We divide this vast planet into four independent parts. Because each part loosely occupies a shell around Earth, we call them spheres. The four spheres include the *geosphere* (solid Earth), the *atmosphere* (gaseous envelope), the *hydrosphere* (water portion), and the *biosphere* (life). It is important to remember that these spheres are not separated by well-defined boundaries; rather, each sphere is intertwined with all of the others. In addition, each of Earth's four major spheres can be thought of as being composed of numerous interrelated parts.

The Geosphere

Lying beneath the atmosphere and the ocean is the solid Earth or **geosphere.** The geosphere extends from the surface to the center of the planet, a depth of about 6400 kilometers (nearly 4000 miles), making it by far the largest of Earth's four spheres.

Based on compositional differences, the geosphere is divided into three principal regions: the dense inner sphere, called the *core;* the less dense *mantle;* and the *crust,* which is the light and very thin outer skin of Earth.

Soil, the thin veneer of material at Earth's surface that supports the growth of plants, may be thought of as part of all four spheres. The solid portion is a mixture of weathered rock debris (geosphere) and organic matter from decayed plant and animal life (biosphere). The decomposed and disintegrated rock debris is the product of weathering processes that require air (atmosphere) and water (hydrosphere). Air and water also occupy the open spaces between the solid particles.

The Atmosphere

Earth is surrounded by a life-giving gaseous envelope called the **atmosphere.** When we watch a high-flying jet plane cross the sky, it seems that the atmosphere extends upward for a great distance (Figure 16). However, when compared to the thickness (radius) of the solid Earth (about 6400 kilometers or 4000 miles), the atmosphere is a very shallow layer. More than 99 percent of the atmosphere is within 30 kilometers (20 miles) of Earth's surface. This thin blanket of air is nevertheless an integral part of the planet. It not only provides the air that we breathe but also acts to protect us from the dangerous radiation emitted by the Sun. The energy exchanges that continually occur between the atmosphere and Earth's surface and between the atmosphere and space produce the effects we call *weather.* If, like the Moon, Earth had no atmosphere, our planet would not only be lifeless, but many of the processes and interactions that make the surface such a dynamic place could not operate.

BOX 1 ▶ MONITORING EARTH FROM SPACE

Scientific facts are gathered in many ways, including laboratory experiments and field observations and measurements. Satellites provide another very important source of data. Satellite images give us perspectives that are difficult to gain from more traditional sources (Figure A). Moreover, the high-tech instruments aboard many satellites enable scientists to gather information from remote regions where data are otherwise scarce.

The image in Figure B is from NASA's *Tropical Rainfall Measuring Mission* (TRMM). TRMM is a research satellite designed to expand our understanding of Earth's water (hydrologic) cycle and its role in our climate system. By covering the region between the latitudes 35°N and 35°S, it provides much needed data on rainfall and the heat release associated with rainfall. Many types of measurements and images are possible.

FIGURE A Hurricane Rita approaching the Texas-Louisiana coast about midday on September 22, 2005. It was the third most powerful Atlantic basin storm ever measured. (NASA)

FIGURE 16 This jet is flying high in the atmosphere at an altitude of more than 9000 meters (30,000 feet). More than two-thirds of the atmosphere is below this height. To someone on the ground, the atmosphere seems to extend for a great distance. However, when compared to the thickness (radius) of the solid Earth, the atmosphere is a very shallow layer. (Photo by Warren Faidley/Weatherstock.)

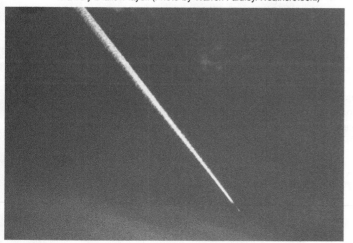

The Hydrosphere

Earth is sometimes called the *blue planet*. Water more than anything else makes Earth unique. The **hydrosphere** is a dynamic mass that is continually on the move, evaporating from the oceans to the atmosphere, precipitating to the land, and running back to the ocean again. The global ocean is certainly the most prominent feature of the hydrosphere, blanketing nearly 71 percent of Earth's surface to an average depth of about 3800 meters (12,500 feet). It accounts for about 97 percent of Earth's water (Figure 17). However, the hydrosphere also includes the fresh water found in clouds, streams, lakes, and glaciers, as well as that found underground.

Although these latter sources constitute just a tiny fraction of the total, they are much more important than their meager percentage indicates. Clouds, of course, play a vital role in many weather and climate processes. In addition to providing the fresh water that is so vital to life on the land, streams, glaciers, and groundwater are responsible for sculpturing and creating many of our planet's varied landforms.

Instruments aboard the *TRMM* satellite have greatly expanded our ability to collect precipitation data. In addition to data for land areas, this satellite provides extremely precise measurements of rainfall over the oceans where conventional land-based instruments cannot see. This is especially important because much of Earth's rain falls in ocean-covered tropical areas, and a great deal of the globe's weather-producing energy comes from heat exchanges involved in the rainfall process. Until the *TRMM*, information on the intensity and amount of rainfall over the tropics was scanty. Such data are crucial to understanding and predicting global climate change.

FIGURE B This map of rainfall for December 7–13, 2004, in Malaysia was constructed using *TRMM* data. Over 800 millimeters (32 inches) of rain fell along the east coast of the peninsula (darkest red area). The extraordinary rains caused extensive flooding and triggered many mudflows. (NASA/*TRMM* image)

The Biosphere

The **biosphere** includes all life on Earth. Ocean life is concentrated in the sunlit surface waters of the sea. Most life on land is also concentrated near the surface, with tree roots and burrowing animals reaching a few meters underground and flying insects and birds reaching a kilometer or so above the surface. A surprising variety of life forms are also adapted to extreme environments. For example, on the ocean floor, where pressures are extreme and no light penetrates, there are places where vents spew hot, mineral-rich fluids that support communities of exotic life forms. On land, some bacteria thrive in rocks as deep as 4 kilometers (2.5 miles) and in boiling hot springs. Moreover, air currents can carry microorganisms many kilometers into the atmosphere. But even when we consider these extremes, life still must be thought of as being confined to a narrow band very near Earth's surface.

Plants and animals depend on the physical environment for the basics of life. However, organisms do more than just respond to their physical environment. Through countless interactions, life forms help maintain and alter their physical environment. Without life, the makeup and nature of the geosphere, hydrosphere, and atmosphere would be very different.

Earth as a System

Anyone who studies Earth soon learns that our planet is a dynamic body with many separate but highly interactive parts or *spheres*. The atmosphere, hydrosphere, biosphere, and geosphere and all of their components can be studied separately. However, the parts are not isolated. Each is related in some way to the others to produce a complex and continuously interacting whole that we call the *Earth system*.

Earth System Science

A simple example of the interactions among different parts of the Earth system occurs every winter as moisture evaporates from the Pacific Ocean and subsequently falls as rain in the

FIGURE 17 Distribution of Earth's water. Obviously most of Earth's water is in the oceans. Glacial ice represents about 85 percent of all the water *outside* the oceans. When only *liquid freshwater* is considered, more than 90 percent is groundwater. (Glacier photo by Bernhard Edmaier/Photo Researchers; stream photo by E.J. Tarbuck; and ground water photo by Michael Collier)

hills of southern California, triggering destructive landslides (Figure 18). The processes that move water from the hydrosphere to the atmosphere and then to the solid Earth have a profound impact on the plants and animals (including humans) that inhabit the affected regions.

Scientists have recognized that in order to more fully understand our planet, they must learn how its individual components (land, water, air, and life forms) are interconnected. This endeavor, called *Earth system science*, aims to study Earth as a *system* composed of numerous interacting parts, or *subsystems*. Using an interdisciplinary approach, those who practice Earth system science attempt to achieve the level of understanding necessary to comprehend and solve many of our global environmental problems.

What Is a System? Most of us hear and use the term *system* frequently. We may service our car's cooling *system*, make use of the city's transportation *system*, and be a participant in the political *system*. A news report might inform us of an approaching weather *system*. Further, we know that Earth is just a small part of a larger system known as the *solar system*, which in turn is a

subsystem of an even larger system called the Milky Way Galaxy.

Loosely defined, a **system** can be any size group of interacting parts that form a complex whole. Most natural systems are driven by sources of energy that move matter and/or energy from one place to another. A simple analogy is a car's cooling system, which contains a liquid (usually water and antifreeze) that is driven from the engine to the radiator and back again. The role of this system is to transfer heat generated by combustion in the engine to the radiator, where moving air removes it from the system. Hence, the term cooling system.

Systems like a car's cooling system are self-contained with regard to matter and are called **closed systems.** Although energy moves freely in and out of a closed system, no matter (liquid in the case of our auto's cooling system) enters or leaves the system. (This assumes you don't get a leak in your radiator). By contrast, most natural systems are **open systems** and are far more complicated than the foregoing example. In an open system both energy and matter flow into and out of the system. In a weather system such as a hurricane, factors such as the quantity of water vapor available for cloud formation, the amount of heat released by condensing water vapor, and the flow of air into and out of the storm can fluctuate a great deal. At times the storm may strengthen; at other times it may remain stable or weaken.

Feedback Mechanisms Most natural systems have mechanisms that tend to enhance change, as well as other mechanisms

FIGURE 18 This image provides an example of interactions among different parts of the Earth system. This deadly debris flow (popularly called a *mudslide* in the press) at La Conchita, California, in January 2005, was triggered by extraordinary rains that saturated the ground on this steep hillside. (Photo by David McNew/Getty Images)

that tend to resist change and thus stabilize the system. For example, when we get too hot, we perspire to cool down. This cooling phenomenon works to stabilize our body temperature and is referred to as a **negative feedback mechanism.** Negative feedback mechanisms work to maintain the system as it is or, in other words, to maintain the status quo. By contrast, mechanisms that enhance or drive change are called **positive feedback mechanisms.**

Most of Earth's systems, particularly the climate system, contain a wide variety of negative and positive feedback mechanisms. For example, substantial scientific evidence indicates that Earth has entered a period of global warming. One consequence of global warming is that many of the world's glaciers and ocean areas covered by sea ice are diminishing in size. Highly reflective snow- and ice-covered surfaces are gradually being replaced by brown soils, green trees, or blue oceans, all of which are darker, so they absorb more sunlight. The result is a positive feedback that contributes to the warming.

On the other hand, an increase in global temperature also causes greater evaporation of water from Earth's land-sea surface. One result of having more water vapor in the air is an increase in cloud cover. Because cloud tops are white and highly reflective, more sunlight is reflected back to space, which diminishes the amount of sunshine reaching Earth's surface and thus reduces global temperatures. Further, warmer temperatures tend to promote the growth of vegetation. Plants in turn remove carbon dioxide (CO_2) from the air. Since carbon dioxide is one of the atmosphere's *greenhouse gases,* its removal has a negative impact on global warming.*

In addition to natural processes, we must also consider the human element. The burning of fossil fuels (oil, natural gas, and coal) and the extensive cutting and clearing of the tropical rain forests result in an increase in atmospheric CO_2. It is highly likely that such activity has contributed to the increase in global temperature that our planet is experiencing. One of the daunting tasks for Earth system scientists is to predict what the climate will be like in the future by taking into account many variables, including technological changes, population trends, and the overall impact of the numerous competing positive and negative feedback mechanisms.

The Earth System

The Earth system has a nearly endless array of subsystems in which matter is recycled over and over again. One example that is described in Box 2 traces the movements of carbon among Earth's four spheres. It shows us, for example, that the carbon dioxide in the air and the carbon in living things and in certain sedimentary rocks is all part of a subsystem described by the *carbon cycle.*

*Greenhouse gases absorb heat energy emitted by Earth and thus help keep the atmosphere warm.

Cycles in the Earth System   A more familiar loop or subsystem is the *hydrologic cycle.* It represents the unending circulation of Earth's water among the hydrosphere, atmosphere, biosphere, and geosphere. Water enters the atmosphere by evaporation from Earth's surface and by transpiration from plants. Water vapor condenses in the atmosphere to form clouds, which in turn produce precipitation that falls back to Earth's surface. Some of the rain that falls onto the land sinks into the ground to be taken up by plants or become groundwater, and some flows across the surface toward the ocean.

Viewed over long spans, the rocks of the geosphere are constantly forming, changing, and reforming (Figure 19). The loop that involves the processes by which one rock changes to another is called the *rock cycle.* The cycles of the Earth system, such as the hydrologic and rock cycles, are not independent of one another. To the contrary, there are many places where they interact. A common boundary where different parts of a system come in contact and interact is known as an **interface.** For example, in Figure 19, weathering at the surface gradually disintegrates and decomposes solid rock. The work of gravity and running water may eventually move this material (sediment) to another place and deposit it. Later, groundwater percolating through the debris may leave behind mineral matter that cements the grains together into solid rock (a rock that is often very different from the rock with which we started). This changing of one rock into another could not have occurred without the movement of water through the hydrologic cycle. There are many places where one cycle or loop in the Earth system interfaces with and is a basic part of another.

Energy for the Earth System   The Earth system is powered by energy from two sources. The Sun drives external

FIGURE 19   Each part of the Earth system is related to every other part to produce a complex interacting whole. The Earth system involves many cycles, including the hydrologic cycle and the rock cycle. Such cycles are not independent of each other. There are many places where they interact.

BOX 2 ▶ THE CARBON CYCLE: ONE OF EARTH'S SUBSYSTEMS

To illustrate the movement of material and energy in the Earth system, let us take a brief look at the *carbon cycle* (Figure C). Pure carbon is relatively rare in nature. It is found predominantly in two minerals: diamond and graphite. Most carbon is bonded chemically to other elements to form compounds such as carbon dioxide, calcium carbonate, and the hydrocarbons found in coal and petroleum. Carbon is also the basic building block of life as it readily combines with hydrogen and oxygen to form the fundamental organic compounds that compose living things.

In the atmosphere, carbon is found mainly as carbon dioxide (CO_2). Atmospheric carbon dioxide is significant because it is a greenhouse gas, which means it is an efficient absorber of energy emitted by Earth and thus influences the heating of the atmosphere. Because many of the processes that operate on Earth involve carbon dioxide, this gas is constantly moving into and out of the atmosphere. For example, through the process of photosynthesis, plants absorb carbon dioxide from the atmosphere to produce the essential organic compounds needed for growth. Animals that consume these plants (or consume other animals that eat plants) use these organic compounds as a source of energy and, through the process of respiration, return carbon dioxide to the atmosphere. (Plants also return some CO_2 to the atmosphere via respiration.) Further, when plants die and decay or are burned, this biomass is oxidized, and carbon dioxide is returned to the atmosphere.

Not all dead plant material decays immediately back to carbon dioxide. A small percentage is deposited as sediment. Over long spans of geologic time, considerable biomass is buried with sediment. Under the right conditions, some of these carbon-rich deposits are converted to fossil fuels—coal, petroleum, or natural gas. Eventually some of the fuels are recovered (mined or pumped from a well) and burned to run

FIGURE C Simplified diagram of the carbon cycle, with emphasis on the flow of carbon between the atmosphere and the hydrosphere, geosphere, and biosphere. The colored arrows show whether the flow of carbon is into or out of the atmosphere.

processes that occur in the atmosphere, hydrosphere, and at Earth's surface. Weather and climate, ocean circulation, and erosional processes are driven by energy from the Sun. Earth's interior is the second source of energy. Heat remaining from when our planet formed, and heat that is continuously generated by decay of radioactive elements powers the internal processes that produce volcanoes, earthquakes, and mountains.

The Parts are Linked The parts of the Earth system are linked so that a change in one part can produce changes in any or all of the other parts. For example, when a volcano erupts, lava from Earth's interior may flow out at the surface and block a nearby valley. This new obstruction influences the region's drainage system by creating a lake or causing streams to change course. The large quantities of volcanic ash and gases that can be emitted during an eruption might be blown high into the atmosphere and influence the amount of solar energy that can reach Earth's surface. The result could be a drop in air temperatures over the entire hemisphere.

Where the surface is covered by lava flows or a thick layer of volcanic ash, existing soils are buried. This causes the soil-forming processes to begin anew to transform the new surface material into soil (Figure 20). The soil that eventually forms will reflect the interactions among many parts of the Earth system—the volcanic parent material, the climate, and the impact of biological activity. Of course, there would also be significant changes in the biosphere. Some organisms and their habitats would be eliminated by the lava and ash, whereas new settings for life, such as the lake, would be created. The potential climate change could also impact sensitive life forms.

The Earth system is characterized by processes that vary on spatial scales from fractions of millimeters to thousands of kilometers. Time scales for Earth's processes range from milliseconds to billions of years. As we learn about Earth, it becomes increasingly clear that despite significant separations in distance or time, many processes are connected, and a change in one component can influence the entire system.

factories and fuel our transportation system. One result of fossil-fuel combustion is the release of huge quantities of CO_2 into the atmosphere. Certainly one of the most active parts of the carbon cycle is the movement of CO_2 from the atmosphere to the biosphere and back again.

Carbon also moves from the geosphere and hydrosphere to the atmosphere and back again. For example, volcanic activity early in Earth's history is thought to be the source of much of the carbon dioxide found in the atmosphere. One way that carbon dioxide makes its way back to the hydrosphere and then to the solid Earth is by first combining with water to form carbonic acid (H_2CO_3), which then attacks the rocks that compose the geosphere. One product of this chemical weathering of solid rock is the soluble bicarbonate ion ($2 HCO_3^-$), which is carried by groundwater and streams to the ocean. Here water-dwelling organisms extract this dissolved material to produce hard parts of calcium carbonate ($CaCO_3$). When the organisms die, these skeletal remains settle to the ocean floor as biochemical sediment and become sedimentary rock. In fact, the geosphere is by far Earth's largest depository of carbon, where it is a constituent of a variety of rocks, the most abundant being limestone (Figure D). Eventually the limestone may be exposed at Earth's surface, where chemical weathering will cause the carbon stored in the rock to be released to the atmosphere as CO_2.

In summary, carbon moves among all four of Earth's major spheres. It is essential to every living thing in the biosphere. In the atmosphere carbon dioxide is an important greenhouse gas. In the hydrosphere, carbon dioxide is dissolved in lakes, rivers, and the ocean. In the geosphere, carbon is contained in carbonate-rich sediments and sedimentary rocks and is stored as organic matter dispersed through sedimentary rocks and as deposits of coal and petroleum.

FIGURE D A great deal of carbon is locked in Earth's geosphere. This rock sample is a form of limestone ($CaCO_3$) called coquina. The raw material for coquina is shell fragments. (Photo by E. J. Tarbuck)

←— 5 cm —→

Close up

Humans are *part of* the Earth system, a system in which the living and nonliving components are entwined and interconnected. Therefore, our actions produce changes in all of the other parts. When we burn gasoline and coal, dispose of our wastes, and clear the land, we cause other parts of the system to respond, often in unforeseen ways. Throughout this book you will learn about some of Earth's subsystems, including the hydrologic system and the climate system. Remember that these components *and we humans* are all part of the complex interacting whole we call the Earth system.

Composition of the Atmosphere

GE⬤De
ATMOSPHERE
Introduction to the Atmosphere
▶ A View of Earth

In the days of Aristotle, air was thought to be one of four fundamental substances that could not be further divided into constituent components. The other three substances were fire,

earth (soil), and water. Even today the term **air** is sometimes used as if it were a specific gas, which of course it is not. The envelope of air that surrounds our planet is a *mixture* of many discrete gases, each with its own physical properties, in which varying quantities of tiny solid and liquid particles are suspended.

Major Components

The composition of air is not constant; it varies from time to time and from place to place (see Box 3). If the water vapor, dust, and other variable components were removed from the atmosphere, we would find that its makeup is very stable up to an altitude of about 80 kilometers (50 miles).

As you can see in Figure 21, two gases—nitrogen and oxygen—make up 99 percent of the volume of clean, dry air. Although these gases are the most plentiful components of the atmosphere and are of great significance to life on Earth, they are of little or no importance in affecting weather phenomena. The remaining 1 percent of dry air is mostly the inert gas

FIGURE 20   When Mount St. Helens erupted in May 1980 (inset), the area shown here was buried by a volcanic mudflow. Now, plants are reestablished and new soil is forming. (Photo by Jack Dykinga/Inset photo by Corbis)

more than one-third remains in the air. Estimates project that by sometime in the second half of the twenty-first century, carbon dioxide levels will be twice as high as they were early in the twentieth century.

Most atmospheric scientists agree that increased carbon dioxide concentrations have contributed to a warming of Earth's atmosphere over the past several decades and will continue to do so in the decades to come. The magnitude of such temperature changes is uncertain and depends partly on the quantities of CO_2 contributed by human activities in the years ahead.

Variable Components

Air includes many gases and particles that vary significantly from time to time and place to place. Important examples include water vapor, dust particles, and ozone. Although usually present in small percentages, they can have significant effects on weather and climate.

Water Vapor   The amount of water vapor in the air varies considerably, from practically none at all up to about 4 percent by volume. Why is such a small fraction of the atmosphere so significant? Certainly the fact that water vapor is the source of all clouds and precipitation would be enough to explain its importance. However, water vapor has other roles. Like carbon dioxide, it has the ability to absorb heat given off by Earth, as well as some solar

argon (0.93 percent) plus tiny quantities of a number of other gases.

Carbon Dioxide

Carbon dioxide, although present in only minute amounts (0.0387 percent or 387 parts per million), is nevertheless a meteorologically important constituent of air. Carbon dioxide is of great interest to meteorologists because it is an efficient absorber of energy emitted by Earth and thus influences the heating of the atmosphere. Although the proportion of carbon dioxide in the atmosphere is relatively uniform, its percentage has been rising steadily for more than a century. Figure 22 is a graph showing the growth in atmospheric CO_2 since 1960. Much of this rise is attributed to the burning of ever increasing quantities of fossil fuels, such as coal and oil. Some of this additional carbon dioxide is absorbed by the waters of the ocean or is used by plants, but

FIGURE 21   Proportional volume of gases composing dry air. Nitrogen and oxygen obviously dominate.

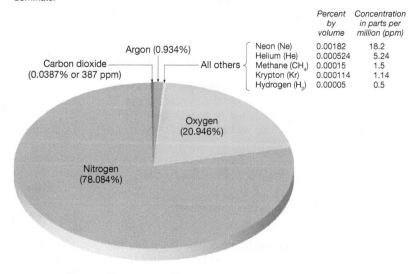

	Percent by volume	Concentration in parts per million (ppm)
Neon (Ne)	0.00182	18.2
Helium (He)	0.000524	5.24
Methane (CH$_4$)	0.00015	1.5
Krypton (Kr)	0.000114	1.14
Hydrogen (H$_2$)	0.00005	0.5

Argon (0.934%)

Carbon dioxide (0.0387% or 387 ppm)

All others

Oxygen (20.946%)

Nitrogen (78.084%)

BOX 3 ▶ EARTH'S ATMOSPHERE EVOLVES

Earth's atmosphere is unlike that of any other body in the solar system. No other planet exhibits the same life-sustaining mixture of gases as Earth. Today the air we breathe is a stable mixture of 78 percent nitrogen, almost 21 percent oxygen, about 1 percent argon (an inert gas), and trace gases like carbon dioxide and water vapor. But our planet's original atmosphere, several billion years ago, was far different.

Earth's very earliest atmosphere probably was swept into space by the *solar wind*, a vast stream of particles emitted by the Sun. As Earth slowly cooled, a more enduring atmosphere formed. The molten surface solidified into a crust, and gases that had been dissolved in the molten rock were gradually released, a process called *outgassing*. Outgassing continues today from hundreds of active volcanoes worldwide. Thus, geologists hypothesize that Earth's original atmosphere was made up of gases similar to those released in volcanic emissions today: water vapor, carbon dioxide, nitrogen, and several trace gases.

As the planet continued to cool, the water vapor condensed to form clouds, and great rains commenced. At first the water evaporated in the hot air before reaching the ground, or quickly boiled away upon contacting the surface, just like water sprayed on a hot grill. This accelerated the cooling of Earth's crust. When the surface had cooled below water's boiling point (100°C, or 212°F), torrential rains slowly filled low areas, forming the oceans. This reduced not only the water vapor in the air but also the amount of carbon dioxide, for it became dissolved in the water. What remained was a nitrogen-rich atmosphere.

If Earth's primitive atmosphere resulted from volcanic outgassing, we have a quandary, because volcanoes do not emit free oxygen. Where did the very significant percentage of oxygen in our present atmosphere (nearly 21 percent) come from?

The major source of oxygen is green plants (Figure E). Put another way, *life itself* has strongly influenced the composition of our present atmosphere. Plants did not just adapt to their environment; they actually influenced it, dramatically altering the composition of the entire planet's atmos-

FIGURE E Life has strongly influenced the composition of our atmosphere. The primary source of the abundant oxygen in Earth's atmosphere is photosynthesis by green plants. (Photo by Art Wolfe/Photo Researchers, Inc.)

phere by using carbon dioxide and releasing oxygen. This is a good example of how Earth operates as a giant system in which living things interact with their environment.

How did plants come to alter the atmosphere? The key is the way in which plants create their own food. They employ *photosynthesis*, in which they use light energy to synthesize food sugars from carbon dioxide and water. The process releases a waste gas—oxygen. Those of us in the animal kingdom rely on oxygen to metabolize our food, and we in turn exhale carbon dioxide as a waste gas. The plants use this carbon dioxide for more photosynthesis, and so on, in a continuing system.

The first life forms on Earth, probably bacteria, did not need oxygen. Their life processes were geared to the earlier, oxygenless atmosphere. Even today many *anaerobic* bacteria thrive in environments that lack free oxygen. Later, primitive plants evolved that used photosynthesis and released oxygen. Slowly the oxygen content

of Earth's atmosphere increased. The geologic record of this ancient time suggests that much of the first free oxygen did not remain free, because it combined with (oxidized) other substances dissolved in water, especially iron. Iron has tremendous affinity for oxygen, and the two elements combine to form iron oxides (rust) at any opportunity (Figure F).

Then, once the available iron satisfied its need for oxygen, substantial quantities of oxygen accumulated in the atmosphere. By the beginning of the Paleozoic era, about 4 billion years into Earth's existence (after seven-eighths of Earth's history had elapsed) the fossil record reveals abundant ocean-dwelling organisms that require oxygen to live. Hence, the composition of Earth's atmosphere has evolved together with its life forms, from an oxygenless envelope to today's oxygen-rich environment.

FIGURE F These ancient layered, iron-rich rocks, called banded iron formations, were deposited during a geologic span known as the Precambrian. Much of the oxygen generated as a by-product of photosynthesis was readily consumed by chemical reactions with iron to produce these rocks. (Photo courtesy of Spencer R. Titley)

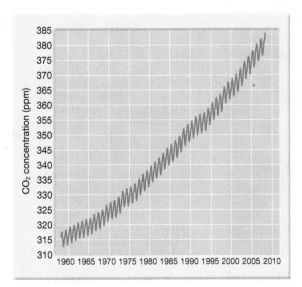

FIGURE 22 Changes in the atmosphere's carbon dioxide (CO_2) as measured at Hawaii's Mauna Loa Observatory. The oscillations reflect the seasonal variations in plant growth and decay in the Northern Hemisphere. (Data from NOAA)

Students Sometimes Ask . . .

Could you explain a little more about why the graph in Figure 22 has so many "ups and downs"?

Sure. Carbon dioxide is removed from the air by photosynthesis, the process by which green plants convert sunlight into chemical energy. In spring and summer, vigorous plant growth removes carbon dioxide from the atmosphere, so the graph takes a dip. As winter approaches, many plants die or shed leaves. The decay of organic matter returns carbon dioxide to the air, causing the graph to spike upward.

energy. It is therefore important when we examine the heating of the atmosphere.

When water changes from one state to another, such as from a gas to a liquid or a liquid to a solid, it absorbs or releases heat. This energy is termed *latent heat*, which means "hidden" heat. Water vapor in the atmosphere transports this latent heat from one region to another, and is the energy source that drives many storms.

Aerosols The movements of the atmosphere are sufficient to keep a large quantity of solid and liquid particles suspended within it. Although visible dust sometimes clouds the sky, these relatively large particles are too heavy to stay in the air for very long. Still, many particles are microscopic and remain suspended for considerable periods of time. They may originate from many sources, both natural and human made,

and include sea salts from breaking waves, fine soil blown into the air, smoke and soot from fires, pollen and microorganisms lifted by the wind, ash and dust from volcanic eruptions, and more (Figure 23a). Collectively, these tiny solid and liquid particles are called **aerosols**.

Aerosols are most numerous in the lower atmosphere near their primary source, Earth's surface. Nevertheless, the upper atmosphere is not free of them, because some dust is carried to great heights by rising currents of air, and other particles are contributed by meteoroids that disintegrate as they pass through the atmosphere.

From a meteorological standpoint, these tiny, often invisible particles can be significant. First, many act as surfaces on which water vapor may condense, an important function in the formation of clouds and fog. Second, aerosols can absorb or reflect incoming solar radiation. Thus, when an air-pollution episode is occurring or when ash fills the sky following a volcanic eruption, the amount of sunlight reaching Earth's surface can be measurably reduced. Finally, aerosols contribute to an optical phenomenon we have all observed—the varied hues of red and orange at sunrise and sunset (Figure 23b).

Ozone Another important component of the atmosphere is **ozone**. It is a form of oxygen that combines three oxygen atoms into each molecule (O_3). Ozone is not the same as the oxygen we breathe, which has two atoms per molecule (O_2). There is very little ozone in the atmosphere. Overall, it represents just three out of every 10 million molecules. Moreover, its distribution is not uniform. In the lowest portion of the atmosphere, ozone represents less than one part in 100 million. It is concentrated well above the surface in a layer called the *stratosphere*, between 10 and 50 kilometers (6 and 31 miles).

In this altitude range, oxygen molecules (O_2) are split into single atoms of oxygen (O) when they absorb ultraviolet radiation emitted by the Sun. Ozone is then created when a single atom of oxygen (O) and a molecule of oxygen (O_2) collide. This must happen in the presence of a third, neutral molecule that acts as *a catalyst* by allowing the reaction to take place without itself being consumed in the process. Ozone is concentrated in the 10- to 50-kilometer height range because a crucial balance exists there: The ultraviolet radiation from the Sun is sufficient to produce single atoms of oxygen, and there are enough gas molecules to bring about the required collisions (see Box 4).

The presence of the ozone layer in our atmosphere is crucial to those of us who dwell on Earth. The reason is that ozone absorbs the potentially harmful ultraviolet (UV) radiation from the Sun. If ozone did not filter a great deal of the ultraviolet radiation, and if the Sun's UV rays reached the surface of Earth undiminished, our planet would be uninhabitable for most life as we know it. Thus, anything that reduces the amount of ozone in the atmosphere could affect the well-being of life on Earth. Just such a problem exists and is described in the next section.

(a)   (b)

FIGURE 23   (a) This satellite image from November 11, 2002, shows two examples of aerosols. First, a large dust storm is blowing across northeastern China toward the Korean Peninsula. Second, a dense haze toward the south (bottom center) is human-generated air pollution. (b) Dust in the air can cause sunsets to be especially colorful. (Image courtesy NASA) (Photo by Steve Elmore/CORBIS/The Stock Market)

Ozone Depletion—A Global Issue

The loss of ozone high in the atmosphere as a consequence of human activities is a serious global-scale environmental problem. For nearly a billion years Earth's ozone layer has protected life on the planet. However, over the past half century, people have unintentionally placed the ozone layer in jeopardy by polluting the atmosphere. The most significant of the offending chemicals are known as chlorofluorocarbons (CFCs for short). They are versatile compounds that are chemically stable, odorless, nontoxic, noncorrosive, and inexpensive to produce. Over the decades many uses were developed for CFCs, including as coolants for air-conditioning and refrigeration equipment, cleaning solvents for electronic components,

Students Sometimes Ask . . .

Isn't ozone some sort of pollutant?

Yes, you're right. Although the naturally occurring ozone in the stratosphere is critical to life on Earth, it is regarded as a pollutant when produced at ground level because it can damage vegetation and be harmful to human health. Ozone is a major component in a noxious mixture of gases and particles called photochemical smog. It forms as a result of reactions triggered by sunlight that occur among pollutants emitted by motor vehicles and industries.

propellants for aerosol sprays, and the production of certain plastic foams.

No one worried about how CFCs might affect the atmosphere until three scientists, Paul Crutzen, F. Sherwood Rowland, and Mario Molina, studied the relationship. In 1974 they alerted the world when they reported that CFCs were probably reducing the average concentration of ozone in the stratosphere. In 1995 these scientists were awarded the Nobel Prize in chemistry for their pioneering work.

They discovered that because CFCs are practically inert (that is, not chemically active) in the lower atmosphere, a portion of these gases gradually makes its way to the ozone layer, where sunlight separates the chemicals into their constituent atoms. The chlorine atoms released this way, through a complicated series of reactions, have the net effect of removing some of the ozone (see Box 4).

The Antarctic Ozone Hole

Although ozone depletion by CFCs occurs worldwide, measurements have shown that ozone concentrations take an especially sharp drop over Antarctica during the Southern Hemisphere spring (September and October). Later, during November and December, the ozone concentration recovers to more normal levels (Figure 24). Between the early 1980s, when it was discovered, and the early 2000s, this well-publicized *ozone hole* intensified and grew larger until it covered an area roughly the size of North America (Figure 25).

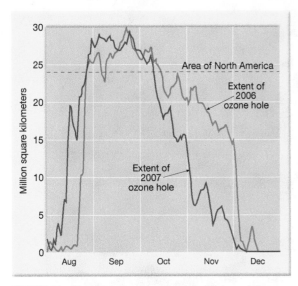

FIGURE 24   Changes in the size of the Antarctic ozone hole during 2006 and 2007. The ozone hole in both years began to form in August and was well developed in September and October. As is typical, each year the ozone hole persisted through November and disappeared in December. At its maximum, the area of the ozone hole was nearly 30 million square kilometers in 2006, an area larger than all of North America. The extent of the hole in 2007 was somewhat smaller than in 2006.

The hole is caused in part by the relatively abundant ice particles in the south polar stratosphere. The ice boosts the effectiveness of CFCs in destroying ozone, thus causing a greater decline than would otherwise occur. The zone of maximum depletion is confined to the Antarctic region by a swirling upper-level wind pattern. When this vortex weakens during the late spring, the ozone-depleted air is no longer restricted, and mixes freely with air from other latitudes where ozone levels are higher.

A few years after the Antarctic ozone hole was discovered, scientists detected a similar but smaller ozone thinning in the vicinity of the North Pole during spring and early summer. When this pool breaks up, parcels of ozone-depleted air move southward over North America, Europe, and Asia.

Effects of Ozone Depletion

Because ozone filters out most of the damaging UV radiation in sunlight, a decrease in its concentration permits more of these harmful wavelengths to reach Earth's surface. Scientists in New Zealand discovered that during the decade of the 1990s, damaging UV radiation gradually increased as concentrations of stratospheric ozone decreased. By 2000, peak sunburning UV levels in New Zealand were about 12 percent higher than 10 years earlier. What are the effects of the increased ultraviolet radiation? Each 1 percent decrease in the concentration of stratospheric ozone increases the amount of UV radiation that reaches Earth's surface by about 2 percent. Therefore, because ultraviolet radiation is known to induce skin cancer, ozone depletion seriously affects human health, especially among fair-skinned people and those who spend considerable time in the sun.

The fact that up to a half-million cases of these cancers occur in the United States annually means that ozone depletion could ultimately lead to many thousands of additional cases each year. In addition to upping the risk of skin cancer, an increase in damaging UV radiation can negatively impact the human immune system, as well as promote cataracts, a clouding of the eye lens that reduces vision and may cause blindness if not treated.

The effects of additional UV radiation on animal and plant life are also important. There is serious concern that crop yields and quality will be adversely affected. Some scientists

FIGURE 25   The view of the South polar region shows the Antarctic ozone hole on September 9, 2007. Dark blue colors correspond to the region with the sparsest ozone. Light blue, green, and yellow indicate progressively more ozone. The small graph shows changes in the average extent of the ozone hole, 1980–2007. (Data from NOAA)

BOX 4 ▶ IMPORTANT REACTIONS INVOLVING OZONE IN THE STRATOSPHERE

Ozone (O_3) is found naturally in the atmosphere, where it is concentrated in the stratosphere, a layer between about 10 and 50 kilometers above Earth's surface. Here natural processes are continually creating and destroying ozone. These reactions account for the higher temperatures that occur in the stratosphere.

Natural Formation and Destruction of Ozone

Ozone is created in two steps. First, high-energy ultraviolet (UV) rays from the Sun strike ordinary oxygen molecules (O_2) and split them into two single oxygen atoms. Second, a freed oxygen atom (O) combines with an oxygen molecule (O_2) to form a molecule of ozone (O_3). Figure G illustrates these steps.

When an ozone molecule (O_3) absorbs UV rays, it splits into an oxygen molecule (O_2) and a single atom of oxygen (O). Usually the single oxygen atom quickly collides with and rejoins an oxygen molecule to form another ozone molecule. These reactions, in which ozone is continually being broken down and re-created, are sometimes called the *ozone-oxygen cycle* and are depicted in Figure H.

Ozone Destruction by CFCs

Scientists have learned that the use of certain chlorine-containing chemicals such as chlorofluorocarbons (CFCs) leads to a loss of ozone in the stratosphere. CFCs drift upward into the stratosphere, where they are bombarded by solar ultraviolet rays. In response, CFC molecules break up by releasing chlorine (Cl) atoms. As shown in the top portion of Figure I, these chlorine atoms react with ozone molecules by taking one oxygen atom to form chlorine monoxide (ClO) and leaving behind an oxygen molecule (O_2). Then whenever a molecule of chlorine monoxide encounters a single atom of oxygen (Figure I, bottom), the oxygen "breaks up" the chlorine monoxide, stealing its oxygen atom and releasing chlorine back to the stratosphere to destroy more ozone. The reactions shown in Figure I occur over and over again. In this manner, every chlorine atom that makes its way to the stratosphere is able to destroy *many* molecules of ozone.

FIGURE G Ozone in the stratosphere is created in two steps.

FIGURE H The absorption of solar ultraviolet radiation by ozone during the two-step *ozone-oxygen cycle* causes temperatures in the stratosphere to rise.

FIGURE I Free chlorine atoms destroy ozone (top). Below, chlorine atoms are released back to the stratosphere where they destroy more ozone. These two reactions occur over and over again.

also fear that increased UV radiation in the Antarctic will penetrate the waters surrounding the continent and impair or destroy the microscopic plants, called phytoplankton, that represent the base of the food chain. A decrease in phytoplankton, in turn, could reduce the population of copepods and krill that sustain fish, whales, penguins, and other marine life in the high latitudes of the Southern Hemisphere.

Montreal Protocol

What has been done to protect the atmosphere's ozone layer? Realizing that the risks of not curbing CFC emissions were difficult to ignore, an international agreement known as the *Montreal Protocol on Substances that Deplete the Ozone Layer* was concluded under the auspices of the United Nations in late 1987. The protocol established legally binding controls on the production and consumption of gases known to cause ozone depletion. As the scientific understanding of ozone depletion improved after 1987 and substitutes and alternatives became available for the offending chemicals, the Montreal Protocol was strengthened several times. More than 190 nations eventually ratified the treaty.

The Montreal Protocol represents a positive international response to a global environment problem. As a result of the action, the total abundance of ozone-depleting gases in the atmosphere has started to decrease in recent years. According to the U.S. Environmental Protection Agency (U.S. EPA), the ozone layer has not grown thinner since 1998 over most of the world.* If the nations of the world continue to follow the provisions of the protocol, the decreases are expected to continue throughout the twenty-first century. Some offending chemicals are still increasing but will begin to decrease in coming decades. Between 2060 and 2075, the abundance of ozone-depleting gases is projected to fall to values that

*U.S. EPA. *Achievements in Stratospheric Ozone Protection, Progress Report.* EPA-430-R-07-001, April 2007, p. 5.

FIGURE 26 Global ozone recovery predictions. Observed values of global total ozone decreased beginning about 1980. As emissions of ozone-depleting gases decrease in the early twenty-first century, computer models indicate that ozone values will increase. Model results show that recovery is expected to be significant by 2050, or perhaps sooner.

existed before the Antarctic ozone hole began to form in the 1980s. Figure 26 shows global ozone recovery predictions to the year 2050.

Extent of the Atmosphere

 GE❍De
ATMOSPHERE
Introduction to the Atmosphere
▸ Extent of the Atmosphere

To say that the atmosphere begins at Earth's surface and extends upward is obvious. However, where does the atmosphere end and outer space begin? There is no sharp boundary; the atmosphere rapidly thins as you travel away from Earth, until there are too few gas molecules to detect.

To understand the vertical extent of the atmosphere, let us examine the changes in atmospheric pressure with height. Atmospheric pressure is simply the weight of the air above. At sea level the average pressure is slightly more than 1000 millibars. This corresponds to a weight of slightly more than 1 kilogram per square centimeter (14.7 pounds per square inch). Obviously, the pressure at higher altitudes is less (Figure 27).

One half of the atmosphere lies below an altitude of 5.6 kilometers (3.5 miles). At about 16 kilometers (10 miles) 90 percent of the atmosphere has been traversed, and above 100 kilometers (62 miles) only 0.00003 percent of all the gases composing the atmosphere remain.

At an altitude of 100 kilometers the atmosphere is so thin that the density of air is less than could be found in the most perfect artificial vacuum at the surface. Nevertheless, the atmosphere continues to even greater heights. The truly rarefied nature of the outer atmosphere is described very well by Richard Craig:

The earth's outermost atmosphere, the part above a few hundred kilometers, is a region of extremely low density. Near sea level, the number of atoms and molecules in a

FIGURE 27 Atmospheric pressure changes with altitude. The rate of pressure decrease with an increase in altitude is not constant. Rather, pressure decreases rapidly near Earth's surface and more gradually at greater heights.

cubic centimeter of air is about 2×10^{19}; near 600 km, it is only about 2×10^7, which is the sea-level value divided by a million million. At sea level, an atom or molecule can be expected, on the average, to move about 7×10^{-6} cm before colliding with another particle; at the 600-km level, this distance, called the "mean free path," is about 10 km. Near sea level, an atom or molecule, on the average, undergoes about 7×10^9 such collisions each second; near 600 km, this number is reduced to about 1 each minute.*

The graphic portrayal of pressure data (Figure 27) shows that the rate of pressure decrease is not constant. Rather, pressure decreases at a decreasing rate with an increase in altitude until, beyond an altitude of about 35 kilometers, the decrease is negligible.

Put another way, data illustrate that air is highly compressible—that is, it expands with decreasing pressure and becomes compressed with increasing pressure. Consequently, traces of our atmosphere extend for thousands of kilometers beyond Earth's surface. Thus, to say where the atmosphere ends and outer space begins is arbitrary and, to a large extent, depends on what phenomenon one is studying. It is apparent that there is no sharp boundary.

*Richard Craig. *The Edge of Space: Exploring the Upper Atmosphere* (New York: Doubleday & Company, Inc. 1968), p. 130.

In summary, data on vertical pressure changes reveal that the vast bulk of the gases making up the atmosphere is very near Earth's surface and that the gases gradually merge with the emptiness of space. When compared with the size of the solid Earth, the envelope of air surrounding our planet is indeed very shallow.

Thermal Structure of the Atmosphere

GE●De
ATMOSPHERE
Introduction to the Atmosphere
▶ Thermal Structure of the Atmosphere

By the early twentieth century much had been learned about the lower atmosphere. The upper atmosphere was partly known from indirect methods. Data from balloons and kites had revealed that the air temperature dropped with increasing height above Earth's surface. This phenomenon is felt by anyone who has climbed a high mountain, and is obvious in pictures of snow-capped mountaintops rising above snow-free lowlands (Figure 28).

Although measurements had not been taken above a height of about 10 kilometers (6 miles), scientists believed that the temperature continued to decline with height to a value of absolute zero (−273°C) at the outer edge of the

atmosphere. In 1902, however, the French scientist Leon Philippe Teisserenc de Bort refuted the notion that temperature decreases continuously with an increase in altitude. In studying the results of more than 200 balloon launchings, Teisserenc de Bort found that the temperature stopped decreasing and leveled off at an altitude between 8 and 12 kilometers (5 and 7.5 miles). This surprising discovery was at first doubted, but subsequent data-gathering confirmed his findings. Later, through the use of radiosondes and rocket-sounding techniques, the temperature structure of the atmosphere up to great heights became clear. Today the atmosphere is divided vertically into four layers on the basis of temperature (Figure 29).

Troposphere

The bottom layer in which we live, where temperature decreases with an increase in altitude, is the **troposphere.** The term was coined in 1908 by Teisserrenc de Bort and literally means the region where air "turns over," a reference to the appreciable vertical mixing of air in this lowermost zone.

The temperature decrease in the troposphere is called the **environmental lapse rate.** Its average value is 6.5°C per kilometer (3.6°F per 1000 feet), a figure known as the *normal lapse rate*. It needs to be emphasized, however, that the environmental lapse rate is not a constant but rather can be highly variable and must be regularly measured using radiosondes. It can vary during the course of a day with fluctuations of the weather, as well as seasonally and from place to place. Sometimes shallow layers where temperatures actually increase with height are observed in the troposphere. When such a reversal occurs, a *temperature inversion* is said to exist.

The temperature decrease continues to an average height of about 12 kilometers (7.5 miles). Yet the thickness of the troposphere is not the same everywhere. It reaches heights in excess of 16 kilometers (10 miles) in the tropics, but in polar regions it is more subdued, extending to 9 kilometers (5.5 miles) or less (Figure 30). Warm surface temperatures and highly developed thermal mixing are responsible for the greater vertical extent of the troposphere near the equator. As a result, the environmental lapse rate extends to great heights; and despite relatively high surface temperatures below, the lowest tropospheric temperatures are found aloft in the tropics and not at the poles.

The troposphere is the chief focus of meteorologists because it is in this layer that essentially all important weather phenomena occur. Almost all clouds and certainly all precipitation, as well as all our violent storms, are born in this lowermost layer of the atmosphere. There should be little wonder why the troposphere is often called the "weather sphere."

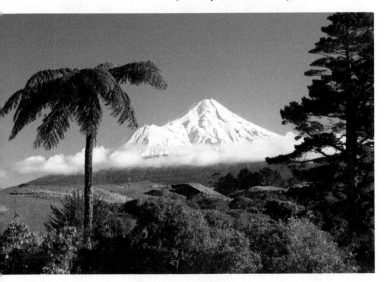

FIGURE 28   Temperatures drop with an increase in altitude in the troposphere. Therefore, it is possible to have snow on a mountaintop and warmer, snow-free lowlands below. Mt Taranaki Mt Egmont Taranaki North Island New Zealand. (Photo by David Wall/Alamy)

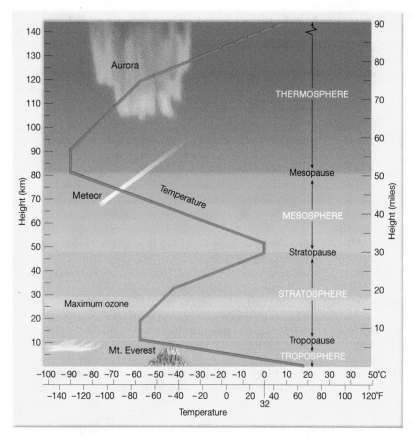

FIGURE 29 Thermal structure of the atmosphere.

approaches −90°C (−130°F). The coldest temperatures anywhere in the atmosphere occur at the mesopause. The pressure at the base of the mesosphere is only about a thousandth that at sea level. At the mesopause, the at-mospheric pressure drops to just a millionth that at sea level. Because accessibility is difficult, the mesosphere is one of the least explored regions of the atmosphere. The reason is that it cannot be reached by the highest flying airplanes and research balloons nor is it accessible to the lowest orbiting satellites. Recent technical developments are just beginning to fill this knowledge gap.

Thermosphere

The fourth layer extends outward from the mesopause and has no well-defined upper limit. It is the **thermosphere**, a layer that contains only a minute fraction of the atmosphere's mass. In the extremely rarefied air of this outermost layer, temperatures again increase, owing to the absorption of very shortwave, high-energy solar radiation by atoms of oxygen and nitrogen.

Temperatures rise to extremely high values of more than 1000°C (1800°F) in the thermosphere. But such temperatures are not comparable to those experienced near Earth's surface. Temperature is defined in terms of the average speed at which molecules move. Because the gases of the thermosphere are moving at very high speeds, the temperature is very high. But the gases are so sparse that collectively they possess only an insignificant quantity of heat. For this reason, the temperature of a satellite orbiting Earth in the thermosphere is determined chiefly by the amount of solar radiation it absorbs and not by the high temperature of the almost nonexistent surrounding air. If an astronaut inside were to expose his or her hand, the air in this layer would not feel hot.

Stratosphere

Beyond the troposphere lies the **stratosphere;** the boundary between the troposphere and the stratosphere is known as the **tropopause.** Below the tropopause, atmospheric properties are readily transferred by large-scale turbulence and mixing, but above it, in the stratosphere, they are not. In the stratosphere, the temperature at first remains nearly constant to a height of about 20 kilometers (12 miles) before it begins a sharp increase that continues until the **stratopause** is encountered at a height of about 50 kilometers (30 miles) above Earth's surface. Higher temperatures occur in the stratosphere because it is in this layer that the atmosphere's ozone is concentrated. Recall that ozone absorbs ultraviolet radiation from the Sun. Consequently, the stratosphere is heated. Although the maximum ozone concentration exists between 15 and 30 kilometers (9 and 19 miles), the smaller amounts of ozone above this height range absorb enough UV energy to cause the higher observed temperatures.

Mesosphere

In the third layer, the **mesosphere,** temperatures again decrease with height until at the **mesopause,** some 80 kilometers (50 miles) above the surface, the average temperature

Vertical Variations in Composition

In addition to the layers defined by vertical variations in temperature, other layers, or zones, are also recognized in the atmosphere. Based on composition, the atmosphere is often divided into two layers: the homosphere and the heterosphere. From Earth's surface to an altitude of about 80 kilometers (50 miles), the makeup of the air is uniform in terms of the proportions of its component gases. That is, the composition is the same as that shown earlier in Figure 21. This lower uniform layer is termed the *homosphere,* the zone of homogeneous composition.

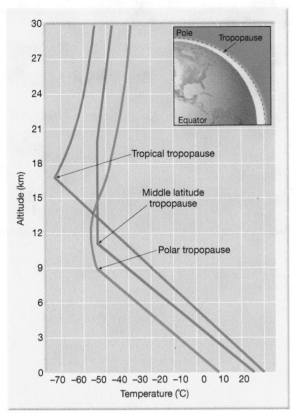

FIGURE 30 Differences in the height of the tropopause. The variation in the height of the tropopause, as shown on the small inset diagram, is greatly exaggerated.

In contrast, the rather tenuous atmosphere above 80 kilometers is not uniform. Because it has a heterogeneous composition, the term *heterosphere* is used. Here the gases are arranged into four roughly spherical shells, each with a distinctive composition. The lowermost layer is dominated by molecular nitrogen (N_2); next, a layer of atomic oxygen (O) is encountered, followed by a layer dominated by helium (He) atoms; and finally a region consisting of hydrogen (H) atoms. The stratified nature of the gases making up the heterosphere varies according to their weights. Molecular nitrogen is the heaviest, and so it is lowest. The lightest gas, hydrogen, is outermost.

Ionosphere

Located in the altitude range between 80 to 400 kilometers (50 to 250 miles), and thus coinciding with the lower portions of the thermosphere and heterosphere, is an electrically charged layer known as the **ionosphere.** Here molecules of nitrogen and atoms of oxygen are readily ionized as they absorb high-energy shortwave solar energy. In this process, each affected molecule or atom loses one or more electrons and becomes a positively charged ion, and the electrons are set free to travel as electric currents.

Although ionization occurs at heights as great as 1000 kilometers (620 miles) and extends as low as perhaps 50 kilometers (30 miles), positively charged ions and negative electrons are most dense in the range of 80 to 400 kilometers (50 to 250 miles). The concentration of ions is not great below this zone because much of the short-wavelength radiation needed for ionization has already been depleted. In addition, the atmospheric density at this level results in a large percentage of free electrons being swiftly captured by positively charged ions. Beyond the 400-kilometer (250-mile) upward limit of the ionosphere, the concentration of ions is low because of the extremely low density of the air. Because so few molecules and atoms are present, relatively few ions and free electrons can be produced.

The electrical structure of the ionosphere is not uniform. It consists of three layers of varying ion density. From bottom to top, these layers are called the D, E, and F layers, respectively. Because the production of ions requires direct solar radiation, the concentration of charged particles changes from day to night, particularly in the D and E zones. That is, these layers weaken and disappear at night and reappear during the day. The uppermost, or F layer, on the other hand, is present both day and night. The density of the atmosphere in this layer is very low, and positive ions and electrons do not meet and recombine as rapidly as they do at lesser heights, where density is higher. Consequently, the concentration of ions and electrons in the F layer does not change rapidly, and the layer, although weak, remains through the night.

The Auroras

As best we can tell, the ionosphere has little impact on our daily weather. But this layer of the atmosphere is the site of one of nature's most interesting spectacles, the auroras (Figure 31). The **aurora borealis** (northern lights) and its Southern Hemisphere couterpart, the **aurora australis** (southern lights), appear in a wide variety of forms. Sometimes the displays consist of vertical streamers in which there can be considerable movement. At other times the auroras appear as a series of luminous expanding arcs or as a quiet glow that has an almost foglike quality.

The occurrence of auroral displays is closely correlated in time with solar-flare activity and, in geographic location, with Earth's magnetic poles. Solar flares are massive magnetic storms on the Sun that emit enormous amounts of energy and great quantities of fast-moving atomic particles. As the clouds of protons and electrons from the solar storm approach Earth, they are captured by its magnetic field, which in turn guides them toward the magnetic poles. Then, as the ions impinge on the ionosphere, they energize the atoms of oxygen and molecules of nitrogen and cause them to emit light—the glow of the auroras. Because the occurrence of solar flares is closely correlated with sunspot activity, auroral displays increase conspicuously at times when sunspots are most numerous.

(a)

(b)

FIGURE 31 (a) Aurora borealis (northern lights) as seen from Wapusk National Park, Manitoba, Canada. The same phenomenon occurs toward the South Pole, where it is called the aurora australis (southern lights). (Photo by Daniel Cox/Oxford Scientific (OSF)/Photolibrary); (b) Aurora australis (southern lights) photographed from the Space Shuttle in May 1991. (NASA)

Chapter Summary

- *Meteorology* is the scientific study of the atmosphere. *Weather* refers to the state of the atmosphere at a given time and place. It is constantly changing, sometimes from hour to hour and other times from day to day. *Climate* is an aggregate of weather conditions, the sum of all statistical weather information that helps describe a place or region. The nature of both weather and climate is expressed in terms of the same basic *elements*, those quantities or properties measured regularly. The most important elements are (1) air temperature, (2) humidity, (3) type and amount of cloudiness, (4) type and amount of precipitation, (5) air pressure, and (6) the speed and direction of the wind.

- All science is based on the assumption that the natural world behaves in a consistent and predictable manner. The process by which scientists gather facts through observation and careful measurement and formulate scientific *hypotheses* and *theories* is called the *scientific method*. To determine what is occurring in the natural world, scientists often (1) collect facts, (2) develop a scientific hypothesis, (3) construct experiments to validate the hypothesis, and (4) accept, modify, or reject the hypothesis on the basis of extensive testing. Other discoveries represent purely theoretical ideas that have stood up to extensive examination. Still other scientific advancements have been made when a totally unexpected event occurred during an experiment.

- *Balloons* play a significant role in the systematic investigation of the atmostphere by carrying *radiosondes* (lightweight packages of instruments that send back data on temperature, pressure, and relative humidity) into the lower atmosphere. Rockets, airplanes, satellites, and weather radar also play important roles in the study of the atmosphere.

- Earth's four spheres include the *atmosphere* (gaseous envelope), the *geosphere* (solid Earth), the *hydrosphere* (water portion), and the *biosphere* (life). Each sphere is composed of many interrelated parts and is intertwined with all other spheres.

- Although each of Earth's four spheres can be studied separately, they are all related in a complex and continuously interacting whole that we call the *Earth system*. *Earth system science* uses an interdisciplinary approach to integrate the knowledge of several academic fields in the study of our planet and its global environmental problems.

- A *system* is a group of interacting parts that form a complex whole. *Closed systems* are those in which energy moves freely in and out, but matter does not enter or leave the system. In an open system, both energy and matter flow into and out of the system.

- Most natural systems have mechanisms that tend to enhance change, called *positive feedback mechanisms*, and other mechanisms, called *negative feedback mechanisms*, that tend to resist change and thus stabilize the system.

- The two sources of energy that power the Earth system are (1) the Sun, which drives the external processes that occur in the atmosphere, hydrosphere, and at Earth's surface, and (2) heat from Earth's interior that powers the internal processes that produce volcanoes, earthquakes, and mountains.

- Air is a mixture of many discrete gases, and its composition varies from time to time and place to place. After water vapor, dust, and other variable components are removed, two gases, *nitrogen* and *oxygen*, make up 99 percent of the volume of the remaining clean, dry air. *Carbon dioxide*, although present in only minute amounts (0.0387 percent or 387 ppm), is an efficient absorber of energy emitted by Earth and thus influences the heating of the atmosphere. Due to the rising level of carbon dioxide in the atmosphere during the past century attributed to the burning of ever increasing quantities of fossil fuels, it is likely that a warming of the lower atmosphere is triggering global climate change.

- The variable components of air include *water vapor, dust particles,* and *ozone*. Like carbon dioxide, water vapor can absorb heat given off by Earth as well as some solar energy. When water vapor changes from one state to another, it absorbs or releases heat. In the atmosphere, water vapor transports this *latent* ("hidden") *heat* from one place to another, and it is the energy source that helps drive many storms. *Aerosols* (tiny solid and liquid particles) are meteorologically important because these often invisible particles act as surfaces on which water can condense and are also absorbers and reflectors of incoming solar radiation. *Ozone*, a form of oxygen that combines three oxygen atoms into each molecule (O_3), is a gas concentrated in the 10- to 50-kilometer height range in the atmosphere that absorbs the potentially harmful ultraviolet (UV) radiation from the Sun.

- Over the past half century, people have placed Earth's ozone layer in jeopardy by polluting the atmosphere with chlorofluorocarbons (CFCs), which remove some of the gas. Ozone concentrations take an especially sharp drop over Antarctica during the Southern Hemisphere spring (September and October). Furthermore, scientists have also discovered a similar but smaller ozone thinning near the North Pole during spring and early summer. Because ultraviolet radiation is known to produce skin cancer, ozone depletion seriously affects human health, especially among fair-skinned people and those who spend considerable time in the Sun. The *Montreal Protocol*, concluded under the auspices of the United Nations, represents a positive international response to the ozone problem.

- No sharp boundary to the upper atmosphere exists. The atmosphere simply thins as you travel away from Earth until there are too few gas molecules to detect. The change that occurs in atmospheric pressure (the weight of the air above) depicts the vertical extent of the atmosphere.

One-half of the atmosphe kilometers (3.5 miles), an meters (10 miles). Traces sands of kilometers beyc

- Using temperature as the into four layers. The t *posphere,* the bottom layer in which *environmental lapse rate*. Its average value is 6.5°C per kilometer, a figure known as the *normal lapse rate*. The environmental lapse rate is not a constant and must be regularly measured using radiosondes. A *temperature inversion,* in which temperatures increase with height, is sometimes observed in shallow layers in the troposphere. The thickness of the troposphere is generally greater in the tropics than in polar regions. Essentially all important weather phenomena occur in the troposphere. Beyond the troposphere lies the *stratosphere;* the boundary between the troposphere and stratosphere is known as the *tropopause*. In the stratosphere, the temperature at first remains constant to a height of about 20 kilometers (12 miles) before it begins a sharp increase due to the absorption of ultraviolet radiation from the Sun by ozone. The temperatures continue to increase until the *stratopause* is encountered at a height of about 50 kilometers (30 miles). In the *mesosphere,* the third layer, temperatures again decrease with height until the *mesopause,* some 80 kilometers (50 miles) above the surface. The fourth layer, the *thermosphere,* with no well-defined upper limit, consists of extremely rarefied air. Temperatures here increase with an increase in altitude.

- Besides layers defined by vertical variations in temperature, the atmosphere is often divided into two layers based on composition. The *homosphere* (zone of homogeneous composition), from Earth's surface to an altitude of about 80 kilometers (50 miles), consists of air that is uniform in terms of the proportions of its component gases. Above 80 kilometers, the *heterosphere* (zone of heterogenous composition) consists of gases arranged into four roughly spherical shells, each with a distinctive composition. The stratified nature of the gases in the heterosphere varies according to their weights.

- Occurring in the altitude range between 80 and 400 kilometers (50 and 250 miles) is an electrically charged layer known as the *ionosphere*. Here molecules of nitrogen and atoms of oxygen are readily ionized as they absorb high-energy, shortwave solar energy. Three layers of varying ion density make up the ionosphere. Auroras (the *aurora borealis,* northern lights, and its Southern Hemisphere counterpart the *aurora australis,* southern lights) occur within the ionosphere. Auroras form as clouds of protons and electrons ejected from the Sun during solar-flare activity enter the atmosphere near Earth's magnetic poles and energize the atoms of oxygen and molecules of nitrogen, causing them to emit light—the glow of the auroras

abulary Review

eview your understanding of important terms in this chapter by defining and explaining the importance of each term listed here. Terms are listed in alphabetical order.

aerosols	environmental lapse rate	negative feedback	system
air	geosphere	mechanism	theory
atmosphere	hydrosphere	open system	thermosphere
aurora australis	hypothesis	ozone	tropopause
aurora borealis	interface	paradigm	troposphere
biosphere	ionosphere	positive feedback	weather
climate	mesopause	mechanism	
closed system	mesosphere	radiosonde	
elements of weather and	meteorology	stratopause	
climate	model	stratosphere	

Review Questions

1. Distinguish between the terms "weather" and "climate."

2. The following statements refer to either weather or climate. On the basis of your answer to Question 1, determine which statements refer to weather and which refer to climate. (*Note:* One statement includes aspects of both weather and climate.)

   a. The baseball game was rained out today.
   b. January is Peoria's coldest month.
   c. North Africa is a desert.
   d. The high this afternoon was 25°C.
   e. Last evening a tornado ripped through Canton.
   f. I am moving to southern Arizona because it is warm and sunny.
   g. The highest temperature ever recorded at this station is 43°C.
   h. Thursday's low of –20°C is the coldest temperature ever recorded for that city.
   i. It is partly cloudy.

3. What are the basic elements of weather and climate?

4. How is a scientific hypothesis different from a scientific theory?

5. What is a radiosonde?

6. List and briefly describe the four "spheres" that constitute our environment.

7. How is an open system different from a closed system?

8. Contrast positive feedback mechanisms and negative feedback mechanisms.

9. What are the two sources of energy for the Earth system?

10. What are the major components of clean, dry air?

11. Describe the stages in the formation of Earth's atmosphere. (See Box 3)

12. What is responsible for the increasing carbon dioxide content of the air? What is one possible effect of increased carbon dioxide in the atmosphere?

13. Why are water vapor and dust important constituents of our atmosphere?

14. a. Why is ozone important to life on Earth?
    b. What are CFCs, and what is their connection to the ozone problem?
    c. What are the effects on human health of a decrease in the stratosphere's ozone?

15. The atmosphere is divided vertically into four layers on the basis of temperature. List the names of these layers and their boundaries in order (from lowest to highest), and list as many characteristics of each as you can.

16. Why does the temperature increase in the stratosphere?

17. Why are temperatures in the thermosphere not strictly comparable to those experienced near Earth's surface?

18. Distinguish between the homosphere and the heterosphere.

19. What is the primary cause of auroral displays?

Problems

1. Refer to the newspaper-type weather map in Figure 4 to answer the following:

   a. Estimate the predicted high temperatures in central New York State and the northwest corner of Arizona.
   b. Where is the coldest area on the weather map? Where is the warmest?
   c. On this weather map, H stands for the center of a region of high pressure. Does it appear as though high pressure is associated with precipitation or fair weather?
   d. Which is warmer—central Texas or central Maine? Would you normally expect this to be the case?

2. Refer to the graph in Figure 6 to answer the following questions about temperatures in New York City:

  a. What is the approximate average daily high temperature in January? In July?

  b. Approximately what are the highest and lowest temperatures ever recorded?

3. Refer to the graph in Figure 8. Which year had the greatest number of billion-dollar weather disasters? How many events occurred that year? In which year was the damage amount greatest?

4. Refer to the graph in Figure 27 to answer the following:

  a. Approximately how much does the air pressure drop (in millibars) between the surface and 4 kilometers? (Use a surface pressure of 1000 mb.)

  b. How much does the pressure drop between 4 and 8 kilometers?

  c. Based on your answers to parts a and b, with an increase in altitude, air pressure decreases at a(n) (constant, increasing, decreasing) rate. Underline the correct answer.

5. If the temperature at sea level were 23°C, what would the air temperature be at a height of 2 kilometers under average conditions?

6. Use the graph of the atmosphere's thermal structure (Figure 29) to answer the following:

  a. What is the approximate height and temperature of the stratopause?

  b. At what altitude is the temperature lowest? What is the temperature at that height?

7. Answer the following questions by examining the graph in Figure 30.

  a. In which one of the three regions (tropics, middle latitudes, poles) is the *surface* temperature lowest?

  b. In which region is the tropopause encountered at the lowest altitude? The highest? What are the altitudes and temperatures of the tropopause in those regions?

8. a. On a spring day a middle-latitude city (about 40° north latitude) has a surface (sea-level) temperature of 10°C. If vertical soundings reveal a nearly constant environmental lapse rate of 6.5°C per kilometer and a temperature at the tropopause of −55°C, what is the height of the tropopause?

  b. On the same spring day a station near the equator has a surface temperature of 25°C, 15°C higher than the middle-latitude city mentioned in part a. Vertical soundings reveal an environmental lapse rate of 6.5°C per kilometer and indicate that the tropopause is encountered at 16 kilometers. What is the air temperature at the tropopause?

Atmospheric Science Online

The Atmosphere 11e website uses the resources and flexibility of the Internet to aid in your study of the topics in this chapter. Written and developed by meteorology instructors, this site will help improve your understanding of meteorology. Visit **www.mygeoscience.com** in order to:

- **Review** key chapter concepts

- **Read** with links to the eBook and to chapter-specific web resources

- **Visualize** and comprehend challenging topics using learning activities in *GEODe: Atmosphere*

- **Test yourself** with online quizzes

GEODe: Atmosphere

GEODe: Atmosphere makes studying more effective by reinforcing key concepts using animation, video, narration, interactive exercises, and practice quizzes. Available at **www.mygeoscience.com**.

Heating Earth's Surface and Atmosphere

From Chapter 2 of *The Atmosphere: An Introduction to Meteorology*, Eleventh Edition, Frederick K. Lutgens, Edward J. Tarbuck, Dennis Tasa. Copyright

Heating Earth's Surface and Atmosphere

Solar radiation provides more than 99.9 percent of the energy that heats Earth's surface. (Photo by Xenon/Shutterstock)

From our everyday experiences, we know that the Sun's rays feel hotter on clear days than on overcast days and that on sunny days paved roads become much hotter than grassy boulevards. Pictures of snowcapped mountains remind us that temperatures decrease with altitude. And we know that the fury of winter is always replaced by the newness of spring. What you may not know is that these occurrences are manifestations of the same phenomenon that causes the blue color of the sky and the red color of a brilliant sunset. All these occurrences are a result of the interaction of solar radiation with Earth's atmosphere and its land–sea surface, which is the essence of this chapter (Figure 1).

Earth–Sun Relationships

Heating Earth's Surface and Atmosphere

THE ATMOSPHERE ▶ Understanding Seasons

Earth intercepts only a minute percentage of the energy given off by the Sun—less than one two-billionth. This may seem an insignificant amount when in fact, the entire Earth receives 174 billion megawatts of energy from the Sun each year. For reference, one billion megawatts is enough energy to power New York City for more than a decade.

Solar energy is not distributed equally over Earth's land–sea surface. The amount of energy received varies with latitude, time of day, and season of the year. Contrasting images of polar bears on ice rafts and palm trees along a remote tropical beach serve to illustrate the extremes. It is the unequal heating of Earth that creates winds and drives the ocean's currents. These movements in turn transport heat from the tropics toward the poles in an unending attempt to balance energy inequalities. The consequences of these processes are the phenomena we call *weather*. If the Sun were "turned off," global winds and ocean currents would quickly cease. Yet as long as the Sun shines, winds *will* blow and weather *will* persist. So to understand how the dynamic weather machine works, we must know why different latitudes receive different quantities of solar energy and why the amount of solar energy received changes during the course of a year to produce the seasons. As you will see, seasonal variations in solar heating are caused by the motions of Earth relative to the Sun and by variations in Earth's land–sea surface.

FIGURE 1   The Sun over a snow-covered Norwegian landscape. (Photo by Per Breiehagen/Getty Images)

Earth's Motions

Earth has two principal motions—rotation and revolution. **Rotation** is the spinning of Earth about its axis that produces the daily cycle of daylight and darkness.

The other motion of Earth, **revolution,** refers to its movement in orbit around the Sun. Hundreds of years ago most people believed that Earth was stationary in space. The reasoning was that if Earth was moving, people would feel the movement of the wind rushing past them. Today we know that Earth is traveling at nearly 113,000 kilometers (70,000 miles) per hour in a slightly elliptical orbit about the Sun.

The distance between Earth and Sun averages about 150 million kilometers (93 million miles). Because Earth's orbit is not perfectly circular, however, the distance varies during the course of a year. Each year, on about January 3, our planet is about 147.3 million kilometers (91.5 million miles) from the Sun, closer than at any other time. This position is called the **perihelion.** About six months later, on July 4, Earth is about 152.1 million kilometers (94.5 million miles) from the Sun, farther away than at any other time. This position is called the **aphelion.** Although Earth is closest to the Sun and receives up to 7 percent more energy in January than in July, this difference plays only a minor role in producing seasonal temperature variations. As proof, consider that Earth is closest to the Sun during the Northern Hemisphere winter.

The Seasons

We know that it is colder in winter than in summer, but if variations in the distance between the Sun and Earth do not cause this seasonal temperature change, what does? We adjust to the continuous changes in the duration of daylight that occur throughout the year by planning our outdoor activities accordingly. The gradual but significant *change in day length* certainly accounts for some of the difference we notice between summer and winter. Furthermore, a gradual change in the angle of the noon Sun above the horizon is quite noticeable (Figure 2). At midsummer the noon Sun is seen high above the horizon. But as summer gives way to autumn, the noon Sun appears lower in the sky, and sunset occurs earlier each evening.

The seasonal variation in the angle of the Sun above the horizon affects the amount of energy received at Earth's surface in two ways. First, when the Sun is directly overhead (at a 90° angle), the solar rays are most concentrated. The lower the angle, the more spread out and less intense is the solar radiation that reaches the surface (Figure 3). You have probably experienced this when using a flashlight. If the beam strikes a surface perpendicularly, a small intense spot is produced. When the flashlight beam strikes the object at an oblique angle, however, the area illuminated is larger—but dimmer.

Second, and of less importance, the angle of the Sun determines the path solar rays take as they pass through the atmosphere (Figure 4). When the Sun is directly overhead, the rays strike the atmosphere at a 90° angle and travel the shortest possible route to the surface. This distance is referred to as *one atmosphere.* However, rays entering the atmosphere at a 30° angle

(a) Summer solstice

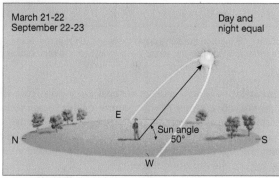

(b) Spring or fall equinox

(c) Winter solstice

FIGURE 2 Daily paths of the Sun for a place located at 40°N latitude for: (a) summer solstice; (b) spring or fall equinox, and (c) winter solstice. As we move from summer to winter, the angle of the noon Sun decreases from 73½ to 26½ degrees—a difference of 47 degrees (see Figure 6). Notice also how the location of sunrise (east) and sunset (west) changes during a year.

must travel twice this distance before reaching the surface, and 5° rays travel through a thickness roughly equal to 11 atmospheres (Table 1). The longer the path, the greater the chance that sunlight will be absorbed, reflected, or scattered by the atmosphere, all of which reduce the intensity at the surface. These same effects account for the fact that we cannot look directly at the midday Sun but we can enjoy gazing at a sunset.

It is important to remember that Earth has a spherical shape. Hence, on any given day, only places located along a

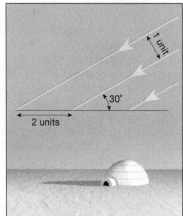

FIGURE 3 Changes in the Sun's angle cause variations in the amount of solar energy reaching Earth's surface. The higher the angle, the more intense the solar radiation.

particular latitude will receive vertical (90°) rays from the Sun. As we move either north or south of this location, the Sun's rays strike at an ever decreasing angle. Thus, the nearer a place is situated to the latitude receiving the vertical rays of the Sun, the higher will be its noon Sun, and the more concentrated will be the radiation it receives.

In summary, the most important reasons for variations in the amount of solar energy reaching a particular location are the seasonal changes in the angle at which the Sun's rays strike the surface and changes in the length of daylight.

Earth's Orientation

What causes fluctuations in Sun angle and length of daylight during the course of a year? Variations occur *because Earth's orientation to the Sun continually changes.* Earth's axis (the imaginary line through the poles around which Earth rotates) is

not perpendicular to the plane of its orbit around the Sun, which is called the **plane of the ecliptic**. Instead, it is tilted 23 1/2° from the perpendicular, as shown in Figure 4. This is called the **inclination of the axis**. As we shall see, if the axis were not inclined, we would have no seasonal changes. In addition, because the axis remains pointed in the same direction (toward the North Star) as Earth journeys around the Sun, the orientation of Earth's axis to the Sun's rays is constantly changing (Figure 5).

For example, on one day in June each year, Earth's position in orbit is such that the Northern Hemisphere is "leaning" 23 1/2° *toward* the Sun (left in Figure 5). Six months later, in December, when Earth has moved to the opposite side of its orbit, the Northern Hemisphere "leans" 23 1/2° *away* from the Sun (Figure 5, right). On days between these extremes, Earth's axis is leaning at amounts less than 23 1/2° to the rays of the Sun. This change in orientation causes the spot where the Sun's rays are vertical to make an annual migration from 23 1/2° north of the equator to 23 1/2° south of the equator. In turn, this migration causes the angle of the noon Sun to

FIGURE 4 Rays striking Earth at a low angle (toward the poles) must traverse more of the atmosphere than rays striking at a high angle (around the equator) and thus are subject to greater depletion by reflection and absorption.

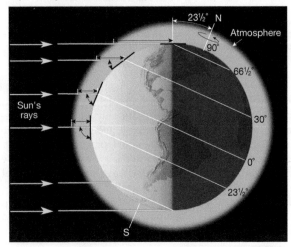

Angle of Sun above horizon	Equivalent number of atmospheres sunlight must pass through
90° (Directly overhead)	1.00
80°	1.02
70°	1.06
60°	1.15
50°	1.31
40°	1.56
30°	2.00
20°	2.92
10°	5.70
5°	10.80
0° (At horizon)	45.00

TABLE 1 Distance Radiation Must Travel Through the Atmosphere

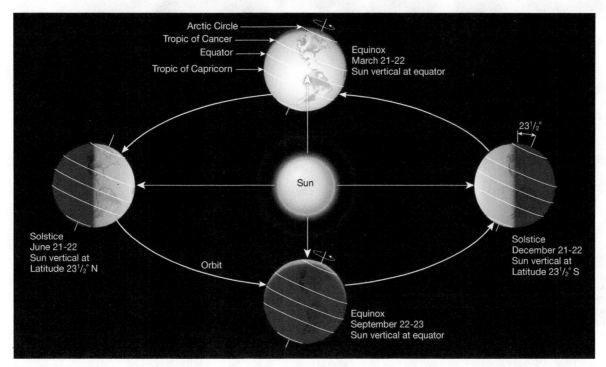

FIGURE 5 Earth–Sun relationships.

vary by up to 47° (23 1/2 + 23 1/2) for many locations during a year. A midlatitude city like New York, for instance, has a maximum noon Sun angle of 73 1/2° when the Sun's vertical rays have reached their farthest northward location in June and a minimum noon Sun angle of 26 1/2° six months later (Figure 6).

Solstices and Equinoxes

Historically, four days each year have been given special significance based on the annual migration of the direct rays of the Sun and its importance to the yearly cycle of weather. On June 21 or 22, Earth is in a position where the axis in the Northern Hemisphere is tilted 23 1/2° toward the Sun (Figure 5). At this time the vertical rays of the Sun are striking 23 1/2° north latitude (23 1/2° north of the equator), a line of latitude

known as the **Tropic of Cancer**. For people living in the Northern Hemisphere, June 21 or 22 is known as the **summer solstice**, the first "official" day of summer (see Box 1).

Six months later, on about December 21 or 22, Earth is in an opposite position, where the Sun's vertical rays are striking at 23 1/2° south latitude. This line is known as the **Tropic of Capricorn**. For those of us in the Northern Hemisphere, December 21 or 22 is the **winter solstice**, the first day of winter. However, at the same time in the Southern Hemisphere, people are experiencing just the opposite—the summer solstice.

The *equinoxes* occur midway between the solstices. September 22 or 23 is the date of the **autumnal equinox** in the Northern Hemisphere, and March 21 or 22 is the date of the **spring equinox** (also called the *vernal equinox*). On these dates the vertical rays of the Sun strike along the equator (0° latitude), because Earth is in such a position in its orbit that the axis is tilted neither toward nor away from the Sun.

The length of daylight versus darkness is also determined by the position of Earth in its orbit. The length of daylight on June 21, the summer solstice in the Northern Hemisphere, is greater than the length of night. This fact can be established by examining Figure 7, which illustrates the **circle of illumination**—that is, the boundary separating the dark half of Earth from the lighted half. The length of daylight is established by comparing the fraction of a line of latitude that is on the "day" side of the circle of illumination with the fraction on the "night" side. Notice that on June 21 all locations in the Northern Hemisphere experience longer periods of daylight than darkness (Figure 7). The opposite is true for the

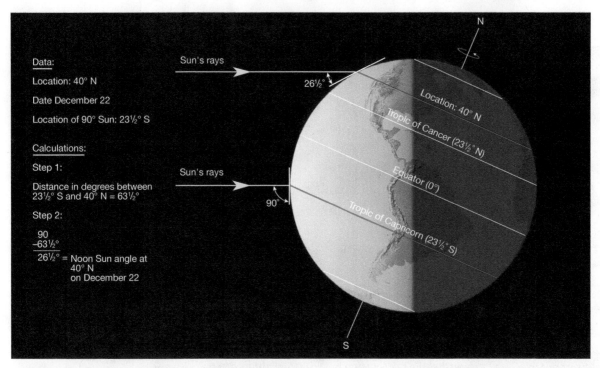

Data:

Location: 40° N

Date December 22

Location of 90° Sun: 23½° S

Calculations:

Step 1:

Distance in degrees between 23½° S and 40° N = 63½°

Step 2:

$$\begin{array}{r} 90 \\ -63\frac{1}{2}° \\ \hline 26\frac{1}{2}° \end{array} = \text{Noon Sun angle at}$$
                    40° N
                    on December 22

FIGURE 6 Calculating the noon Sun angle. Recall that on any given day, only one latitude receives vertical (90°) rays of the Sun. A place located 1° away (either north or south) receives an 89° angle; a place 2° away, an 88° angle, and so forth. To calculate the noon Sun angle, simply find the number of degrees of latitude separating the location you want to know about from the latitude that is receiving the vertical rays of the Sun. Then subtract that value from 90°. The example in this figure illustrates how to calculate the noon Sun angle for a city located at 40° north latitude on December 22 (winter solstice).

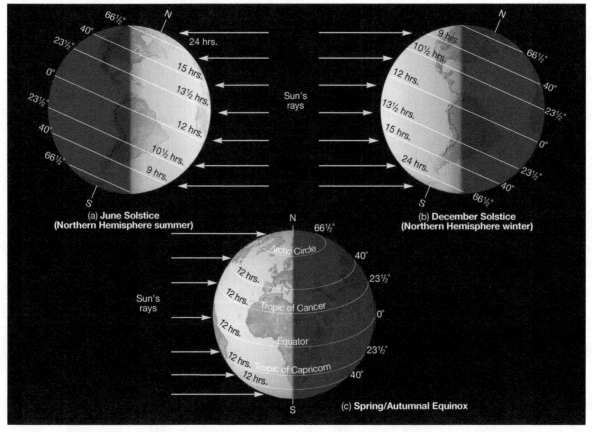

FIGURE 7 Characteristics of the solstices and equinoxes.

TABLE 2	Length of Daylight		
Latitude (degrees)	Summer solstice	Winter solstice	Equinoxes
0	12 hr	12 hr	12 hr
10	12 hr 35 min	11 hr 25 min	12 hr
20	13 hr 12 min	10 hr 48 min	12 hr
30	13 hr 56 min	10 hr 04 min	12 hr
40	14 hr 52 min	9 hr 08 min	12 hr
50	16 hr 18 min	7 hr 42 min	12 hr
60	18 hr 27 min	5 hr 33 min	12 hr
70	2 mo	0 hr 00 min	12 hr
80	4 mo	0 hr 00 min	12 hr
90	6 mo	0 hr 00 min	12 hr

As a review of the characteristics of the summer solstice for the Northern Hemisphere, examine Figure 7 and Table 2 and consider the following facts:

1. The date of occurrence is June 21 or 22.
2. The vertical rays of the Sun are striking the Tropic of Cancer (23 1/2° north latitude).
3. Locations in the Northern Hemisphere are experiencing their longest length of daylight and highest Sun angle (opposite for the Southern Hemisphere).
4. The farther north a location is from the equator, the longer the period of daylight until the Arctic Circle is reached, where the length of daylight becomes 24 hours long (opposite for the Southern Hemisphere).

The facts about the winter solstice are just the opposite. It should now be apparent why a midlatitude location is warmest in the summer. It is then that the days are longest and the angle of the Sun is highest (see Box 2).

During an equinox (meaning "equal night"), the length of daylight is 12 hours everywhere on Earth because the circle of illumination passes directly through the poles, thus dividing the latitudes in half.

In summary, *seasonal fluctuations in the amount of solar energy reaching various places on Earth's surface are caused by the migrating vertical rays of the Sun and the resulting variations in Sun angle and length of daylight.* These changes in turn cause the month-to-month variations in temperature observed at most

December solstice, when the length of darkness exceeds the length of daylight at all locations in the Northern Hemisphere. Again, for comparison, consider New York City (about 40°N), which has 15 hours of daylight on June 21 and only nine hours on December 21.

Also note, from Table 2, that the farther north a location is from the equator on June 21, the longer the period of daylight. When you reach the Arctic Circle (66 1/2°N), the length of daylight is 24 hours. This is the "midnight Sun," which does not set for about six months at the North Pole (Figure 8).

FIGURE 8 Multiple exposures of the midnight Sun in late June or July in high northern latitudes—Alaska, Scandinavia, Northern Canada, etc. (Photo by Brian Stablyk/Getty Images, Inc./Stone Allstock)

BOX 1 ▶ WHEN ARE THE SEASONS?

Have you ever been caught in a snow-storm around Thanksgiving, only to be told by the TV weatherperson that winter does not begin until December 21? Or perhaps you have endured several consecutive days of 100° temperatures only to discover that summer has not "officially" started? The idea of dividing the year into four seasons clearly originated from the Earth–Sun relationships discussed in this chapter (Table A). This astronomical definition of the seasons defines winter (Northern Hemisphere) as the period from the winter solstice (December 21–22) to the spring equinox (March 21–22) and so forth. This is also the definition used most widely by the news media, yet it is not unusual for portions of the United States and Canada to have significant snowfalls

TABLE A Occurrence of the Seasons in the Northern Hemisphere

Season	Astronomical season	Climatological season
Spring	March 21 or 22 to June 21 or 22	March, April, May
Summer	June 21 or 22 to September 22 or 23	June, July, August
Autumn	September 22 or 23 to December 21 or 22	September, October, November
Winter	December 21 or 22 to March 21 or 22	December, January, February

weeks before the "official" start of winter (Figure A).

Because the weather phenomena we normally associate with each season do not coincide well with the astronomical seasons, meteorologists prefer to divide the year into four three-month periods based primarily on temperature. Thus, winter is defined as December, January, and February, the three coldest months of the year in

the Northern Hemisphere. Summer is defined as the three warmest months, June, July, and August. Spring and autumn are the transition periods between these two seasons. Inasmuch as these four three-month periods better reflect the temperatures and weather that we associate with the respective seasons, this definition of the seasons is more useful for meteorological discussions.

FIGURE A Stream in autumn woods. (Photo by Corbis/Superstock)

locations outside the tropics. Figure 9 shows mean monthly temperatures for selected cities at different latitudes. Notice that the cities located at more poleward latitudes experience larger temperature differences from summer to winter than do cities located nearer the equator. Also notice that temperature minimums for Southern Hemisphere locations occur in July, whereas they occur in January for most places in the Northern Hemisphere.

All places situated at the same latitude have identical Sun angles and lengths of daylight. If the Earth–Sun relationships just described were the only controls of temperature, we would expect these places to have identical temperatures as well. Obviously, such is not the case. Although the angle of the Sun above the horizon and the length of daylight are the main controls of temperature, they are not the only controls.

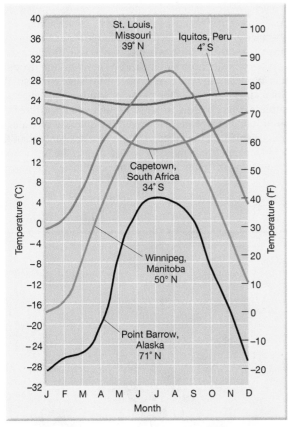

FIGURE 9 Mean monthly temperatures for five cities located at different latitudes. Note that Capetown, South Africa, experiences winter in June, July, and August.

Energy, Heat, and Temperature

The universe is made up of a combination of matter and energy. The concept of matter is easy to grasp because it is the "stuff" we can see, smell, and touch. Energy, on the other hand, is abstract and therefore more difficult to describe and understand. Energy comes to Earth from the Sun in the form of electromagnetic radiation, which we see as light and feel as heat. There are countless places and situations where energy is present. It is found in the food we eat, the water located at the top of a waterfall, and the waves that break along the shore.

For our purposes we will define **energy** simply as *the capacity to do work.* We can think of work as being done whenever matter is moved. Everyday examples include the chemical energy from gasoline that powers automobiles, the heat energy from stoves that excite water molecules (boils water), and the gravitational energy that has the capacity to move snow down a mountain slope in the form of an avalanche. These examples illustrate that energy takes many forms. Moreover, energy can change from one form to another. For example, the chemical energy in gasoline is first converted to heat in the engine of an automobile, which is then converted to mechanical energy that moves the automobile along.

Forms of Energy

You are undoubtedly familiar with some of the common forms of energy, such as heat, chemical, nuclear, radiant (light), and gravitational energy. In addition, some forms of energy are classified into two major categories: *kinetic energy* and *potential energy.*

Kinetic Energy *Energy associated with an object by virtue of its motion* is described as **kinetic energy**. A simple example of kinetic energy is the motion of a hammer when driving a nail. Because of its motion, the hammer is able to move another object (do work). The faster the hammer is swung, the greater its kinetic energy (energy of motion). Similarly, a larger (more massive) hammer will possess more kinetic energy than a smaller one, provided both are swung at the same velocity. Likewise, the winds associated with a hurricane possess much more kinetic energy than do light, localized breezes. Hurricane-force winds are both larger in scale (more massive) and travel at higher velocities.

Kinetic energy is also significant at the atomic level. All matter is composed of atoms and molecules that are continually vibrating. Thus, by virtue of this motion, the atoms or molecules in matter have kinetic energy. When a pan of water is placed over a fire, the water becomes warmer, because the heat from the fire causes the water molecules to vibrate faster. We can conclude that when a solid, liquid, or gas is heated, its atoms or molecules move faster and possess more kinetic energy.

Potential Energy As the term implies, **potential energy** has the capability to do work. For example, large hailstones suspended by an updraft in a towering cloud have potential energy because of their position. Should the updraft subside, these hailstones could do destructive work on roofs and vehicles. Many substances, including wood, gasoline, and the food you eat, contain potential energy, which is capable of doing work given the right circumstances.

Temperature

Temperature is a quantity that describes how warm or cold an object is with respect to some standard measure. In the United States the Fahrenheit scale is used most often for everyday expressions of temperature. However, laboratories and most of the rest of the world use the Celsius and Kelvin temperature scales.

Temperature can also be described as a *measure of the average kinetic energy of the atoms or molecules in a substance.* When a substance gains energy, its particles move faster and its temperature rises. By contrast, when energy is lost, the atoms and molecules vibrate more slowly and its temperature drops.

It is important to note that temperature is *not* a measure of the total kinetic energy of the particles within a substance. For example, a cup of boiling water has a higher temperature than a tub of lukewarm water. However, the quantity of water in the cup is small, so it contains far less kinetic energy than the water in the tub. Much more ice would melt in the tub of lukewarm water than in the cup of boiling water. The temperature

---

BOX 2 ▶ THE ANALEMMA

The analemma is a graph resembling a figure 8 that can be used as a reference when calculating the angle of noon Sun for any location on the globe, for any day of the year. An analemma shows the latitude where the noon Sun is directly overhead (90-degree angle) for each day of the year. Notice that on March 21–22 and September 21–22 the Sun is directly overhead at the equator, a fact we considered earlier (Figure B).

By knowing where the noon Sun is overhead, you can readily calculate the angle of the noon Sun at any other latitude for any date. For each degree of latitude that a particular location is from the latitude where the Sun is overhead, the angle of the noon Sun at that location is one degree less than 90 degrees. For example, if you want to know the angle of the noon Sun at New York City (40°N) on May 14, you first find that date on the analemma to establish the latitude where the noon Sun is directly overhead. In this case it is 18 degrees north latitude. *It is important to note whether the location is north or south of the equator.* Thus, New York City is 22 degrees (40° N − 18°N = 22°) from the location where the Sun is directly overhead on May 14. Consequently, the angle of the noon Sun at New York City on May 14 is 68 degrees above the horizon. (Note that New York is 22 degrees from the location where the Sun is directly overhead. Subtracting that figure from 90 degrees yields 68 degrees [90 − 22 = 68]). Can you calculate the noon Sun angle for a place located at 40°S latitude on May 14? (*Hint:* See Figure 6.)

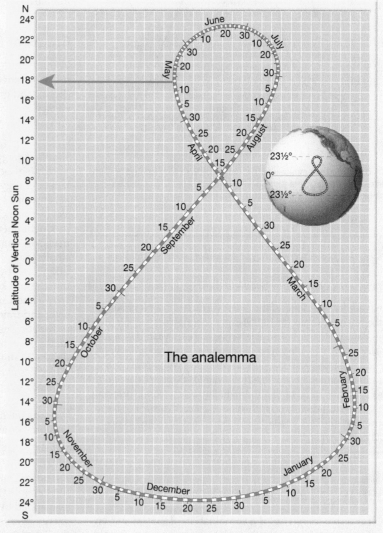

FIGURE B The analemma, a graph showing the latitude of the overhead (vertical) noon Sun throughout the year.

of the water in the cup is higher because the atoms and molecules are vibrating faster, but the total amount of kinetic energy is much smaller because there are many fewer particles.

Heat

When you touch a hot stove, heat enters your hand because the stove is warmer than your hand. By contrast, when you hold an ice cube, heat is transferred from your hand to the ice cube. The transfer of energy into or out of an object because of temperature differences between that object and its surroundings is called **heat.** Heat flows from a region of higher temperature to one of lower temperature. Once the temperatures become equal, heat flow stops.

When an object absorbs heat, it appears as an increase in internal energy, often in the form of increased molecular motion. (Sometimes, as when ice melts, a substance absorbs heat without an increase in kinetic energy.) However, we do not say that a substance has heat, because heat describes energy that is flowing or being transferred. We can examine the flow of energy between substances of different temperatures by imagining a warm bottle of wine placed in a bucket of chilled water. According to the concept of kinetic energy, the average speed of the molecules in the bottle of wine is greater than those in the cold water. As the molecules collide with the sides of the wine bottle, the faster molecules (warm wine) tend to slow down, while the slower molecules (cold water) tend to speed up. Assuming no other source of energy, the average speed of the molecules in these liquids (and therefore their temperatures) eventually becomes equal. The net result is that energy has flowed from the warm wine to the cold water. So heat can be thought of as internal energy of matter that transfers from one thing to another by virtue of temperature differences.

Mechanisms of Heat Transfer

GE●De   Heating Earth's Surface and Atmosphere
THE ATMOSPHERE   ▶ Solar Radiation

As we consider heat-transfer mechanisms, recall that heat flows from warmer substances to cooler substances. If two objects are in contact, the one that is warmer will become cooler

and the cooler one will become warmer, until they reach a common temperature. This flow of energy called *heat* can occur in three ways: *conduction, convection,* and *radiation* (Figure 10). Although they are presented separately, all three mechanisms of heat transfer can operate simultaneously. In addition, these processes transfer heat between the Sun and Earth and between Earth's surface, the atmosphere, and outer space.

Conduction

Conduction is familiar to most of us through our everyday experiences. Anyone who has attempted to pick up a metal spoon that was left in a boiling pot of soup realized that heat was transmitted along the entire length of the spoon. The transfer of heat in this manner is called conduction. The hot soup caused the molecules at the lower end of the spoon to vibrate more rapidly. These molecules and free electrons collided more vigorously with their neighbors and so on up the handle of the spoon. Thus, **conduction** is the transfer of heat through electron and molecular collisions from one molecule to another. The ability of substances to conduct heat varies considerably. Metals are good conductors, as those of us who have touched a hot spoon have quickly learned. Air, in contrast, is a very poor conductor of heat. Consequently, conduction is important only between Earth's surface and the air immediately in contact with the surface. As a means of heat transfer for the atmosphere as a whole, conduction is the least significant and can be disregarded when considering most meteorological phenomena.

Objects that are poor conductors, like air, are called *insulators*. Most objects that are good insulators, such as cork, plastic foams, or goose down, contain many small air spaces. It is the poor conductivity of the trapped air that gives these materials their insulating value. Snow is also a poor conductor (good insulator). Like other insulators, fresh snow contains numerous air spaces that serve to retard the flow of heat. Thus, a wild animal will often burrow into a snowbank to escape the "cold." The snow, like a down-filled comforter, does not supply heat; it simply retards the loss of the animal's own body heat.

FIGURE 10   The three mechanisms of heat transfer: conduction, convection, and radiation.

Convection

Much of the heat transport that occurs in the atmosphere and ocean is carried on by convection. **Convection** is heat transfer that involves the actual movement or circulation of a substance. It takes place in fluids (liquids like water and gases like air) where the material is able to flow. Because the atoms or molecules in solids vibrate around a fixed point, heat transfer in solids takes place by conduction.

The pan of water being heated over a campfire in Figure 10 illustrates the nature of a simple convective circulation. The fire warms the bottom of the pan, which conducts heat to the water inside. Because water is a relatively poor conductor, only the water in close proximity to the bottom of the pan is heated by conduction. Heating causes water to expand and become less dense. Thus, the hot, buoyant water near the bottom of the pan rises while the cooler, denser water above sinks. As long as the water is heated from the bottom and cools near the top, it will continue to "turn over," producing a *convective circulation.*

In a similar manner, much of the heat acquired in the lowest layer of the atmosphere by way of radiation and conduction is transported by convection. For example, on a hot, sunny day the air above a large asphalt parking lot will be heated more than the air above the surrounding woodlands. As warm, less dense air above the parking lot buoys upward, it is replaced by the cooler air above the woodlands. In this way a convective flow is established. The warm parcels of rising air are called **thermals** and are what hang-glider pilots use to keep their crafts soaring. Convection of this type not only transfers heat but also transports moisture aloft. The result is an increase in cloudiness that frequently can be observed on warm summer afternoons.

On a much larger scale is the global convective circulation of the atmosphere, which is driven by the unequal heating of Earth's surface. These complex movements are responsible for the redistribution of heat between hot equatorial regions and frigid polar latitudes.

Students Sometimes Ask . . .

In the morning when I get out of bed, why does the tile flooring in the bathroom feel much colder than the carpeted area, even though both materials are the same temperature?

The difference you feel is due mainly to the fact that floor tile is a much better conductor of heat than carpet. Hence, heat is more rapidly conducted from your bare feet when you are standing on the tile floor than when you are on the carpeted floor. Even at room temperature (20°C or 68°F), objects that are good conductors can feel chilly to the touch. (Remember, body temperature is about 98.6°F.)

Atmospheric circulation consists of vertical as well as horizontal components, so both vertical and horizontal heat transfer occurs. Meteorologists often use the term *convection* to describe that part of the atmospheric circulation that involves *upward and downward* heat transfer. By contrast, the term **advection** is used to denote the horizontal component of convective flow. (The common term for advection is "wind.") Those who reside in the midlatitudes often experience the effects of heat transfer by advection. For example, when frigid Canadian air invades the Midwest in January, it brings bitterly cold winter weather. By contrast, the northward flow of air from the Gulf of Mexico is associated with warm temperatures.

Radiation

The third mechanism of heat transfer is radiation. Unlike conduction and convection, which need a medium in which to travel, radiant energy does not. Radiation is the only mechanism of heat transfer that travels through the vacuum of space. Therefore, it is the heat-transfer mechanism by which solar energy reaches our planet.

Solar Radiation As noted earlier, the Sun is the ultimate source of energy that drives the weather machine. For this reason, we consider the nature of solar radiation in more detail. We know that the Sun emits light and heat as well as the rays that burn or darken skin pigmentation. Although these forms of energy constitute a major portion of the total energy that radiates from the Sun, they are only a part of a large array of energy called **radiation** or **electromagnetic radiation.** This array or spectrum of electromagnetic energy is shown in Figure 11.

All types of radiation, whether X-rays, radio waves, or heat waves, travel through the vacuum of space at 300,000 kilometers (186,000 miles) per second, a value known as the *speed of light.* To help visualize radiant energy, imagine ripples made in a calm pond when a pebble is tossed in. Like the waves produced in the pond, electromagnetic waves come in various sizes or **wavelengths**—the distance from one crest to the next (Figure 11). Radio waves have the longest wavelengths, up to tens of kilometers in length. Gamma waves are the shortest, being less than a billionth of a centimeter long. Visible light is roughly in the middle of this range.

Radiation is often identified by the effect that it produces when it interacts with an object. The retinas of our eyes, for instance, are sensitive to a range of wavelengths that we call **visible light.** We often refer to visible light as white light, for it appears "white" in color. It is easy to show, however, that white light is really an array of colors, each color corresponding to a specific range of wavelengths. By using a prism, white light can be divided into the colors of the rainbow, from violet with the shortest wavelength, 0.4 micrometer (1 micrometer is 0.001 centimeter), to red with the longest wavelength, 0.7 micrometer.

Located adjacent to the color red, and having a longer wavelength, is **infrared radiation,** which we cannot see but our skin detects as heat. (Only the infrared energy that is

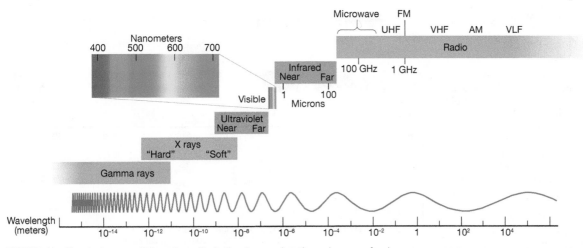

FIGURE 11 The electromagnetic spectrum, illustrating the wavelengths and names of various types of radiation.

nearest the visible part of the spectrum is intense enough to be felt as heat.) The invisible waves located next to violet are called **ultraviolet radiation.** These are the wavelengths that are responsible for sunburn (see Box 3).

Although we divide radiant energy into categories based on our ability to perceive them, all wavelengths of radiation behave in a similar manner. When an object absorbs any form of electromagnetic energy, the waves excite subatomic particles (electrons). This results in an increase in molecular motion and a corresponding increase in temperature. Thus, the rapid vibrations of extremely hot molecules on the Sun create electromagnetic waves that travel through space and, upon being absorbed, increase the molecular motion of other groups of molecules—including those that make up the atmosphere, Earth's land–sea surface, and even our bodies.

One important difference among the various wavelengths of radiant energy is that shorter wavelengths are more energetic. This accounts for the fact that relatively short (high-energy) ultraviolet waves can damage human tissue more readily than similar exposures to longer wavelength radiation. The damage can result in skin cancer and cataracts.

It is important to note that the Sun emits all forms of radiation, as shown in Figure 11, but in varying quantities. Over 95 percent of all solar radiation is emitted in wavelengths between 0.1 and 2.5 micrometers, with much of this energy concentrated in the visible and near-visible parts of the electromagnetic spectrum (Figure 12). The narrow band of visible light, between 0.4 and 0.7 micrometer, represents over 43 percent of the total energy emitted. The bulk of the remainder lies in the infrared zone (49 percent) and ultraviolet

(UV) section (7 percent). Less than 1 percent of solar radiation is emitted as X-rays, gamma rays, and radio waves.

Laws of Radiation To obtain a better appreciation of how the Sun's radiant energy interacts with Earth's atmosphere and land–sea surface, it is helpful to have a general understanding of the basic radiation laws. The principles that follow were set forth by physicists during the late 1800s and early 1900s. Although the mathematics of these laws is beyond the scope of this text, the concepts are fundamental to understanding radiation:

FIGURE 12 Comparison of the intensity of solar radiation and radiation emitted by Earth. Because of the Sun's high surface temperature, most of its energy is radiated at wavelengths shorter than 4 micrometers, with the greatest intensity in the visible range of the electromagnetic spectrum. Earth, in contrast, radiates most of its energy in wavelengths longer than 4 micrometers, primarily in the infrared band. Thus, we call the Sun's radiation *short-wave* and Earth's radiation *longwave*. (*After Tom L. McKnight,* Physical Geography, © 1990, *Prentice Hall, Inc.*)

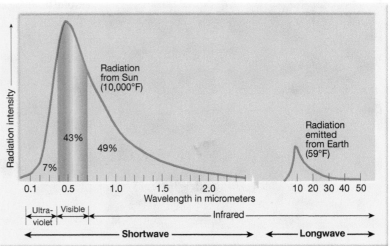

BOX 3 ▶ THE ULTRAVIOLET INDEX

Gong-Yuh Lin *

Most people welcome sunny weather. On warm days, when the sky is cloudless and bright, many spend a great deal of time outdoors "soaking up" the sunshine (Figure C). For many, the goal is to develop a dark tan, one that sunbathers often describe as "healthy-looking." Ironically, there is strong evidence that too much sunshine (specifically, too much ultraviolet radiation) can lead to serious health problems, mainly skin cancer and cataracts.

Since June 1994 the National Weather Service (NWS) has issued the next-day ultraviolet index (UVI) for the United States to warn the public of potential health risks of exposure to sunlight (Figure D). The UV index is determined by taking into account the predicted cloud cover and reflectivity of the surface, as well as the Sun angle and atmospheric depth for each forecast location. Because atmospheric ozone strongly absorbs ultraviolet radiation, the extent of the ozone layer is also considered. The UVI values lie on a scale from 0 to 11 and higher, with larger values representing greatest risk.

The U.S. Environmental Protection Agency has established five exposure categories based on UVI values—Low, Moderate, High, Very High, and Extreme (Table B). Precautionary measures have been developed for each category. The public is advised to minimize outdoor activities when the UVI is Very High or Extreme. Sunscreen with a sun-protection factor (SPF) of 15 or higher is recommended for all exposed skin. This is especially important after swimming or while sunbathing, even on cloudy days with the UVI in the Low category.

Table B shows the range of minutes to burn for the most susceptible skin type (pale or milky white) for each exposure category. Note that the exposure that results in sunburn varies from over 60 minutes for the Low category to less than 10 minutes for the Extreme category. It takes approximately five times longer to cause sunburn of the least susceptible skin type, brown to dark. The most susceptible skin type develops red sunburn, painful swelling, and skin peeling when exposed to excessive sunlight. By contrast, the least susceptible skin type rarely burns and shows very rapid tanning response.

---

*Professor Lin is a faculty member in the Department of Geography at California State University, Northridge.

TABLE B	The UV Index: Minutes to Burn for the Most Susceptible Skin Type.		
UVI value	Exposure category	Description	Minutes to burn
0–2	Low	Low danger from the Sun's UV rays for the average person.	>60
3–5	Moderate	Moderate risk from unprotected Sun exposure. Take precautions during the mid-day when Sun is strongest.	40–60
6–7	High	Protection against sunburn is needed. Cover up, wear a hat and sunglasses, and use sunscreen.	25–40
8–10	Very High	Try to avoid the Sun between 11 AM and 4 PM. Otherwise, cover up and use sunscreen.	10–25
11–15	Extreme	Take all precautions. Unprotected skin will burn in minutes. Do not pursue outdoor activities if possible. If out of doors, apply sunscreen liberally every 2 hours.	<10

FIGURE C Exposing sensitive skin to too much solar ultraviolet radiation has potential health risks. (Photo by Eddie Gerald/Rough Guides)

FIGURE D UV Index forecast for June 8, 2008.

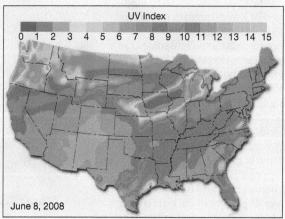

1. **All objects continually emit radiant energy over a range of wavelengths.*** Thus, not only do hot objects like the Sun continually emit energy, but Earth does as well, even its polar ice caps.

2. **Hotter objects radiate more total energy per unit area than do colder objects.** The Sun, which has a surface temperature of 6000 K (10,000°F), emits about 160,000 times more energy per unit area than does Earth, which has an average surface temperature of 288 K (59°F). This concept is called the *Stefan–Boltzman law* and is expressed mathematically in Box 4.

3. **Hotter objects radiate more energy in the form of short wavelength radiation than do cooler objects.** We can visualize this law by imagining a piece of metal that, when heated sufficiently (as occurs in a blacksmith's shop), produces a white glow. As it cools, the metal emits more of its energy in longer wavelengths and glows a reddish color. Eventually, no light is given off, but if you place your hand near the metal, the still longer infrared radiation will be detectable as heat. The Sun radiates maximum energy at 0.5 micrometer, which is in the visible range (Figure 12). The maximum radiation emitted from Earth occurs at a wavelength of 10 micrometers, well within the infrared (heat) range. Because the maximum Earth radiation is roughly 20 times longer than the maximum solar radiation, it is often referred to as **longwave radiation,** whereas solar radiation is called **shortwave radiation.** This concept is known as *Wien's displacement law* and is expressed mathematically in Box 4.

4. **Objects that are good absorbers of radiation are also good emitters.** The perfect absorber (and emitter) is a theoretical object called a **blackbody.** In the visible wavelengths, black coal dust is an excellent absorber (reflects very little light), hence the name blackbody. However, blackbodies do not have to be black in color, they simply must absorb and emit all possible radiation for their respective temperatures. Earth's surface and the Sun approach being blackbodies because they absorb and radiate with nearly 100 percent efficiency. By contrast, the gases that compose our atmosphere are *selective* absorbers and emitters of radiation. For some wavelengths the atmosphere is nearly transparent (little radiation absorbed). For others, however, it is nearly opaque (absorbs most of the radiation that strikes it). Experience tells us that the atmosphere is quite transparent to visible light emitted by the Sun because it readily reaches Earth's surface.

To summarize, although the Sun is the ultimate source of radiant energy, all objects continually radiate energy over a range of wavelengths. Hot objects, like the Sun, emit mostly shortwave radiation. By contrast, most objects at everyday temperatures (Earth's surface and atmosphere) emit mostly longwave (low-energy) radiation. Objects that are good absorbers of radiation, like Earth's surface, are also good emitters. By contrast, most gases are only good absorbers (emitters) in certain wavelengths but poor absorbers in other wavelengths.

What Happens to Incoming Solar Radiation?

GEODe THE ATMOSPHERE — Heating Earth's Surface and Atmosphere ▸ What Happens to Incoming Solar Radiation?

When radiation strikes an object, there are usually three different things that can happen at the same time. First, some of the energy may be *absorbed*. Recall that when radiant energy is absorbed, the molecules begin to vibrate faster, which causes an increase in temperature. The amount of energy absorbed by an object depends on the intensity of the radiation and the object's **absorptivity**. In the visible range, the degree of absorptivity is largely responsible for the brightness of an object. Surfaces that are good absorbers of all wavelengths of visible light appear black in color, whereas light-colored surfaces have a much lower absorptivity. That is why wearing light-colored clothing on a sunny summer day will help keep you cooler. Second, substances such as water and air, which are transparent to certain wavelengths of radiation, may simply *transmit* energy. Radiation that is transmitted does not contribute energy to the object. Third, some radiation may "bounce off" the object without being absorbed or transmitted. *Reflection* and *scattering* are responsible for redirecting incoming solar radiation. In summary, *radiation may be absorbed, transmitted, or redirected (reflected or scattered).*

Figure 13 shows the fate of incoming solar radiation averaged for the entire globe. Notice that the atmosphere is quite

FIGURE 13 Average distribution of incoming solar radiation by percentage. More solar energy is absorbed by Earth's surface than by the atmosphere. Consequently, the air is not heated directly by the Sun, but is heated indirectly from Earth's surface.

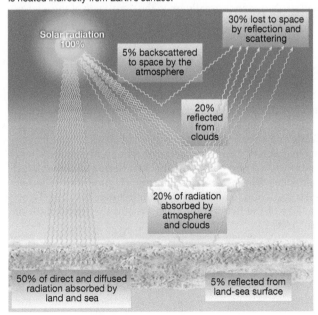

*The temperature of the object must be above a theoretical value called *absolute zero* (−273°C) for it to emit radiant energy. The letter K is used for values on the Kelvin temperature scale.

BOX 4 ▶ RADIATION LAWS

Gregory J. Carbone *

All bodies radiate energy. Both the rate and the wavelength of radiation emitted depend on the temperature of the radiating body.

Stefan–Boltzman Law

This law mathematically expresses the rate of radiation emitted per unit area:

$$E = \sigma T^4$$

E, the rate of radiation emitted by a body, is proportional to the fourth power of the body's temperature (T). The Stefan–Boltzmann constant (σ) is equal to $5.67 \times 10^{-8}\ \mathrm{W/m^2\,K^4}$. Compare the difference between the radiation emission from the Sun and Earth. The Sun, with an average temperature of 6000 K, emits 73,483,200 watts per square meter ($\mathrm{Wm^{-2}}$)

$$E = (5.67 \times 10^{-8}\ \mathrm{W/m^2\,K^4})$$
$$(6000\ \mathrm{K})^4$$

$$= 73{,}483{,}200\ \mathrm{W/m^2}$$

By contrast, Earth has an average temperature of only 288 K. If we round the value to 300 K, we have

$$E = (5.67 \times 10^{-8}\ \mathrm{W/m^2\,K^4})$$
$$(300\ \mathrm{K})^4$$

$$= 459\ \mathrm{W/m^2}$$

The Sun has a temperature that is approximately 20 times higher than Earth and thus emits approximately 160,000 times more radiation per unit area. This makes sense because $20^4 = 160{,}000$.

Wien's Displacement Law

This law describes mathematically the relationship between the temperature (T) of a radiating body and its wavelength of maximum emission (λ_{max})

$$\lambda_{max} = C/T$$

Wien's constant (C) is equal to 2898 μmK. If we use the Sun and Earth as examples, we find

$$\lambda_{max}(\text{Sun}) = \frac{2898\ \mu\mathrm{mK}}{6000\ \mathrm{K}} = 0.483\ \mu\mathrm{m}$$

and

$$\lambda_{max}(\text{Earth}) = \frac{2898\ \mu\mathrm{mK}}{300\ \mathrm{K}} = 9.66\ \mu\mathrm{m}$$

Note that the Sun radiates its maximum energy within the visible portion of the electromagnetic spectrum. The cooler Earth radiates its maximum energy in the infrared portion of the electromagnetic spectrum.

_____

*Professor Carbone is a faculty member in the Department of Geography at the University of South Carolina.

---

transparent to incoming solar radiation. On average, about 50 percent of the energy reaching the top of the atmosphere is absorbed at Earth's surface. Another 30 percent is reflected back to space by the atmosphere, clouds, and reflective surfaces such as snow and water. The remaining 20 percent is absorbed by clouds and the atmosphere's gases.

What determines whether solar radiation will be transmitted to the surface, scattered, reflected back to space, or absorbed by the gases and particles in the atmosphere? As you will see, it depends greatly upon the *wavelength* of the energy being transmitted, as well as upon the size and nature of the intervening material.

Reflection and Scattering

Reflection is the process whereby light bounces back from an object at the same angle at which it encounters a surface and with the same intensity (Figure 14a). By contrast, **scattering** produces a larger number of weaker rays, traveling in different directions. Although scattering disperses light both forward and backward (**backscattering**), more energy is dispersed in the forward direction (Figure 14b). Whether solar radiation is reflected or scattered depends largely on the size of the intervening particles and the wavelength of the light.

Reflection and Earth's Albedo Energy is returned to space from Earth in two ways: reflection and emission of radiant energy. The portion of solar energy that is reflected back to space leaves in the same short wavelengths in which it came

to Earth. About 30 percent of the solar energy that reaches our planet is reflected back to space (Figure 13). Included in this figure is the amount sent skyward by backscattering. This energy is lost to Earth and does not play a role in heating the atmosphere.

The fraction of radiation that is reflected by an object is called its **albedo.** The albedo for Earth as a whole (planetary albedo) is 30 percent. The amount of light reflected from Earth's land–sea surface represents only about 5 percent of the total planetary albedo (Figure 13). Clouds are largely responsible

FIGURE 14 Reflection and scattering. (a) Reflected light bounces back from a surface at the same angle at which it strikes that surface and with the same intensity. (b) When a beam of light is scattered, it results in a larger number of weaker rays, traveling in different directions. Usually more energy is scattered in the forward direction than is backscattered.

(a) Reflection   (b) Scattering

for most of Earth's "brightness" as seen from space. The high reflectivity of clouds should not surprise anyone who has tried to drive on a very foggy night with bright lights.

In comparison to Earth, the Moon, which is without clouds or an atmosphere, has an average albedo of only 7 percent. Even though a full Moon gives us a good bit of light, the much brighter and larger Earth would provide an astronaut on the Moon with far more light for an "Earth-lit" walk at night.

Figure 15 gives the albedo for various surfaces. Fresh snow and thick clouds have high albedos (good reflectors). By contrast, dark soils and parking lots have low albedos and thus absorb much of the radiation they receive. In the case of a lake or the ocean, note that the angle at which the Sun's rays strike the water surface greatly affects its albedo.

Diffused Light   Although incoming solar radiation travels in a straight line, small dust particles and gas molecules in the atmosphere scatter some of this energy in different directions. The result, called **diffused light,** explains how light reaches into the area beneath a shade tree, and how a room is lit in the absence of direct sunlight. Further, scattering accounts for the brightness and even the blue color of the daytime sky. In contrast, bodies like the Moon and Mercury, which are without atmospheres, have dark skies and "pitch-black" shadows, even during daylight hours. Overall, about one-half of solar radiation that is absorbed at Earth's surface arrives as scattered light.

Blue Skies and Red Sunsets   Recall that sunlight appears white, but it is composed of all colors. Gas molecules more effectively scatter the shorter wavelengths (blue and violet) of

FIGURE 16   At sunset, clouds often appear red because they are illuminated by sunlight in which most of the blue light has been lost due to scattering. (Photo by Dennis Frates / Alamy)

visible light than the longer wavelengths (red and orange). This fact explains the blue color of the sky and the orange and red colors seen at sunrise and sunset (Figure 16). When the Sun is overhead, you can look in any direction away from the direct Sun and see predominantly blue light, which is the wavelength more readily scattered by the atmosphere.

Conversely, the Sun appears to have an orangish-to-reddish tint when viewed near the horizon (Figure 17). This is the result of the great distance solar radiation must travel through the atmosphere before it reaches your eyes (see Table 1). As a consequence, most of the blue and violet wavelengths will be scattered out, leaving light that consists mostly of reds and oranges. The reddish appearance of clouds during sunrise and sunset also results because the clouds are illuminated by light from which the blue color has been subtracted by scattering.

The most spectacular sunsets occur when large quantities of fine dust or smoke particles penetrate the stratosphere. For three years after the great eruption of the Indonesian volcano Krakatau in 1883, brilliant sunsets occurred worldwide. In addition, the European summer that followed this colossal explosion was cooler than normal, which has been attributed to an increase in the amount of backscattering.

Large particles associated with haze, fog, or smog scatter light more equally in all wavelengths. Because no color is predominant over any other, the sky appears white or gray on days when large particles are abundant. Scattering of sunlight by haze, water droplets, or dust particles makes it possible for us to observe bands (or rays) of sunlight called *crepuscular rays*. These bright fan-shaped bands are most commonly seen when the Sun shines through a break in the clouds, as shown in Figure 18. Crepuscular rays can also be observed around twilight when towering clouds cause alternating lighter and darker bands (light rays and shadows) to streak across the sky.

FIGURE 15   Albedo (reflectivity) of various surfaces. In general, light-colored surfaces tend to be more reflective than dark-colored surfaces and thus have higher albedos.

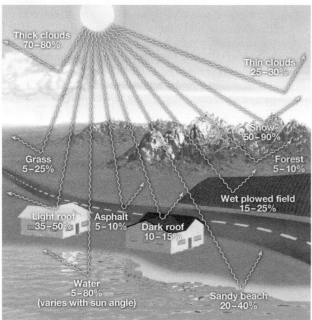

Thick clouds
70–80%

Thin clouds
25–30%

Snow
50–90%

Grass
5–25%

Forest
5–10%

Wet plowed field
15–25%

Light roof
35–50%

Asphalt
5–10%

Dark roof
10–15%

Water
5–80%
(varies with sun angle)

Sandy beach
20–40%

Midday sun

Midday–observer sees whitish sun, blue sky

Sunset–observer sees reddish sunset

Sun at sunset

FIGURE 17 Short wavelengths (blue and violet) of visible light are scattered more effectively than are longer wavelengths (red, orange). Therefore, when the Sun is overhead, an observer can look in any direction and see predominantly blue light that was selectively scattered by the gases in the atmosphere. By contrast, at sunset, the path that light must take through the atmosphere is much longer. Consequently, most of the blue light is scattered before it reaches an observer. Thus, the Sun appears reddish in color.

In summary, the color of the sky gives an indication of the number of large or small particles present. Numerous small particles produce red sunsets, whereas large particles produce white (gray) skies. Thus, the bluer the sky, the cleaner the air.

Absorption by Earth's Surface and Atmosphere

Although Earth's surface is a relatively good absorber (effectively absorbs most wavelengths of solar radiation), the atmosphere is not. This accounts for the fact that 50 percent of the solar radiation that reaches Earth is absorbed by Earth's land–sea surface, whereas only 20 percent of this energy is absorbed directly by the atmosphere (see Figure 13). The atmosphere is not as effective an absorber because gases are selective absorbers (and emitters) of radiation. As you will see in the following section, this fact greatly influences how the atmosphere is heated.

Freshly fallen snow is another example of a selective absorber. Anyone who has experienced the blinding reflection of sunlight from snow is aware that fresh snow is a poor absorber of visible light (reflects up to 85 percent). Because of this, the temperature directly above a snow-covered surface is colder than it would otherwise be because much of the incoming radiation is reflected away. However, snow is a very good absorber (absorbs up to 95 percent) of the infrared (heat) radiation that is emitted from Earth's surface. As the ground radiates heat upward, the lowest layer of snow absorbs this energy and reradiates most of it downward. Thus, the depth at which a winter's frost can penetrate into the ground is much less when the ground has a snow cover than in an equally cold region without snow. The statement "The ground is blanketed with snow" can be taken literally. Farmers who plant winter wheat desire a deep snow cover because it insulates their crops from bitter midwinter temperatures.

FIGURE 18 Crepuscular rays are produced when haze scatters light. Crepuscular rays are most commonly seen when the Sun shines through a break in the clouds. (Photo by Adam Jones/Visuals Unlimited, Inc.)

Radiation Emitted by Earth

GE🌎De
THE ATMOSPHERE
Heating Earth's Surface and Atmosphere
▶ The Greenhouse Effect

Although we often talk about radiation in terms of the Sun, recall that *all* objects continuously emit radiation. Because Earth is much cooler than the Sun, it emits considerably less radiant energy. Furthermore, radiation emanating from Earth's surface and atmosphere is emitted at longer wavelengths than most solar radiation. Over 95 percent of Earth's radiation has wavelengths between 2.5 and 30 micrometers, placing it in the long end of the infrared band of the electromagnetic spectrum (Figure 19). Recall that the bulk of solar radiation is emitted in wavelengths shorter than 2.5 micrometers (shortwave radiation). This difference between incoming solar radiation and radiation emitted by Earth is very important to our understanding of how our atmosphere is heated.

Heating the Atmosphere

As stated earlier, gases are selective absorbers, meaning that they absorb strongly in some wavelengths, moderately in others, and only slightly in still others. When a gas molecule absorbs radiation, this energy is transformed into internal molecular motion, which is detectable as a rise in temperature. *Thus, it is the gases that are the most effective absorbers of radiation that play the primary role in heating the atmosphere.*

At first glance Figure 19 may appear complicated; nevertheless, it is a useful aid to understanding how the atmosphere is heated. The upper portion shows that most (95 percent) incoming solar radiation has wavelengths between 0.1 and 2.5 micrometers (abbreviated μm) and includes the band of visible light (shown as the colors of the rainbow). The lower half of Figure 19 gives the absorptivity of the principal atmospheric gases. Note that nitrogen, the most abundant constituent in the atmosphere (78 percent), is a relatively poor absorber of incoming solar radiation because it absorbs best in that part of the electromagnetic spectrum, with wavelengths greater than 2.5 micrometers.

The only significant absorbers of incoming solar radiation are water vapor, oxygen, and ozone, which together accounts for most of the solar energy absorbed directly by the atmosphere. Oxygen and ozone are efficient absorbers of high-energy, shortwave radiation. Oxygen removes most of the shorter-wavelength UV radiation high in the atmosphere, and ozone absorbs UV rays in the stratosphere between 10 and 50 kilometers (6 and 30 miles). The absorption of UV energy in the stratosphere accounts for the high temperatures experienced there. More important, without the removal of UV radiation, human life would not be possible because UV energy disrupts the genetic code.

Looking at the bottom of Figure 19, you can see that for the atmosphere as a whole, none of the gases are effective absorbers of radiation that has wavelengths between 0.3 and 0.7 micrometers. This region of the spectrum corresponds to the visible light band, which constitutes about 43 percent of the

FIGURE 19 The absorptivity of selected gases of the atmosphere and the atmosphere as a whole. The atmosphere as a whole is quite transparent to solar radiation between 0.3 and 0.7 micrometer, which includes the band of visible light. Most solar radiation falls in this range, explaining why a large amount of solar radiation penetrates the atmosphere and heats Earth's surface. Also, note that longwave infrared radiation in the zone between 8 and 12 micrometers can escape the atmosphere most readily. This zone is called the atmospheric window. *(Data after R. G. Fleagle and J. A. Businger,* An Introduction to Atmospheric Physics. *1963 by Academic Press)*

What causes leaves on deciduous trees to change color each fall?

The leaves of all deciduous trees contain the pigment chlorophyll, which gives them a green color. The leaves of some trees also contain the pigment carotene, which is yellow, and still others produce a class of pigments that appear red in color. During summer, leaves are factories generating sugar from carbon dioxide and water by the action of light on chlorophyll. As the dominant pigment, chlorophyll causes the leaves of most trees to appear green. The shortening days and cool nights of autumn trigger changes in deciduous trees. With a drop in chlorophyll production, the green color of the leaves fades allowing other pigments to be seen. If the leaves contain carotene, as do birch and hickory, they will change to bright yellow. Other trees, such as red maple and sumac, display the brightest reds and purples in the autumn landscape.

energy radiated by the Sun. Because the atmosphere is a poor absorber of visible radiation, most of this energy is transmitted to Earth's surface. Thus, we say that *the atmosphere is nearly transparent to incoming solar radiation and that direct solar energy is not an effective "heater" of Earth's atmosphere.*

We can also see in Figure 19 that the atmosphere as a whole is a relatively efficient absorber of longwave (infrared) radiation emitted by Earth (see bottom right of Figure 19). Water vapor and carbon dioxide are the principal absorbing gases, with water vapor absorbing about 60 percent of the radiation emitted by Earth. Therefore, water vapor accounts (more than any other gas) for the warm temperatures of the lower troposphere, where it is most highly concentrated.

Although the atmosphere is an effective absorber of radiation emitted by Earth's surface, it is nevertheless quite transparent to the band of radiation between 8 and 12 micrometers. Notice in Figure 19 (lower right) that the gases in the atmosphere absorb very little energy in these wavelengths. Because the atmosphere is transparent to radiation between 8 and 12 micrometers, much like window glass is transparent to visible light, this band is called the **atmospheric window**. Although other "atmospheric windows" exist, the one located between 8 and 12 micrometers is the most significant because it is located where Earth's radiation is most intense.

By contrast, clouds that are composed of tiny liquid droplets are excellent absorbers of this energy. Clouds absorb outgoing radiation and reradiate much of this energy back to Earth's surface. Thus, clouds serve a purpose similar to window blinds because they effectively block the atmospheric window and lower the rate at which the surface cools. This explains why nighttime temperatures remain higher on cloudy nights than on clear nights.

Because the atmosphere is largely transparent to solar (shortwave) radiation but more absorptive of the longwave radiation emitted by Earth, the atmosphere is heated from the ground up. This explains the general drop in temperature with increased altitude in the troposphere. The farther from the "radiator" (Earth's surface), the colder it gets. On average, the temperature drops 6.5°C for each kilometer increase in altitude, a figure known as the *normal lapse rate.* The fact that the atmosphere does not acquire the bulk of its energy directly from the Sun, but is heated by Earth's surface, is of utmost importance to the dynamics of the weather machine.

The Greenhouse Effect

If Earth had no atmosphere, it would experience an average surface temperature far below freezing. But the atmosphere warms the planet and makes Earth livable. The extremely important role the atmosphere plays in heating Earth's surface has been named the **greenhouse effect**.

As discussed earlier, cloudless air is largely transparent to incoming shortwave solar radiation and, hence, transmits it to Earth's surface. By contrast, a significant fraction of the longwave radiation emitted by Earth's land–sea surface is absorbed by water vapor, carbon dioxide, and other trace gases in the atmosphere. This energy heats the air and increases the rate at which it radiates energy, both out to space and back toward Earth's surface. The energy that is emitted back to the surface causes it to heat up more, which then results in greater emissions from the surface. This complicated game of "pass the hot potato" keeps Earth's average temperature 33°C (59°F) warmer than it would otherwise be (Figure 20). Without these absorptive gases in our atmosphere, Earth would not provide a suitable habitat for humans and other life forms.

This natural phenomenon was named the greenhouse effect because it was once thought that greenhouses were heated in a similar manner. The glass in a greenhouse allows shortwave solar radiation to enter and be absorbed by the objects inside. These objects, in turn, radiate energy but at longer wavelengths, to which glass is nearly opaque. The heat, therefore, is "trapped" in the greenhouse. It has been shown, however, that air inside greenhouses attains higher temperatures than outside air mainly because greenhouses restrict the exchange of air between the inside and outside. Nevertheless, the term "greenhouse effect" remains.

The popular press frequently points to the greenhouse effect as the "villain" of the global warming problem. It is important to note that the greenhouse effect and global warming *are not* the same thing. Without the greenhouse effect Earth would be uninhabitable. Scientists have mounting evidence that human activity (particularly the release of carbon dioxide into the atmosphere) is responsible for a rise in global temperature. Thus, human activity seems to be adding to an otherwise natural process (the greenhouse effect). Nevertheless, it is incorrect to equate the greenhouse phenomenon, which makes life possible, with undesirable changes to our atmosphere caused by human activities.

FIGURE 20 The heating of the atmosphere. Most of the short-wavelength radiation from the Sun passes through the atmosphere and is absorbed by Earth's land–sea surface. This energy is then emitted from the surface as longer-wavelength radiation, much of which is absorbed by certain gases in the atmosphere. Some of the energy absorbed by the atmosphere will be reradiated Earthward. This so-called greenhouse effect is responsible for keeping Earth's surface much warmer than it would be otherwise.

Students Sometimes Ask . . .

Is Venus so much hotter than Earth because it is closer to the Sun?

Proximity to the Sun is actually not the primary factor. On Earth, water vapor and carbon dioxide are the primary greenhouse gases and are responsible for elevating Earth's average surface temperature by 33°C (59°F). However, greenhouse gases make up less than 1 percent of Earth's atmosphere. By contrast, the Venusian atmosphere is much denser and consists of 97 percent carbon dioxide. Thus, the Venusian atmosphere experiences extraordinary greenhouse warming, which is estimated to raise its surface temperature by 523°C (941°F).

Role of Clouds in Heating Earth

Clouds, like water vapor and carbon dioxide, are good absorbers of infrared radiation emitted by Earth (see Box 5). Thus, at night clouds play a key role in keeping the surface warm. A thick cloud cover absorbs most outward directed radiation and radiates much of that energy back to the surface. This explains why on clear, dry nights the surface cools considerably more than on cloudy or humid evenings. Furthermore, although desert areas often experience high daytime temperatures, they are also likely to experience cold nights because of their generally cloudless skies.

During daylight hours the effect of clouds on heating Earth's surface depends on the type of clouds present. High, thin clouds primarily transmit incoming solar radiation. At the same time these clouds absorb a portion of the outgoing infrared radiation emitted by Earth and radiate some of that energy back to the surface. The net effect is that high thin clouds tend to warm the surface.

The impact of low, thick clouds is opposite that of high clouds. Thick, low clouds have a high albedo and therefore reflect a significant portion of incoming solar radiation back to space. Because less solar radiation is transmitted, Earth's surface is cooler than it would otherwise be.

Whether a cloud will cause the surface temperature to be higher or lower than when the sky is clear depends on several factors, including the time of day, the cloud's thickness, its height, and the nature of the particles that compose it. The balance between the cooling and warming effects of clouds is quite close; however, averaging the influence of all the clouds around the globe, cooling predominates.

Heat Budget

Worldwide, Earth's average temperature remains relatively constant, despite seasonal cold spells and heat waves. This stability indicates that a balance exists between the amount of incoming solar radiation and the amount of radiation emitted back to space; otherwise, Earth would be getting progressively colder or progressively warmer. The annual balance of incoming and outgoing radiation is called Earth's **heat budget**. The following examination of this budget provides a good review of the process just discussed.

BOX 5 ▶ INFRARED IMAGING

It is worth noting that our eyes have evolved to be sensitive to the wavelengths of solar radiation having the greatest intensities (visible radiation). If early humans had been solely dependent upon hunting nocturnal mammals (warm-blooded), evolutionary changes might have resulted in "eyes" sensitive to infrared radiation (heat), just like those of some reptiles. Despite our inability to naturally see infrared energy, we have developed artificial detectors (including infrared film) capable of extending our vision into the long-wavelength part of the electromagnetic spectrum.

One type of infrared imaging employs satellites to detect infrared radiation emit-ted by Earth's surface and atmosphere. From these images the temperatures of objects emitting radiation, such as clouds, large bodies of water, and various landforms, can be established. Recall that the wavelengths of radiation emitted by an object are temperature-dependent. When more of the energy is emitted in shorter wavelengths, it translates to objects at higher temperatures, whereas longer wavelengths indicate surfaces at lower temperatures.

One technique uses infrared images to determine which clouds are the most probable precipitation producers. The high tops of towering thunderstorms are colder than the tops of clouds at lower altitudes (less vertically developed clouds). In the image shown in Figure E the highest (coldest) cloud tops are associated with towering storm clouds that are part of Hurricane Isidore in the Gulf of Mexico. The tallest clouds and thus the heaviest rain are in the areas shaded in red and yellow.

Unlike photos produced by exposing film to visible light, infrared images can be made at any time of the day or night. The military uses infrared imaging in their "night vision" technology to detect such things as troop movements made under the cover of darkness.

FIGURE E This infrared image shows the tops of the towering storm clouds (red and yellow) that were part of Hurricane Isidore as it crossed the Gulf of Mexico in late September 2002. (Image courtesy of NASA)

Figure 21 illustrates Earth's heat budget. For simplicity we will use 100 units to represent the solar radiation intercepted at the outer edge of the atmosphere. You have already seen that, of the total radiation that reaches Earth, roughly 30 units (30 percent) are reflected back to space. The remaining 70 units are absorbed, 20 units within the atmosphere and 50 units by Earth's land–sea surface. How does Earth transfer this energy back to space?

If all of the energy absorbed by our planet was reradiated directly and immediately back to space, Earth's heat budget would be simple—100 units of radiation received and 100 units returned to space. In fact, this does happen *over time* (minus small quantities of energy that become locked up in biomass that may eventually become fossil fuel). What complicates the heat budget is the behavior of certain greenhouse gases, particularly water vapor and carbon dioxide. As you learned, these greenhouse gases absorb a large share of outward-directed infrared radiation and radiate much of that energy back to Earth. This "recycled" energy significantly increases the radiation received by Earth's surface. In addition to the 50 units received directly from the Sun, Earth's surface receives another 94 units from the atmosphere, bringing the total absorbed to 144 units. A balance is maintained, however, because all 144 units are returned to the atmosphere and eventually lost to space.

Earth's surface loses the 144 units mainly by emitting long-wave radiation skyward. As Figure 21 illustrates, 102 units are emitted from Earth's surface and absorbed by the

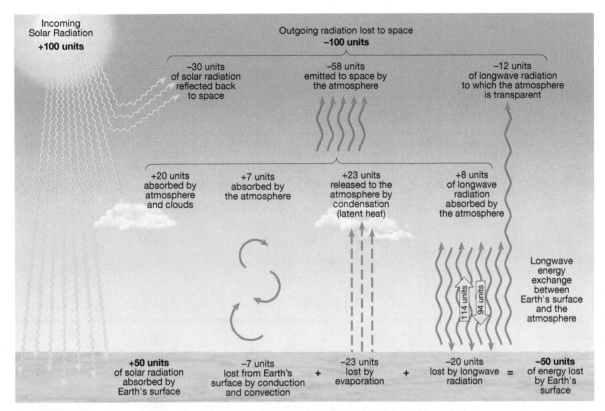

FIGURE 21 Heat budget of Earth and atmosphere. These estimates of the average global energy budget come from satellite observations and radiation studies. As more data are accumulated these numbers will be modified. (Data from Kiehl, Trenberth, Liou, and others.)

atmosphere. In addition, 12 units are transmitted through the atmosphere without being absorbed. (Recall that radiation between 8 and 12 micrometers escapes the troposphere most readily because water vapor and carbon dioxide do not absorb these wavelengths.) In addition, energy is carried from Earth's land–sea surface to the atmosphere by water molecules during the process of evaporation (23 units) and by conduction and convection (7 units).

The energy transferred to the atmosphere is reradiated skyward as well as toward the surface. However, a balance has been established, so that on average the atmosphere radiates back to space the same amount of energy as it receives. A careful examination of Figure 21 confirms that incoming shortwave radiation is in fact balanced by outgoing longwave radiation.

Latitudinal Heat Balance

Because the amount of incoming solar radiation is nearly equal to the amount of outgoing radiation for Earth as a whole, the average worldwide temperature remains constant. However, the balance of incoming and outgoing radiation that holds for the entire planet is not maintained at each latitude. Averaged over the entire year, a zone around Earth between 38°N and 38°S *receives more solar radiation than is lost to space* (Figure 22). Not surprisingly, this zone, centered on the equator, includes the southern United States and the warm tropical areas of Earth. The opposite is true for higher latitudes, where *more heat is lost through radiation emitted by Earth than is received from the Sun.*

We might assume, therefore, that the tropics are getting hotter and the poles are getting colder. But we know that is not the case. Instead, the atmosphere and the oceans act as giant thermal engines transferring surplus heat from the tropics poleward. In effect, it is this energy imbalance that drives the winds and the ocean currents.

The amount of solar radiation received at a given location fluctuates with changes in cloud cover and atmospheric composition (see Box 6). For example, the tropics often experience thick cloud cover, which reduces incoming radiation. Events such as forest fires, dust storms, and volcanic eruptions can also reduce the amount of incoming solar radiation. More important, however, are seasonal changes in Sun angle and length of daylight, which determine, to a large degree, the amount of radiation reaching the ground at any given latitude.

Notice in December (Figure 23) that the zone of maximum heating is centered roughly over the Tropic of Capricorn, be-

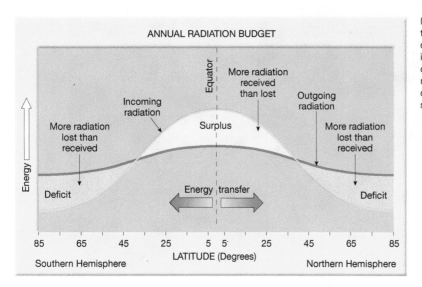

ANNUAL RADIATION BUDGET

More radiation
lost than
received

Incoming
radiation

More radiation
received
than lost

Outgoing
radiation

Surplus

More radiation
lost than
received

Deficit

Energy transfer

Deficit

Energy

Equator

| 85 | 65 | 45 | 25 | 5 | 5 | 25 | 45 | 65 | 85 |

LATITUDE (Degrees)

Southern Hemisphere

Northern Hemisphere

FIGURE 22 Latitudinal heat balance averaged over the entire year. We see that in a zone extending 38 degrees on both sides of the equator, the amount of incoming solar radiation exceeds the loss from outgoing Earth radiation. The reverse is true for the middle and high (polar) latitudes, where losses from outgoing Earth radiation exceed gains from incoming solar radiation.

BOX 6 ▸ SOLAR POWER

Nearly 95 percent of the world's energy needs are derived from fossil fuels, primarily oil, coal, and natural gas. Present estimates indicate that the amount of recoverable fossil fuels may equal 10 trillion barrels of oil, which at the present rate of consumption is enough to last about 150 years. However, with the rapid increase in demand by developing countries, the rate of consumption continues to climb. Thus, reserves will be in short supply sooner, rather than later. In the meantime, the adverse environmental impacts associated with burning huge quantities of fossil fuels will likely grow more severe. How can a growing demand for energy be met without radically altering the planet we inhabit? Although no clear answer has yet emerged,

we must consider greater use of alternate energy sources, such as solar power.

The term *solar energy* generally refers to the direct use of the Sun's rays to supply energy for the needs of people. The simplest, and perhaps most widely used, *passive solar collectors* are south-facing windows. As shortwave sunlight passes through the glass, its energy is absorbed by objects in the room. These objects, in turn, radiate longwave heat that warms the air in the room.

More elaborate systems used for home heating involve an *active solar collector*. These roof-mounted devices are normally large blackened boxes that are covered with glass. The heat they collect can be transferred to where it is needed by circulating air or fluids through pipes. Solar collectors are also used

successfully to heat water for domestic and commercial needs. In Israel, for example, about 80 percent of all homes are equipped with solar collectors that provide hot water.

Research is currently underway to improve the technologies for concentrating sunlight. One method uses parabolic troughs as solar energy collectors. Each collector resembles a large tube that has been cut in half. Their highly-polished surfaces reflect sunlight onto a collection pipe (Figure F). A fluid (usually oil) runs through the pipe and absorbs the concentrated sunlight. The fluid is heated to over 400° F and is typically used to make steam that drives a turbine to produce electricity. Parabolic troughs usually have a north-south alignment and gradually rotate to track the Sun.

FIGURE F Parabolic troughs, like the one shown here are very efficient solar collectors. The troughs focus sunlight onto collection pipes filled with a fluid. This heat is typically used to make steam that drives turbines used to generate electricity. (Photo by A.G. Schott, EPA)

cause this is the latitude that experiences the direct rays of the Sun. By contrast, short days and low Sun angles are mainly responsible for the relatively small amounts of solar radiation reaching the middle and high latitudes in the Northern Hemisphere. Also notice that Antarctica receives what might appear to be an unusually large amount of solar radiation in December. This occurs because in December much of Antarctica experiences nearly continuous daylight. Despite the abundance of energy received during the Antarctic summer, it is not enough to balance the outflows that occur during the long winter. Moreover, much of the summer sunshine in Antarctica is reflected back to space by its snow- and ice-covered surface. The top part of Figure 23 shows the opposite situation, summer in the Northern Hemisphere. In June the

incoming solar radiation is most intense near the Tropic of Cancer, and the Northern Hemisphere is bathed in sunshine.

The shift in incoming solar radiation from the Southern to Northern Hemisphere and back again can be clearly seen by comparing the June and December maps in Figure 23. Because energy imbalances drive Earth's general circulation, the regions of greatest energy transfer also migrate seasonally.

It should be of interest to those who live in the middle latitudes—in the Northern Hemisphere, from the latitude of New Orleans at 30°N to the latitude of Winnipeg, Manitoba, at 50°N—that the most heat transfer takes place across this region. Consequently, much of the stormy weather experienced in the middle latitudes can be attributed to this unending transfer of heat from the tropics toward the poles.

FIGURE G This solar facility near Los Angeles consists of a 20,000-dish array using Stirling dish technology. (Photo by Randy J. Montoya/ Sandia National Laboratories)

Another type of collector uses photovoltaic (solar) cells that convert the Sun's energy directly into electricity. Photovoltaic cells are usually connected together to create solar panels in which sunlight knocks electrons into higher energy states, to produce electricity. For many years solar cells were used mainly to power calculators and novelty devices. Today, however, large photovoltaic power stations are connected to electric grids to supplement other power generating facilities. The leading countries in photovoltaic capacity are Germany,

Japan, Spain, and the United States, and large power plants have recently been completed in Australia and Portugal. The high cost of solar cells makes generating solar electricity more expensive than electricity created by other sources. As the cost of fossil fuels continues to increase, advances in photovoltaic technology should narrow the price differential.

Southern California Edison is nearing completion of a massive 4,500-acre solar-generating facility located 70 miles northeast of Los Angeles. The technology being

employed, called the *Stirling dish*, converts thermal energy to electricity by using a mirror array to focus the Sun's rays on the receiver end of a Stirling engine (Figure G). The internal side of a receiver then heats hydrogen gas, causing it to expand. The pressure created by the expanding gas drives a piston, which turns a small electric generator. When completed in 2011 this facility will consist of a 20,000-dish array that will produce 500 megawatts of electricity, enough to serve 278,000 homes.

FIGURE 23 These false-color images show the average rate of incoming solar radiation at Earth's surface for the months of June and December. The colors correspond to values (kilowatt hours per square meter per day) measured by a variety of Earth-observing satellites and averaged over a 10-year period. Because the measurements are taken at Earth's surface, cloud cover reduces the radiation reaching the ground. This effect is apparent in some tropical regions where cloud cover is extensive.

Chapter Summary

- Earth has two principal motions—*rotation* and *revolution*. Rotation is the spinning of Earth about its axis. Revolution refers to the movement of Earth in its orbit around the Sun.

- The two most important reasons for the variation in solar energy reaching a particular location are the seasonal changes in the angle at which the Sun's rays strike the surface and the length of daylight. The seasonal variation in the angle of the Sun affects where on Earth the solar rays are most concentrated and the thickness of atmosphere the rays must penetrate.

- The four days each year given special significance based on the annual migration of the direct rays of the Sun and its importance to the yearly cycle of weather are (1) June 21/22, the *summer solstice* in the Northern Hemisphere, when the vertical rays of the Sun are striking 23½° north latitude (*Tropic of Cancer*); (2) December 21/22, the *winter solstice* in the Northern Hemisphere, when the vertical rays of the Sun are striking 23½° south latitude (*Tropic of Capricorn*); (3) September 22/23, the *autumnal equinox* in the Northern Hemisphere, when the vertical rays of the Sun strike the equator; and (4) March 21/22, the *spring*, or *vernal, equinox* in the Northern Hemisphere, when the vertical rays of the Sun also strike the equator.
- *Energy* is the ability to do work. The two major categories of energy are (1) *kinetic energy*, which can be thought of as energy of motion; and (2) *potential energy*, energy that has the capability to do work.
- *Heat* is the transfer of energy into or out of an object because of temperature differences between that object and its surroundings.
- The three mechanisms of energy transfer are (1) *conduction*, the transfer of heat through matter by molecular activity; (2) *convection*, the transfer of heat by mass movement or circulation within a substance; and (3) *radiation*, the transfer mechanism by which solar energy reaches our planet.
- *Radiation* or *electromagnetic radiation*, whether X-rays, visible light, heat waves, or radio waves, travels as various size waves through the vacuum of space at 300,000 kilometers per second. Shorter wavelengths of radiation are associated with greater energy. The wavelength of visible light ranges from 0.4 micrometer (violet) to 0.7 micrometer (red). Although the Sun emits many forms of radiation, most of the energy is concentrated in the visible and near visible (infrared and ultraviolet) parts of the spectrum. The basic laws of radiation are (1) all objects emit radiant energy; (2) hotter objects radiate more total energy per unit area than colder objects; (3) the hotter the radiating body, the shorter is the wavelength of maximum radiation; and (4) objects that are good absorbers of radiation are also good emitters.

- Approximately 50 percent of the solar energy that strikes the top of the atmosphere reaches Earth's surface. About 30 percent is reflected back to space. The remaining 20 percent of the energy is absorbed by clouds and the atmosphere's gases. The wavelength of the energy being transmitted, as well as the size and nature of the absorbing or reflecting substance, determine whether solar radiation will be scattered, reflected back to space, or absorbed. The fraction of radiation reflected by a surface is called its *albedo*.
- Radiant energy that is absorbed, heats Earth and eventually is reradiated skyward. Because Earth has a much lower surface temperature than the Sun, its radiation is in the form of longwave infrared radiation. Because the atmospheric gases, primarily water vapor and carbon dioxide, are more efficient absorbers of terrestrial (longwave) radiation, the atmosphere is heated from the ground up. The general drop in temperature with increased altitude in the troposphere (about 6.5°C/kilometer, a figure called the *normal lapse rate*) supports the fact that the atmosphere is heated from below. The transmission of shortwave solar radiation by the atmosphere, coupled with the selective absorption of Earth radiation by atmospheric gases that results in the warming of the atmosphere, is referred to as the *greenhouse effect*.
- Because of the annual balance that exists between incoming and outgoing radiation, called the *heat budget*, Earth's average temperature remains relatively constant despite seasonal cold spells and heat waves.
- Although the balance of incoming and outgoing radiation holds for the entire planet, it is not maintained at each latitude. Averaged over the entire year, a zone around Earth between 38°N and 38°S receives more solar radiation than is lost to space. The opposite is true for higher latitudes, where more heat is lost through outgoing longwave radiation than is received. It is this energy imbalance between the low and high latitudes that drives the global winds and ocean currents, which in turn transfer surplus heat from the tropics poleward. Furthermore, the radiation balance of a given place fluctuates with changes in cloud cover, atmospheric composition, and most important, Sun angle and length of daylight. Thus, areas of radiation surplus and deficit migrate seasonally as the Sun angle and length of daylight change.

Vocabulary Review

absorptivity	convection	perihelion	spring equinox
advection	diffused light	plane of the ecliptic	summer solstice
albedo	energy	potential energy	temperature
aphelion	greenhouse effect	radiation or electro-	thermal
atmospheric window	heat	magnetic radiation	Tropic of Cancer
autumnal equinox	heat budget	reflection	Tropic of Capricorn
backscattering	inclination of the axis	revolution	ultraviolet radiation
blackbody	infrared radiation	rotation	visible light
circle of illumination	kinetic energy	scattering	wavelength
conduction	longwave radiation	shortwave radiation	winter solstice

Review Questions

1. Can the annual variations in Earth–Sun distance adequately account for seasonal temperature changes? Explain.

2. Why does the amount of solar energy received at Earth's surface change when the angle of the Sun changes?

3. List four characteristics of the summer solstice for the Northern Hemisphere. For the Southern Hemisphere.

4. What is meant by temperature? Heat?

5. Describe the three basic mechanisms of energy transfer. Which mechanism is least important meteorologically?

6. What is the difference between convection and advection?

7. Compare visible, infrared, and ultraviolet radiation. For each, indicate whether it is considered short wavelength or long wavelength.

8. In what part of the electromagnetic spectrum does solar radiation have the highest intensity?

9. Describe the relationship between the temperature of a radiating body and the wavelengths it emits.

10. Why does the daytime sky usually appear blue?

11. Why may the sky appear to have a red or orange tint near sunrise or sunset?

12. What factors influence albedo from time to time and from place to place?

13. Explain why the atmosphere is heated chiefly by radiation from Earth's surface rather than by direct solar radiation.

14. Which gases are the primary heat absorbers in the lower atmosphere? Which one is most influential in weather?

15. How does Earth's atmosphere act as a "greenhouse"?

16. What is responsible for absorbing the largest portion of incoming solar radiation?

17. What is the atmospheric window? How is it "closed"?

18. What two phenomena are driven by the imbalance of heating that exists between the tropics and poles?

Problems

1. Refer to Figure 6 and calculate the noon Sun angle on June 21 and December 21 at 50° north latitude, 0° latitude (the equator), and 20° south latitude. Which of these latitudes has the greatest variation in noon Sun angle between summer and winter?

2. For the latitudes listed in Problem 1, determine the length of daylight and darkness on June 21 and December 21 (refer to Table 2). Which of these latitudes has the largest seasonal variation in length of daylight? Which latitude has the smallest variation?

3. How would our seasons be affected if Earth's axis were not inclined 23 1/2° to the plane of its orbit but were instead perpendicular?

4. Describe the seasons if Earth's axis were inclined 40°. Where would the tropics of Cancer and Capricorn be located? How about the Arctic and Antarctic circles?

5. Calculate the noon Sun angle at your location for the equinoxes and solstices.

6. Calculate the noon Sun angle for a city located at 52°N latitude on August 5. What about the same location on January 17? (Hint: See Box 2.)

7. If Earth had no atmosphere, its longwave radiation emission would be lost quickly to space, making the planet approximately 33 K cooler. Calculate the rate of radiation emitted (E), and the wavelength of maximum radiation emission (λ_{max}) for Earth at 255 K.

8. The intensity of solar radiation can be calculated using trigonometry, as shown in Figure 24. For simplicity, consider a solar beam of 1 unit width. The surface area over which the beam would be spread changes with Sun angle, such that

$$\text{Surface area} = \frac{1 \text{ unit}}{\sin (\text{Sun angle})}$$

Therefore, if the Sun angle at solar noon is 56°:

$$\text{Surface area} = \frac{1 \text{ unit}}{\sin 56°} = \frac{1 \text{ unit}}{0.829} = 1.206 \text{ units}$$

Using this method and your answers to Problem 5, calculate the intensity of solar radiation (surface area) for your location at noon during the summer and winter solstices.

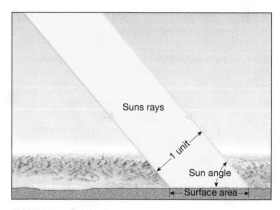

FIGURE 24   Calculating solar intensity.

Atmospheric Science Online

The Atmosphere 11e website uses the resources and flexibility of the Internet to aid in your study of the topics in this chapter. Written and developed by meteorology instructors, this site will help improve your understanding of meteorology. Visit **www.mygeoscience.com** in order to:

- **Review** key chapter concepts

- **Read** with links to the eBook and to chapter-specific web resources
- **Visualize** and comprehend challenging topics using learning activities in *GEODe: Atmosphere*
- **Test yourself** with online quizzes

GEODe: Atmosphere

GEODe: Atmosphere makes studying more effective by reinforcing key concepts using animation, video, narration, interactive exercises, and practice quizzes. Available at **www.mygeoscience.com**.

Temperature

From Chapter 3 of *The Atmosphere: An Introduction to Meteorology*, Eleventh Edition, Frederick K. Lutgens, Edward J. Tarbuck, Dennis Tasa. Copyright © 2010 by Pearson Education, Inc. Published by Pearson Prentice Hall. All rights reserved.

Temperature

Altitude is one basic control of temperature. Temperatures drop with an increase in altitude. (Photo by Ritschel/ Photolibrary)

Temperature is one of the basic elements of weather and climate. When someone asks what the weather is like outside, air temperature is often the first element we mention (Figure 1). From everyday experience, we know that temperatures vary on different time scales: seasonally, daily, and even hourly. Moreover, we all realize that substantial temperature differences exist from one place to another. In this chapter you will focus on several other aspects of this very important atmospheric property, including factors other than Earth–Sun relationships that act as temperature controls. You will also look at how temperature is measured and expressed and see that temperature data can be of very practical value to us all. Applications include calculations that are useful in evaluating energy consumption, crop maturity, and human comfort.

For the Record: Air-Temperature Data

GE●De   Temperature
THE ATMOSPHERE   ▶ Basic Temperature Data

Temperatures recorded daily at thousands of weather stations worldwide provide much of the temperature data compiled by meteorologists and climatologists (see Box 1). Hourly temperatures may be recorded by an observer or obtained from automated observing systems that continually monitor the atmosphere. At many locations only the maximum and minimum temperatures are obtained. The **daily mean temperature** is determined by averaging the 24 hourly readings or more frequently by adding the maximum and minimum temperatures for a 24-hour period and dividing by 2. From the maximum and minimum, the **daily temperature range** is computed by finding the difference

between these figures. Other data involving longer periods are also compiled:

1. The **monthly mean temperature** is calculated by adding together the daily means for each day of the month and dividing by the number of days in the month.
2. The **annual mean temperature** is an average of the 12 monthly means.
3. The **annual temperature range** is computed by finding the difference between the warmest and coldest monthly mean temperatures.

Mean temperatures are especially useful for making daily, monthly, or annual comparisons. It is common to hear a weather reporter state, "Last month was the warmest February on record" or "Today Omaha was 10 degrees warmer than Chicago." Temperature ranges are also useful statistics because

FIGURE 1 People living in the middle latitudes can experience a wide range of temperatures during a year. (left) Digging out in frigid weather following a major snowstorm in Buffalo, New York, in December 2001. (Photo by Mike Groll/Getty Images). (right) Beating the heat on a hot summer day at Chicago's Millenum Park. (Photo by Andre Jenny/ Alamy Images)

BOX 1 ▶ NORTH AMERICA'S HOTTEST AND COLDEST PLACES

Most people living in the United States have experienced temperatures of 38°C (100°F) or more. When statistics for the 50 states are examined for the past century or longer, we find that every state has a maximum temperature record of 38°C or higher. Even Alaska has recorded a temperature this high. Its record was set June 27, 1915, at Fort Yukon, a town along the Arctic Circle in the interior of the state.

Maximum Temperature Records

Surprisingly, the state that ties Alaska for the "lowest high" is Hawaii. Panala, on the south coast of the big island, recorded 38°C on April 27, 1931. Although humid tropical and subtropical places like Hawaii are known for being warm throughout the year, they seldom experience maximum temperatures that surpass the low to mid-30s Celsius (90s Fahrenheit).

The highest accepted temperature record for the United States as well as the entire Western Hemisphere is 57°C (134°F). This long-standing record was set at Death Valley, California, on July 10, 1913. Summer temperatures at Death Valley are consistently among the highest in the Western Hemisphere. During June, July, and August, temperatures exceeding 49°C (120°F) are to be expected. Fortunately, Death Valley has few human summertime residents.

Why are summer temperatures at Death Valley so high? In addition to having the lowest elevation in the Western Hemisphere (53 meters/174 feet below sea level), Death Valley is a desert. Although it is only about 300 kilometers (less than 200 miles) from the Pacific Ocean, mountains cut off the valley from the ocean's moderating influence and moisture. Clear skies allow a maximum of sunshine to strike the dry, barren surface. Because no energy is used to evaporate moisture as occurs in humid regions, all of

the energy is available to heat the ground. In addition, subsiding air that warms by compression as it descends is also common to the region and contributes to its high maximum temperatures.

Minimum Temperature Records

The temperature controls that produce truly frigid temperatures are predictable, and they should come as no surprise. We should expect extremely cold temperatures during winter in high-latitude places that lack the moderating influence of the ocean (Figure A). Moreover, stations located on ice sheets and glaciers should be especially cold, as should stations positioned high in the mountains. *All* of these criteria apply to Greenland's Northice station (elevation 2307 meters/7567 feet). Here on January 9,

1954, the temperature plunged to −66°C (−87°F). If we exclude Greenland from consideration, Snag, in Canada's Yukon Territory, holds the record for North America. This remote outpost experienced a temperature of −63°C (−81°F) on February 3, 1947. When only locations in the United States are considered, Prospect Creek, located north of the Arctic Circle in the Endicott Mountains of Alaska, came close to the North American record on January 23, 1971, when the temperature plunged to −62°C (−80°F). In the lower 48 states the record of −57°C (−70°F) was set in the mountains at Rogers Pass, Montana, on January 20, 1954. Remember that many other places have no doubt experienced equally low or even lower temperatures; they just were not recorded.

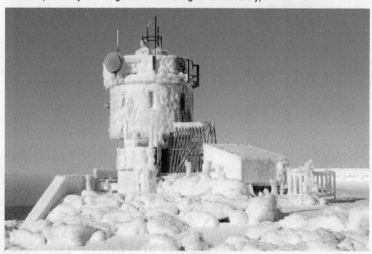

FIGURE A At 1886 meters (6288 feet), Mount Washington is the highest peak in the White Mountains and in fact the entire Northeast. It is considered by some to be "the Home of the World's Worst Weather" due to its extreme cold, heavy snows, high winds, frequent icing, and dense fog. The observatory at its summit keeps detailed weather records. (Photo by Jim Salge/Mount Washington Observatory)

they give an indication of extremes, a necessary part of understanding the weather and climate of a place or an area.

To examine the distribution of air temperatures over large areas, isotherms are commonly used. An **isotherm** is a line that connects points on a map that have the same temperature (*iso* = equal, *therm* = temperature). Therefore, all points through which an isotherm passes have identical temperatures for the time period indicated. Generally, isotherms representing 5° or 10° temperature differences are used, but any interval may be chosen. Figure 2 illustrates how isotherms are drawn on a map. Notice that most isotherms do not pass directly through the observing stations, because the station

readings may not coincide with the values chosen for the isotherms. Only an occasional station temperature will be exactly the same as the value of the isotherm, so it is usually necessary to draw the lines by estimating the proper position between stations.

Isothermal maps are valuable tools because they clearly make temperature distribution visible at a glance. Areas of low and high temperatures are easy to pick out. In addition, the amount of temperature change per unit of distance, called the **temperature gradient,** is easy to visualize. Closely spaced isotherms indicate a rapid rate of temperature change, whereas more widely spaced lines indicate a more gradual

FIGURE 2 Isothermal map for a spring day. Isotherms are lines that connect points of equal temperature. Showing temperature distribution in this way makes patterns easier to see. Notice that most isotherms do not pass directly through the observing stations. It is usually necessary to draw isotherms by estimating their proper position between stations. On television and in many newspapers, temperature maps are in color. Rather than labeling isotherms, the area *between* isotherms is labeled. For example, the zone between the 60° and 70° isotherms is labeled "60s."

rate of change. For example, notice in Figure 2 that the isotherms are more closely spaced in Colorado and Utah (steeper temperature gradient), whereas the isotherms are spread farther apart in Texas (gentler temperature gradient).

Without isotherms a map would be covered with numbers representing temperatures at tens or hundreds of places, which would make patterns difficult to see.

Why Temperatures Vary: The Controls of Temperature

GE🌐De **Temperature**
THE ATMOSPHERE ▸ Controls of Temperature

The **controls of temperature** are factors that cause temperatures to vary from place to place and from time to time (see Box 2). Because variations in Sun angle and length of daylight depend on latitude, they are responsible for warm temperatures in the tropics and colder temperatures poleward. Of course, seasonal temperature changes at a given latitude occur as the Sun's vertical rays migrate toward and away from a place during the year.

But latitude is not the only control of temperature. If it were, we would expect all places along the same parallel to have identical temperatures. Such is clearly not the case. For instance, Eureka, California, and New York City are both coastal cities at about the same latitude, and both places have an annual mean temperature of 11°C (51.8°F). Yet New York City is 9.4°C (16.9°F) warmer than Eureka in July and 9.4°C (16.9°F) colder than Eureka in January. In another example, two cities in Ecuador—Quito and Guayaquil—are relatively close to one another, but the mean annual temperatures at these two cities differ by 12.2°C (22°F). To explain these situations and countless others, we must realize that factors other than latitude also exert a strong influence on temperature. In the next sections we examine these other controls, which include:

1. differential heating of land and water
2. ocean currents
3. altitude
4. geographic position
5. cloud cover and albedo

Land and Water

The heating of Earth's surface controls the heating of the air above it. Therefore, to understand variations in air temperature, we must understand the variations in heating properties of the different surfaces that Earth presents to the Sun—soil, water, trees, ice, and so on. Different land surfaces reflect and absorb varying amounts of incoming solar energy, which in turn cause variations in the temperature of the air above. The greatest contrast, however, is not between different land surfaces but between land and water. Figure 3 illustrates this idea nicely. This satellite image shows surface temperatures in portions of Nevada, California, and the adjacent Pacific Ocean on the afternoon of May 2, 2004, during a spring heat wave. Land-surface temperatures are clearly much higher than water-surface temperatures. The image shows the extreme high surface temperatures in southern California and Nevada in dark red.* Surface temperatures in the Pacific Ocean are much lower. The peaks of the Sierra Nevada, still capped with snow, form a cool blue line down the eastern side of California.

In side-by-side bodies of land and water, such as those shown in Figure 3, *land heats more rapidly and to higher temperatures than water, and it cools more rapidly and to lower temperatures than water*. Variations in air temperatures, therefore, are much greater over land than over water. Why do land and water heat and cool differently? Several factors are responsible.

1. An important reason that the surface temperature of water rises and falls much more slowly than the surface temperature of land is that *water is highly mobile*. As water is heated, convection distributes the heat through a considerably larger mass. Daily temperature changes occur to depths of 6 meters (20 feet) or more below the surface, and yearly, oceans and deep lakes experience

*Realize that air temperatures are cooler than surface temperatures. For example, the surface of a sandy beach can be painfully hot even though the temperature of the air above the sand is comfortable.

FIGURE 3 The differential heating of land and water is an important control of air temperatures. In this satellite image from the afternoon of May 2, 2004, water-surface temperatures in the Pacific Ocean are much lower than land-surface temperatures in California and Nevada. The narrow band of cool temperatures in the center of the image is associated with mountains (the Sierra Nevada). The cooler water temperatures immediately offshore are associated with the California Current (see Figure 7). (NASA image)

temperature variations through a layer between 200 and 600 meters thick (650 and 2000 feet).

In contrast, heat does not penetrate deeply into soil or rock; it remains near the surface. Obviously, no mixing can occur on land because it is not fluid. Instead, heat must be transferred by the slow process of conduction. Consequently, daily temperature changes are small below a depth of 10 centimeters (4 inches), although some change can occur to a depth of perhaps 1 meter (3 feet). Annual temperature variations usually reach depths of 15 meters (50 feet) or less. Thus, as a result of the mobility of water and the lack of mobility in the solid Earth, a relatively thick layer of water is heated to moderate temperatures during the summer. On land only a thin layer is heated but to much higher temperatures.

During winter the shallow layer of rock and soil that was heated in summer cools rapidly. Water bodies, in contrast, cool slowly as they draw on the reserve of heat stored within. As the water surface cools, vertical motions are established. The chilled surface water, which is dense, sinks and is replaced by warmer water from below, which is less dense. Consequently, a larger mass of water must cool before the temperature at the surface will drop appreciably.

BOX 2 ▶ ATMOSPHERIC HAZARD

Heat Waves—Deadly Events

A *heat wave* is a prolonged period of abnormally hot and usually humid weather that typically lasts from a few days to several weeks. The impact of heat waves on individuals varies greatly. The elderly are the most vulnerable because heat puts more stress on weak hearts and bodies. The poor, who often cannot afford air-conditioning, also suffer disproportionally. Studies also show that the temperatures at which death rates increase varies from city to city. In Dallas, Texas, a temperature of 39°C (103°F) is required before the death rate climbs. In San Francisco the key temperature is just 29°C (84°F).

Heat waves do not elicit the same sense of fear or urgency as tornadoes, hurricanes, and flash floods. One reason is that it may take many days of oppressive temperatures for a heat wave to exact its toll rather than just a few minutes or a few hours. Another reason is that they cause far less property damage than other extreme weather events. Nevertheless, heat waves can be deadly.

One notable example occurred in the summer of 2003 when much of Europe experienced perhaps its worst heat wave in more than a century. The image in Figure B relates to this deadly event. An estimate

Land Surface Temperature difference (°C)

-10   -5   0   5   10

FIGURE B This image is derived from satellite data and shows the difference in daytime land surface temperatures during the 2003 European heat wave (July 20–August 20) as compared to the years 2000, 2001, 2002, and 2004. The zone of deep red shows where temperatures were 10°C (18°F) hotter than in the other years. France was hardest hit. (NASA)

2. Because land surfaces are opaque, heat is absorbed only at the surface. This fact is easily demonstrated at a beach on a hot summer afternoon by comparing the surface temperature of the sand to the temperature just a few centimeters beneath the surface. Water, being more transparent, allows some solar radiation to penetrate to a depth of several meters.

3. The **specific heat** (the amount of heat needed to raise the temperature of 1 gram of a substance 1°C) is more than three times greater for water than for land. Thus, water requires considerably more heat to raise its temperature the same amount as an equal quantity of land.

4. Evaporation (a cooling process) from water bodies is greater than from land surfaces. Energy is required to evaporate water. When energy is used for evaporation, it is not available for heating.

All these factors collectively cause water to warm more slowly, store greater quantities of heat, and cool more slowly than land.

Monthly temperature data for two cities will demonstrate the moderating influence of a large water body and the extremes associated with land (Figure 4). Vancouver, British Columbia, is located along the windward Pacific coast, whereas Winnipeg, Manitoba, is in a continental position far from the influence of water. Both cities are at about the same latitude and thus experience similar sun angles and lengths of daylight. Winnipeg, however, has a mean January temperature that is 20°C lower than Vancouver's. Conversely, Winnipeg's July mean is 2.6°C higher than Vancouver's. Although their latitudes are nearly the same, Winnipeg, which has no water influence, experiences much greater temperature extremes than does Vancouver. The key to Vancouver's moderate year-round climate is the Pacific Ocean.

On a different scale, the moderating influence of water may also be demonstrated when temperature variations in based on government records puts the death toll at between 20 and 35 thousand. The majority died during the first two weeks of August—the hottest span. France suffered the greatest number of heat-related fatalities—about 14 thousand.

The dangerous impact of summer heat is also reinforced when examining Figure C, which shows average annual weather-related deaths in the United States for the 10-year period 1998–2007. A comparison of values reveals that the number of heat deaths surpasses those of any other weather condition.

In July 1995 a brief but intense heat wave developed in the central United States. A total of 830 deaths were attributed to this severe five-day event, the worst in 50 years in the northern Midwest. The greatest loss of life occurred in Chicago, where there were 525 fatalities. The *Chicago Tribune* appropriately labeled the event "a citywide tragedy."

The severity of heat waves is usually greater in cities because of the *urban heat island* (see Box 4). Large cities do not cool off as much at night during heat waves as rural areas do, and this can be a critical difference in the amount of heat stress within the inner city. In addition, the stagnant atmospheric conditions usually associated with heat waves trap pollutants in urban areas and add the stresses of severe air pollution to

FIGURE C   Average annual weather-related fatalities for the 10-year period 1998–2007. The figure for the hurricane category was dramatically affected by a single storm— Hurricane Katrina in 2005. Katrina was responsible for 1016 of the 1170 hurricane-related fatalities that occurred during this 10-year span. (Data from NOAA)

the already dangerous stresses caused by the high temperatures.

In addition to the tragic loss of life, the 1995 Midwest heat wave had many other impacts, including the following:

- Energy use vastly increased. This resulted in some power failures during peak stress hours and, of course, in substantially higher electric bills.
- Highways and railroads were damaged due to heat-induced heaving and buckling of roadway joints and rails.
- Many companies reported a substantial reduction in employee work efficiency.
- Shopping declined dramatically.
- In rural areas, livestock were affected. For example, on July 14 the *Wisconsin Journal* reported that 850 dairy cattle had died, major flocks of poultry were killed, and milk production was off by 25 percent.

Not everyone is adversely affected by a heat wave. In response to the 1995 event, tourism from Chicago to nearby (and cooler) Wisconsin increased 10 percent. As we would expect, sales of air conditioners in the Midwest rose as well—more than 50 percent over the previous year.

The 1995 heat wave in the upper Midwest was the most intense in half a century. It provided a sobering lesson by focusing attention on the need for more effective warning and response plans, especially in major urban areas where heat stress is greatest.

---

the Northern and Southern hemispheres are compared. The views of Earth in Figure 5 show the uneven distribution of land and water over the globe. Water covers 61 percent of the Northern Hemisphere; land represents the remaining 39 percent. However, the figures for the Southern Hemisphere (81 percent water, 19 percent land) reveal why it is correctly called the *water hemisphere*. Between 45° north and 79° north latitude there is actually more land than water, whereas between 40° south and 65° south latitude there is almost no land to interrupt the oceanic and atmospheric circulation. Table 1 portrays the considerably smaller annual temperature ranges in the water-dominated Southern Hemisphere compared with the Northern Hemisphere.

Ocean Currents

You probably have heard of the Gulf Stream, an important surface current in the Atlantic Ocean that flows northward along the East Coast of the United States (Figure 6).

Surface currents like this one are set in motion by the wind. At the water surface, where the atmosphere and ocean meet, energy is passed from moving air to the water through friction. As a consequence, the drag exerted by winds blowing steadily across the ocean causes the surface layer of water to move. Thus, major horizontal movements of surface waters are closely related to the circulation of the atmosphere, which in turn is driven by the unequal heating of Earth by the Sun (Figure 7).

Surface ocean currents have an important effect on climate. It is known that for Earth as a whole, the gains in solar energy equal the losses to space of heat radiated from the surface. When most latitudes are considered individually, however, this is not the case. There is a net gain of energy in lower latitudes and a net loss at higher latitudes. Because the tropics are not becoming progressively warmer, nor the polar regions

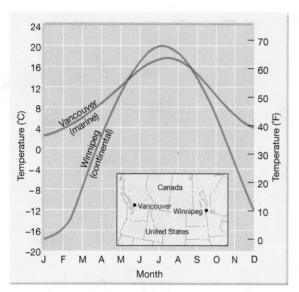

FIGURE 4 Mean monthly temperatures for Vancouver, British Columbia, and Winnipeg, Manitoba. Vancouver has a much smaller annual temperature range owing to the strong marine influence of the Pacific Ocean. Winnipeg illustrates the greater extremes associated with an interior location.

colder, there must be a large-scale transfer of heat from areas of excess to areas of deficit. This is indeed the case. *The transfer of heat by winds and ocean currents equalizes these latitudinal energy imbalances.* Ocean water movements account for about a quarter of this total heat transport, and winds the remaining three-quarters.

The moderating effect of poleward-moving warm ocean currents is well known. The North Atlantic Drift, an extension of the warm Gulf Stream, keeps wintertime temperatures in Great Britain and much of Western Europe warmer than would be expected for their latitudes (London is farther north than St. John's, Newfoundland). Because of the prevailing westerly winds, the moderating effects are carried far inland. For example, Berlin (52° north latitude) has a mean January temperature similar to that experienced at New York City, which lies 12° latitude farther south. The January mean at London (51° north latitude) is 4.5°C (8.1°F) higher than at New York City.

In contrast to warm ocean currents like the Gulf Stream, the effects of which are felt most during the winter, cold currents exert their greatest influence in the tropics or during the summer months in the middle latitudes. For example, the cool Benguela Current off the western coast of southern Africa moderates the tropical heat along this coast. Walvis Bay (23° south latitude), a town adjacent to the Benguela Current, is 5°C (9°F) cooler in summer than Durban, which is 6° latitude farther poleward but on the eastern side of South Africa, away from the influence of the current (Figure 7). The east and west coasts of South America provide another example. Figure 8 shows monthly mean temperatures for Rio de Janeiro, Brazil, which is influenced by the warm Brazilian Current and Arica, Chile, which is adjacent to the cold Peruvian Current. Closer

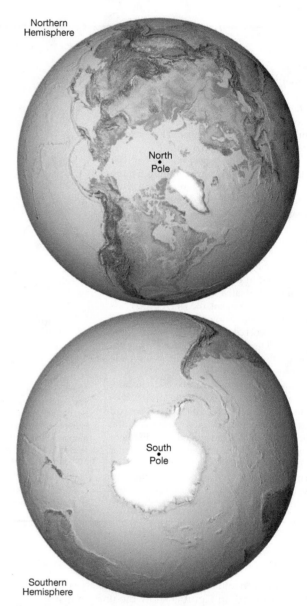

FIGURE 5 The uneven distribution of land and water between the Northern and Southern hemispheres. Almost 81 percent of the Southern Hemisphere is covered by the oceans—20 percent more than the Northern Hemisphere.

TABLE 1 Variation in Mean Annual Temperature Range (°C) with Latitude.

Latitude	Northern Hemisphere	Southern Hemisphere
0	0	0
15	3	4
30	13	7
45	23	6
60	30	11
75	32	26
90	40	31

FIGURE 6 This satellite image shows sea-surface temperatures off the East Coast of the United States on April 18, 2005. The warm waters of the Gulf Stream (lighter shades) extend diagonally from bottom left to top right. The current transports heat from the tropics far into the North Atlantic. This image shows several deep bends in the path of the Gulf Stream. In fact, the northernmost of the two deep bends actually loops back on itself, creating a closed-off eddy. On the northern side of the current, cold waters (blue) dip southward into the Gulf Stream's warmth. Gray areas indicate clouds. (NASA image)

to home, because of the cold California current, summer temperatures in subtropical coastal southern California are lower by 6°C (10.8°F) or more compared to East Coast stations.

Altitude

The two cities in Ecuador mentioned earlier, Quito and Guayaquil, demonstrate the influence of altitude on mean temperature. Both cities are near the equator and relatively close to one another, but the annual mean temperature at Guayaquil is 25.5°C (77.9°F) compared with Quito's mean of 13.3°C (55.9°F). The difference may be understood when the cities' elevations are noted. Guayaquil is only 12 meters (39 feet) above sea level, whereas Quito is high in the Andes Mountains at 2800 meters (9200 feet) (Figure 9).

Recall that temperatures drop an average of 6.5°C per kilometer (3.5°F per 1000 feet) in the troposphere; thus, cooler temperatures are to be expected at greater heights. Yet the magnitude of the difference is not totally explained by the normal lapse rate. If this figure were used, we would expect

FIGURE 7 Major surface ocean currents. Poleward-moving currents are warm, and equatorward-moving currents are cold. Surface ocean currents are driven by global winds and play an important role in redistributing heat around the globe. Note that cities mentioned in the text discussion are shown on this map.

FIGURE 8   Monthly mean temperatures for Rio de Janeiro, Brazil, and Arica, Chile. Both are coastal cities near sea level. Even though Arica is closer to the equator than Rio de Janeiro, its temperatures are cooler. Arica is influenced by the cold Peruvian Current, whereas Rio de Janeiro is adjacent to the warm Brazilian Current.

Students Sometimes Ask . . .

Can high mountain areas in the tropics be cold enough for glaciers?

Yes. Glaciers do indeed occur in the tropics at high elevations. Near the equator, glaciers sometimes form above about 5000 meters (16,400 feet). Examples of equatorial glaciers include those atop Mount Kenya and Mount Kilimanjaro in East Africa and those in the tall mountains of New Guinea.

ing atmosphere absorbs and reflects a smaller portion of the incoming solar radiation. Consequently, with an increase in altitude, the intensity of solar radiation increases, resulting in relatively rapid and intense daytime heating. Conversely, rapid nighttime cooling is also the rule in high mountain locations. Therefore, stations located high in the mountains generally have a greater daily temperature range than do stations at lower elevations.

Geographic Position

The geographic setting can greatly influence the temperatures experienced at a specific location. A coastal location where prevailing winds blow from the ocean onto the shore (a *windward* coast) experiences considerably different temperatures than does a coastal location where prevailing winds blow from the land toward the ocean (a *leeward* coast). In the first situation the windward coast will experience the full moderating influence of the ocean—cool summers and mild winters—compared to an inland station at the same latitude.

Quito to be about 18.2°C (32.7°F) cooler than Guayaquil, but the difference is only 12.2°C (22°F). The fact that high-altitude places, such as Quito, are warmer than the value calculated using the normal lapse rate results from the absorption and reradiation of solar energy by the ground surface.

In addition to the effect of altitude on mean temperatures, the daily temperature range also changes with variations in height. Not only do temperatures drop with an increase in altitude but atmospheric pressure and density also diminish. Because of the reduced density at high altitudes, the overly-

FIGURE 9   (a) Graph comparing monthly mean temperatures at Quito and Guayaquil, Ecuador. (b) Because Quito is high in the Andes, it experiences much cooler temperatures than Guayaquil, which is near sea level. (Photo by Pablo Corral Vega/ CORBIS) (c) Although Guayaquil is not far from Quito, it is near sea level and therefore significantly warmer. (Photo by Jeff Greenberg/Omni-Photo Communications, Inc.)

(a) **Temperature graph**

(b) **Quito is high in the Andes**

(c) **Guayaquil is at sea level**

A leeward coastal situation, however, will have a more continental temperature regime because the winds do not carry the ocean's influence onshore. Eureka, California, and New York City, the two cities mentioned earlier, illustrate this aspect of geographic position (Figure 10). The annual temperature range at New York City is 19°C (34°F) greater than Eureka's.

Seattle and Spokane, both in the state of Washington, illustrate a second aspect of geographic position: mountains acting as barriers. Although Spokane is only about 360 kilometers (225 miles) east of Seattle, the towering Cascade Range separates the cities. Consequently, Seattle's temperatures show a marked marine influence, but Spokane's are more typically continental (Figure 11). Spokane is 7°C (12.6°F) cooler than Seattle in January and 4°C (7.2°F) warmer than Seattle in July. The annual range at Spokane is 11°C (nearly 20°F) greater than at Seattle. The Cascade Range effectively cuts off Spokane from the moderating influence of the Pacific Ocean.

Cloud Cover and Albedo

You may have noticed that clear days are often warmer than cloudy ones and that clear nights usually are cooler than cloudy ones. This demonstrates that cloud cover is another factor that influences temperature in the lower atmosphere. Studies using satellite images show that at any particular time about half of our planet is covered by clouds. Cloud cover is important because many clouds have a high albedo and therefore reflect a significant proportion of the sunlight that strikes them back to space. By reducing the amount of incoming solar

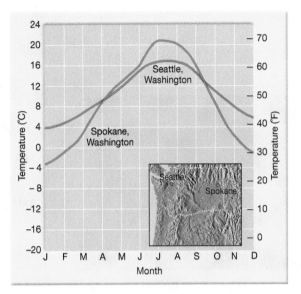

FIGURE 11 Monthly mean temperatures for Seattle and Spokane, Washington. Because the Cascade Mountains cut off Spokane from the moderating influence of the Pacific Ocean, its annual temperature range is greater than Seattle's.

radiation, daytime temperatures will be lower than if the clouds were absent and the sky were clear (Figure 12). The albedo of clouds depends on the thickness of the cloud cover and can vary from 25 to 80 percent.

At night, clouds have the opposite effect as during daylight. They absorb outgoing Earth radiation and emit a portion of it toward the surface. Consequently, some of the heat that otherwise would have been lost remains near the ground. Thus, nighttime air temperatures do not drop as low as they would on a clear night. The effect of cloud cover is to reduce the daily temperature range by lowering the daytime maximum and raising the nighttime minimum. This is illustrated nicely by the graph in Figure 12.

The effect of cloud cover on reducing maximum temperatures can also be detected when monthly mean temperatures are examined for some stations. For example, each year much of southern Asia experiences an extended period of relative drought during the cooler low-Sun period; it is then followed by heavy monsoon rains.* The graph for Yangon, Myanmar (Rangoon, Burma), illustrates this pattern (Figure 13). Notice that the highest monthly mean temperatures occur in April and May, before the summer solstice, rather than in July and August, as normally occurs at most stations in the Northern Hemisphere. Why?

The reason is that during the summer months when we would usually expect temperatures to climb, the extensive cloud cover increases the albedo of the region, which reduces incoming solar radiation at the surface. As a result, the highest monthly mean temperatures occur in late spring when the skies are still relatively clear.

FIGURE 10 Monthly mean temperatures for Eureka, California, and New York City. Both cities are coastal and located at about the same latitude. Because Eureka is strongly influenced by prevailing winds from the ocean and New York City is not, the annual temperature range at Eureka is much smaller.

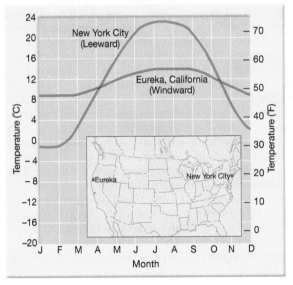

---

*This pattern is associated with monsoon circulation.

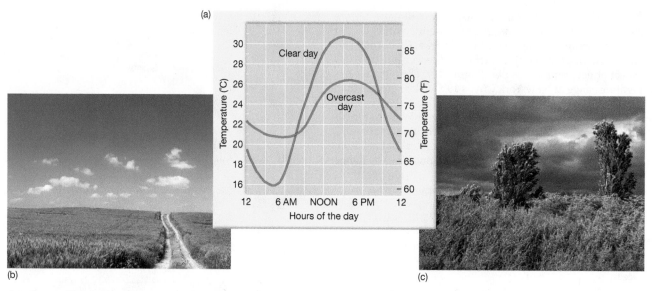

(a)

(b)

(c)

FIGURE 12 (a) The graph shows the daily temperature cycle at Peoria, Illinois, for two July days—one clear and the other overcast. (b) On a clear day the maximum temperature is higher, and the minimum temperature is lower than if the day had been overcast. (Photo by Linux Patrol/Shutterstock) (c) On an overcast day, the daily temperature range is lower than if it had been cloud free. (Photo by Serp/Shutterstock)

Cloudiness is not the only phenomenon that increases albedo and thereby reduces air temperature. We also recognize that snow- and ice-covered surfaces have high albedos. This

FIGURE 13 Monthly mean temperatures (curve) and monthly mean precipitation (bar graph) for Yangon, Myanmar. The highest mean temperature occurs in April, just before the onset of heavy summer rains. The abundant cloud cover associated with the rainy period reflects back into space the solar energy that otherwise would strike the ground and raise summer temperatures.

is one reason why mountain glaciers do not melt away in the summer and why snow may still be present on a mild spring day. In addition, during the winter when snow covers the ground, daytime maximums on a sunny day are cooler than they otherwise would be, because energy that the land would have absorbed and used to heat the air is reflected and lost.

World Distribution of Temperatures

Take a moment to study the two world isothermal maps (Figures 14 and 15). From hot colors near the equator to cool colors toward the poles, these maps portray sea-level temperatures in the seasonally extreme months of January and July. On these maps you can study global temperature patterns and the effects of the controls of temperature, especially latitude, the distribution of land and water, and ocean currents (see Box 3). Like most isothermal maps of large regions, all temperatures on these world maps have been reduced to sea level to eliminate the complications caused by differences in altitude.

On both maps the isotherms generally trend east and west and show a decrease in temperatures poleward from the tropics. They illustrate one of the most fundamental aspects of world temperature distribution: that the effectiveness of incoming solar radiation in heating Earth's surface and the atmosphere above it is largely a function of latitude.

Moreover, there is a latitudinal shifting of temperatures caused by the seasonal migration of the Sun's vertical rays. To see this, compare the color bands by latitude on the two maps. For example, on the January map the "hot spots" of 30°C are *south* of the equator, but in July they have shifted *north* of the equator.

FIGURE 14 World mean sea-level temperatures in January in degrees Celsius.

If latitude were the only control of temperature distribution, our analysis could end here, but this is not the case. The added effect of the differential heating of land and water is clearly reflected on the January and July temperature maps. The warmest and coldest temperatures are found over land—note the coldest area, a purple oval in Siberia, and the hottest areas, the deep orange ovals—all over land. Consequently, because temperatures do not fluctuate as much over water as over land, the north–south migration of isotherms is greater over the continents than over the oceans. In addition,

it is clear that the isotherms in the Southern Hemisphere, where there is little land and where the oceans predominate, are much more regular than in the Northern Hemisphere, where they bend sharply northward in July and southward in January over the continents.

Isotherms also reveal the presence of ocean currents. Warm currents cause isotherms to be deflected toward the poles, whereas cold currents cause an equatorward bending. The horizontal transport of water poleward warms the overlying air and results in air temperatures that are higher than would

FIGURE 15 World mean sea-level temperatures in July in degrees Celsius.

BOX 3 ▶ LATITUDE AND TEMPERATURE RANGE

Gregory J. Carbone*

Latitude, because of its influence on Sun angle, is the most important temperature control. Figures 14 and 15 clearly show higher temperatures in tropical locations and lower temperatures in polar regions. The maps also show that higher latitudes experience a greater range of temperatures during the year than do lower latitudes. Notice also that the temperature gradient between the subtropics and the poles is greatest during the winter season. A look at two cities—San Antonio, Texas, and Winnipeg, Manitoba—illustrates how seasonal differences in Sun angle and day length account for these temperature patterns. Figure D shows the annual march of temperature for the two cities, whereas Figure E illustrates the Sun angles for the June and December solstices.

San Antonio and Winnipeg are a fixed distance apart (approximately 20.5° latitude), so the difference in Sun angles between the two cities is the same throughout the year. However, in December, when the Sun's rays are least direct, this difference more strongly affects the intensity of solar radiation received at Earth's surface. Therefore, we expect a greater difference in temperatures between the two stations in winter than in summer. Moreover, the seasonal difference in intensity (spreading out of the light beam) at Winnipeg is considerably greater than at San Antonio. This helps to explain the greater annual temperature range at the more northerly station.

*Professor Carbone is a faculty member in the Department of Geography at the University of South Carolina.

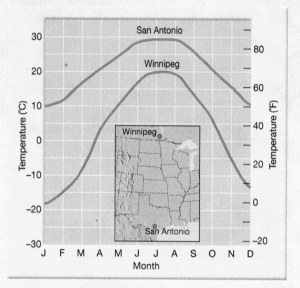

FIGURE D The annual temperature range at Winnipeg is much greater than at San Antonio.

FIGURE E A comparison of Sun angles (solar noon) for summer and winter solstices at San Antonio and Winnipeg. The space covered by a 90° angle = 1.00.

otherwise be expected for the latitude. Conversely, currents moving toward the equator produce cooler-than-expected air temperatures.

Figures 14 and 15 show the seasonal extremes of temperature, so comparing them enables us to see the annual range of temperature from place to place. Comparing the two maps shows that a station near the equator has a very small annual range because it experiences little variation in the length of daylight and it always has a relatively high Sun angle. A station in the middle latitudes, however, experiences wide variations in Sun angle and length of daylight and hence large variations in temperature. Therefore, we can state that the annual temperature range increases with an increase in latitude (see Box 3).

Moreover, land and water also affect seasonal temperature variations, especially outside the tropics. A continental location must endure hotter summers and colder winters than a coastal location. Consequently, outside the tropics the annual range will increase with an increase in continentality.

Figure 16, which shows the global distribution of annual temperature ranges, serves to summarize the preceding two paragraphs. By examining this map, it is easy to see the influence of latitude and continentality on this temperature sta-

FIGURE 16 Global annual temperature ranges in degrees Celsius. Annual ranges are small near the equator and increase toward the poles. Outside the tropics, annual temperature ranges increase as we move away from the ocean toward the interior of large landmasses. (After Robert W. Christopherson, *Geosystems: An Introduction to Physical Geography*, Fifth Edition, Prentice Hall, 2003)

Students Sometimes Ask

Where in the world would I experience the greatest contrast between summer and winter temperatures?

Among places for which records exist, it appears as though Yakutsk, a station in the heart of Siberia, is the best candidate. The latitude of Yakutsk is 62° north, just a few degrees south of the Arctic Circle. Moreover, it is far from the influence of water. The January mean at Yakutsk is a frigid −43°C (−45°F), whereas its July mean is a pleasant 20°C (68°F). The result is an average annual temperature range of 63°C (113°F), among the highest anywhere on the globe.

tistic. The tropics clearly experience small annual temperature variations. As expected, the highest values occur in the middle of large landmasses in the subpolar latitudes. It is also obvious that annual temperature ranges in the ocean-dominated Southern Hemisphere are much smaller than in the Northern Hemisphere with its large continents.

Cycles of Air Temperature

You know from experience that a rhythmic rise and fall of air temperature occurs almost every day. Your experience is confirmed by thermograph records like the one in Figure 17 (a thermograph is an instrument that continuously records temperature). The temperature curve reaches a minimum around

FIGURE 17 Thermograph of temperatures in Peoria, Illinois, during a seven-day span in May 1992. The typical daily rhythm, with minimums around sunrise and maximums in mid- to late afternoon, occurred on most days. The obvious exception occurred on May 23, when the maximum was reached at midnight and temperatures dropped throughout the day.

(a)

(b)

FIGURE 18   The minimum daily temperature usually occurs near the time of sunrise. As the ground and air cool during the nighttime hours, familiar early morning phenomena such as the frost in photo (a) and the ground fog in photo (b) may form. (Photo (a) by AP Photo/Daily Telegram/Jed Carlson. Photo (b) by Michael Collier)

sunrise (Figure 18). It then climbs steadily to a maximum between 2 PM and 5 PM The temperature then declines until sunrise the following day.

Daily Temperature Variations

The primary control of the daily cycle of air temperature is as obvious as the cycle itself: It is Earth's daily rotation, which causes a location to move into daylight for part of each day and then into darkness. As the Sun's angle increases throughout the morning, the intensity of sunlight also rises, reaching a peak at local noon and gradually diminishing in the afternoon.

Figure 19 shows the daily variation of incoming solar energy versus outgoing Earth radiation and the resulting temperature curve for a typical middle-latitude location at the time of an equinox. During the night the atmosphere and the surface of Earth cool as they radiate heat away that is not replaced by incoming solar energy. The minimum temperature, therefore, occurs about the time of sunrise, after which the Sun again heats the ground, which in turn heats the air.

It is apparent that the time of highest temperature does not generally coincide with the time of maximum radiation. By comparing Figures 17 and 19, you can see that the curve for incoming solar energy is symmetrical with respect to noon, but the daily air temperature curves are not. The delay in the occurrence of the maximum until mid- to late afternoon is termed the *lag of the maximum*.

Although the intensity of solar radiation drops in the afternoon, it still exceeds outgoing energy from Earth's surface for a period of time. This produces an energy surplus for up to several hours in the afternoon and contributes substantially to the lag of the maximum. In other words, as long as

the solar energy gained exceeds the rate of Earth radiation lost, the air temperature continues to rise. When the input of solar energy no longer exceeds the rate of energy lost by Earth, the temperature falls.

The lag of the daily maximum is also a result of the process by which the atmosphere is heated. Recall that air is a poor absorber of most solar radiation; consequently, it is heated

FIGURE 19   The daily cycle of incoming solar radiation, Earth's radiation, and the resulting temperature cycle. This example is for a midlatitude site around the time of an equinox. As long as solar energy gained exceeds outgoing energy emitted by Earth, the temperature rises. When outgoing energy from Earth exceeds the input of solar energy, temperature falls. Note that the daily temperature cycle *lags* behind the solar radiation input by a couple of hours.

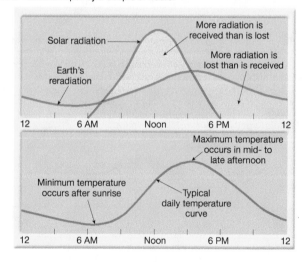

primarily by energy reradiated from Earth's surface. The rate at which Earth supplies heat to the atmosphere through radiation, conduction, and other means, however, is not in balance with the rate at which the atmosphere radiates heat away. Generally, for a few hours after the period of maximum solar radiation, more heat is supplied to the atmosphere by Earth's surface than is emitted by the atmosphere to space. As a result, most locations experience an increase in air temperature during the afternoon.

In dry regions, particularly on cloud-free days, the amount of radiation absorbed by the surface will generally be high. Therefore, the time of the maximum temperature at these locales will often occur quite late in the afternoon. Humid locations, in contrast, will frequently experience a shorter time lag in the occurrence of their temperature maximum.

Magnitude of Daily Temperature Changes

The magnitude of daily temperature changes is variable and may be influenced by locational factors, or local weather conditions, or both (see Box 4). Four common examples illustrate this point. The first two relate to location, and the second two pertain to local weather conditions.

1. Variations in Sun angle are relatively great during the day in the middle and low latitudes. However, points near the poles experience a low Sun angle all day. Consequently, the temperature change experienced during a day in the high latitudes is small.
2. A windward coast is likely to experience only modest variations in the daily cycle. During a typical 24-hour period the ocean warms less than 1°C. As a result, the air above it shows a correspondingly slight change in temperature. For example, Eureka, California, a windward coastal station, consistently has a lower daily temperature range than Des Moines, Iowa, an inland city at about the same latitude. Annually the daily range at Des Moines averages 10.9°C (19.6°F) compared with 6.1°C (11°F) at Eureka, a difference of 4.8°C (8.6°F).
3. As mentioned earlier, an overcast day is responsible for a flattened daily temperature curve (see Figure 13). By day, clouds block incoming solar radiation and so reduce daytime heating. At night the clouds retard the loss of radiation by the ground and air. Therefore, nighttime temperatures are warmer than they otherwise would have been.
4. The amount of water vapor in the air influences daily temperature range because water vapor is one of the atmosphere's important heat-absorbing gases. When the air is clear and dry, heat rapidly escapes at night, and the temperature falls rapidly. When the air is humid, absorption of outgoing long-wavelength radiation by water vapor slows nighttime cooling, and the temperature does not fall to as low a value. Thus, dry conditions are associated with a higher daily temperature range because of greater nighttime cooling.

Although the rise and fall of daily temperatures usually reflects the general rise and fall of incoming solar radiation, such is not always the case. For example, a glance back at Figure 17 reveals that on May 23 the maximum temperature occurred at midnight, after which temperatures fell throughout the day. If records for a station are examined for a period of several weeks, apparently random variations are seen. Obviously these are not Sun-controlled. Such irregularities are caused primarily by the passage of atmospheric disturbances (weather systems) that are often accompanied by variable cloudiness and winds that bring air having contrasting temperatures. Under these circumstances, the maximum and minimum temperatures may occur at any time of the day or night.

Annual Temperature Variations

In most years the months with the highest and lowest mean temperatures do not coincide with the periods of maximum and minimum incoming solar radiation. Poleward of the tropics the greatest intensity of solar radiation occurs at the time of the summer solstice in June, yet the months of July and August are generally the warmest of the year in the Northern Hemisphere. Conversely, a minimum of solar energy is received in December at the time of the winter solstice, but January and February are usually colder.

The fact that the occurrence of annual maximum and minimum radiation does not coincide with the times of temperature maximums and minimums indicates that the amount of solar radiation received is not the only factor determining the temperature at a particular location. Places equatorward of about 38° N and 38° S receive more solar radiation than is lost to space and that the opposite is true of more poleward regions. Based on this imbalance between incoming and outgoing radiation, any location in the southern United States, for example, should continue to get warmer late into autumn.

But this does not occur, because more poleward locations begin experiencing a negative radiation balance shortly after the summer solstice. As the temperature contrasts become greater, the atmosphere and ocean currents "work harder" to transport heat from lower latitudes poleward.

Temperature Measurement

GE**⊙**De   Temperature
THE ATMOSPHERE   ▸ Basic Temperature Data

Thermometers are "meters of therms": They measure temperature. Thermometers measure temperature either mechanically or electrically.

Mechanical Thermometers

Most substances expand when heated and contract when cooled, so many common thermometers are based on this property. More precisely, they rely on the fact that different substances react to temperature changes differently.

BOX 4 ▶ HOW CITIES INFLUENCE TEMPERATURE: THE URBAN HEAT ISLAND

One of the most apparent human impacts on climate is the modification of the atmospheric environment by the building of cities. The construction of every factory, road, office building, and house destroys microclimates and creates new ones of great complexity.

The most studied and well-documented urban climatic effect is the *urban heat island*. The term refers to the fact that temperatures within cities are generally higher than in rural areas. The heat island is evident when temperature data such as that which appears in Table A are examined. As is typical, the data for Philadelphia show the heat island is most pronounced when minimum temperatures are examined. The magnitude of the temperature differences shown by Table A is probably even greater than the figures indicate, because temperatures observed at suburban airports are usually higher than those in truly rural environments.

Figure F, which shows the distribution of average minimum temperatures in the Washington, D.C., metropolitan area for the three-month winter period (December through February) over a five-year span, also illustrates a well-developed heat island. The warmest winter temperatures occurred in the heart of the city, whereas the suburbs and surrounding countryside experienced average minimum temperatures that were as much as 3.3°C (6°F) lower. Remember that these temperatures are averages. On many clear, calm nights the temperature difference between the city center and the countryside was considerably greater, often 11°C (20°F) or more. Conversely, on many overcast or windy nights the temperature differential approached zero degrees.

A recent study indicates that one effect of the urban heat island is to influence the biosphere by extending the plant cycle.* After examining data for 70 cities in eastern North America, researchers found that the growing cycle in cities was about 15 days

*Reported in *Weatherwise*, Vol. 57, No. 6, Nov/Dec 2004, p. 20.

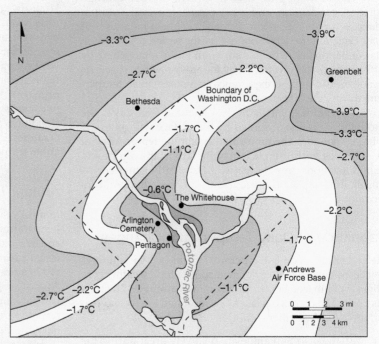

FIGURE F   The heat island of Washington, D.C., as shown by the average minimum temperatures (°C) during the winter season (December through February). The city center had an average minimum that was nearly 4°C higher than some outlying areas. (After Clarence A. Woolum, "Notes from the Study of the Microclimatology of the Washington, D.C. Area for the Winter and Spring Seasons," Weatherwise, 17, no. 6 (1964), 264, 267.)

TABLE A	Average Temperatures (°C) for Suburban Philadelphia Airport and Downtown Philadelphia (10-year Averages)	
	Airport	Downtown
Annual mean	12.8	13.6
Mean June max	27.8	28.2
Mean December max	6.4	6.7
Mean June min	16.5	17.7
Mean December min	−2.1	−0.4

Source: After H. Neuberger and J. Cahir, Principles of Climatology (New York: Holt, Rinehart and Winston, 1969), 128.

The **liquid-in-glass thermometer** shown in Figure 20 is a simple instrument that provides relatively accurate readings over a wide temperature range. Its design has remained essentially unchanged ever since it was developed in the late 1600s. When temperature rises, the molecules of fluid grow more active and spread out (the fluid expands).

Expansion of the fluid in the bulb is much greater than the expansion of the enclosing glass. As a consequence, a thin "thread" of fluid is forced up the capillary tube. Conversely, when temperature falls, the liquid contracts and the thread of fluid moves back down the tube toward the bulb. The movement of the end of this thread (known as the *meniscus*)

Temperature (°C)

18   24   30

FIGURE G This pair of satellite images provides two views of Atlanta, Georgia, on September 28, 2000. The urban core is in the center of the images. The top image is a photo-like view in which vegetation is green, roads and dense development appear gray, and bare ground is tan or brown. The bottom image is a land surface temperature map in which cooler temperatures are yellow and hotter temperatures are red. It is clear that where development is densest, the land surface temperatures are highest. (NASA)

longer than surrounding rural areas. Plants began the growth cycle an average of about seven days earlier in spring and continued growing an average of eight days longer in fall.

Why are cities warmer? The radical change in the surface that results when rural areas are transformed into cities is a significant cause of the urban heat island (Figure G). First, the tall buildings and the concrete and asphalt of the city absorb and store greater quantities of solar radiation than do the vegetation and soil typical of rural areas. In addition, because the city surface is impermeable, the runoff of water following a rain is rapid, resulting in a significant reduction in the evaporation rate. Hence, heat that once would have been used to convert liquid water to a gas now goes to increase further the surface temperature. At night, as both the city and countryside cool by radiative losses, the stonelike surface of the city gradually releases the additional heat accumulated during the day, keeping the urban air warmer than that of the outlying areas.

A portion of the urban temperature rise is also attributed to waste heat from sources such as home heating and air-conditioning, power generation, industry, and transportation. In addition, the "blanket" of pollutants over a city contributes to the heat island by absorbing a portion of the upward-directed long-wave radiation emitted by the surface and reemitting some of it back to the ground.

is calibrated against an established scale to indicate the temperature.

The highest and lowest temperatures that occur each day are of considerable importance and are often obtained by using specially designed liquid-in-glass thermometers. Mercury is the liquid used in the **maximum thermometer**, which has a narrowed passage called a *constriction* in the bore of the glass tube just above the bulb (Figure 21a). As the temperature rises, the mercury expands and is forced through the constriction. When the temperature falls, the constriction prevents a return of mercury to the bulb. As a result, the top of the mercury column remains at the highest point (maximum

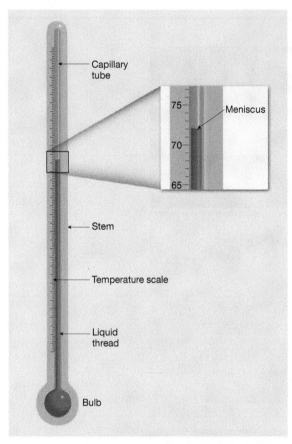

FIGURE 20 The main components of a liquid-in-glass thermometer.

temperature attained during the measurement period). The instrument is reset by shaking or by whirling it to force the mercury through the constriction back into the bulb. Once the thermometer is reset, it indicates the current air temperature.

In contrast to a maximum thermometer that contains mercury, a **minimum thermometer** contains a liquid of low density, such as alcohol. Within the alcohol, and resting at the top of the column, is a small dumbbell-shaped index (Figure 21b). As the air temperature drops, the column shortens and the index is pulled toward the bulb by the effect of surface tension with the meniscus. When the temperature subsequently rises, the alcohol flows past the index, leaving it at the lowest temperature reached. To return the index to the top of the alcohol column, the thermometer is simply tilted. Because the index is free to move, the minimum thermometer must be mounted horizontally; otherwise the index will fall to the bottom.

Another commonly used mechanical thermometer is the **bimetal strip**. As the name indicates, this thermometer consists of two thin strips of metal that are bonded together and have widely different expansion properties. When the temperature changes, both metals expand or contract, but they do so unequally, causing the strips to curl. This change corresponds to the change in temperature.

The primary meteorological use of the bimetal strip is in the construction of a **thermograph**, an instrument that continuously records temperature. The changes in the curvature of the strip can be used to move a pen arm that records the temperature on a calibrated chart that is attached to a clock-driven, rotating drum (Figure 22). Although very convenient, thermograph records are generally less accurate than readings obtained from a mercury-in-glass thermometer. To obtain the most reliable values, it is necessary to check and correct the thermograph periodically by comparing it with an accurate, similarly exposed thermometer.

Electrical Thermometers

Some thermometers do not rely on differential expansion but instead measure temperature electrically.

A resistor is a small electronic part that resists the flow of electrical current. A **thermistor** (thermal resistor) is similar, but its resistance to current flow varies with temperature. As

FIGURE 21 (a) Maximum thermometer and (b) minimum thermometer.

Maximum Thermometer

Minimum Thermometer

FIGURE 22 A common use of the bimetal strip is in the construction of a thermograph, an instrument that continuously records temperatures.

Bimetal strip

temperature increases, so does the resistance of the thermistor, reducing the flow of current. As temperature drops, so does the resistance of the thermistor, allowing more current to flow. The current operates a meter or digital display that is calibrated in degrees of temperature. The thermistor thus is used as a temperature sensor—an electrical thermometer.

Thermistors are rapid-response instruments that quickly register temperature changes. Therefore, they are commonly used in radiosondes where rapid temperature changes are often encountered. The National Weather Service also uses a thermistor system for ground-level readings. The sensor is mounted inside a shield made of louvered plastic rings, and a digital readout is placed indoors (Figure 23).

FIGURE 23 This modern shelter contains an electrical thermometer called a *thermistor*. (Photo by Bobbé Christopherson)

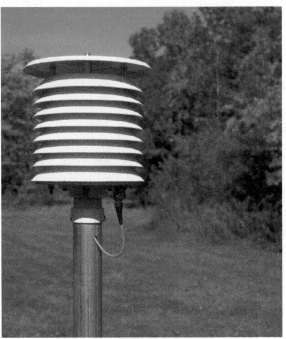

Instrument Shelters

How accurate are thermometer readings? It depends not only on the design and quality of the instruments but also on where they are placed. Placing a thermometer in the direct sunlight will give a grossly excessive reading, because the instrument itself absorbs solar energy much more efficiently than the air. Placing a thermometer near a heat-radiating surface, such as a building or the ground, also yields inaccurate readings. Another way to assure false readings is to prevent air from moving freely around the thermometer.

So where should a thermometer be placed to read air temperature accurately? The ideal location is an instrument shelter (Figure 24). The shelter is a white box that has louvered sides to permit the free movement of air through it, while shielding the instruments from direct sunshine, heat from the

FIGURE 24 This traditional standard instrument shelter is white (for high albedo) and louvered (for ventilation). It protects instruments from direct sunlight and allows for the free flow of air. (Courtesy of Qualimetrics, Inc.)

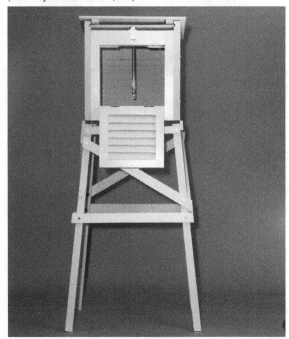

ground, and precipitation. Furthermore, the shelter is placed over grass whenever possible and as far away from buildings as circumstances permit. Finally, the shelter must conform to a standardized height so that the thermometers will be mounted at 1.5 meters (5 feet) above the ground.

Temperature Scales

In the United States, TV weather reporters give temperatures in degrees Fahrenheit. But scientists as well as most people outside of the United States use degrees Celsius. Scientists sometimes also use the Kelvin or absolute scale. What are the differences among these three temperature scales? To make quantitative measurement of temperature possible, it was necessary to establish scales. Such temperature scales are based on the use of reference points, sometimes called **fixed points.** In 1714, Gabriel Daniel **Fahrenheit,** a German physicist, devised the temperature scale that bears his name. He constructed a mercury-in-glass thermometer in which the zero point was the lowest temperature he could attain with a mixture of ice, water, and common salt. For his second fixed point he chose human body temperature, which he arbitrarily set at 96°.

On this scale, he determined that the melting point of ice (the **ice point**) was 32° and the boiling point of water (the **steam point**) was 212°. Because Fahrenheit's original reference points were difficult to reproduce accurately, his scale is now defined by using the ice point and the steam point. As thermometers improved, average human body temperature was later changed to 98.6°F.*

In 1742, 28 years after Fahrenheit invented his scale, Anders Celsius, a Swedish astronomer, devised a decimal scale on which the melting point of ice was set at 0° and the boiling point of water at 100°.** For many years it was called the *centigrade scale,* but it is now known as the **Celsius scale,** after its inventor.

Because the interval between the melting point of ice and the boiling point of water is 100° on the Celsius scale and 180° on the Fahrenheit scale, a Celsius degree (°C) is larger than a Fahrenheit degree (°F) by a factor of 180/100, or 1.8. So, to convert from one system to the other, allowance must be made for this difference in the size of the degrees. Also, conversions must be adjusted because the ice point on the Celsius scale is at 0° rather than at 32°. This relationship is shown graphically in Figure 25.

The Celsius–Fahrenheit relationship also is shown by the following formulas:

$$°F = (1.8 × °C) + 32$$

or

$$°C = \frac{°F - 32}{1.8}$$

---

*This traditional value for "normal body temperature" was established in 1868. A recent assessment places the value at 98.2°F with a range of 4.8°F.

**The boiling point referred to in the Celsius and Fahrenheit scales pertains to pure water at standard sea-level pressure. It is necessary to remember this fact, because the boiling point of water gradually decreases with altitude.

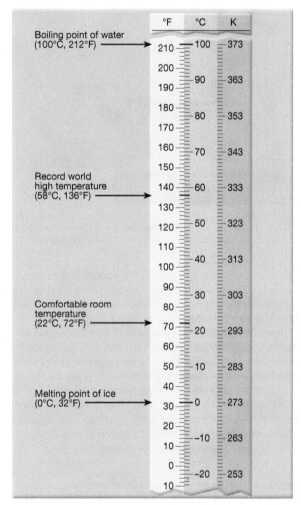

FIGURE 25   The three temperature scales compared.

You can see that the formulas adjust for degree size with the 1.8 factor, and adjust for the different 0° points with the ±32 factor.

The Fahrenheit scale is best known in the United States, where its official use is declining along with the British system of weights and measures. In other parts of the world as well as in the scientific community, where the metric system is used, the Celsius temperature scale is also used.

For some scientific purposes a third temperature scale is used, the **Kelvin** or **absolute scale.** On this scale, degrees Kelvin are called *Kelvins* (abbreviated K). It is similar to the Celsius scale because its divisions are exactly the same; there are 100° separating the melting point of ice and the boiling point of water. However, on the Kelvin scale, the ice point is set at 273 and the steam point at 373 (see Figure 25). The reason is that the zero point represents the temperature at which all molecular motion is presumed to cease (called **absolute zero**). Thus, unlike the Celsius and Fahrenheit scales, it is not possible to have a negative value when using the Kelvin scale, for there is no temperature lower than absolute zero. The relationship between Kelvin and Celsius scales is easily written as follows:

$$°C = K - 273 \text{ or } K = °C + 273$$

Applications of Temperature Data

To make weather data more useful to people, many different applications have been developed over the years. In this section, we examine some commonly used practical applications. First, we will look at three indices that all have the term *degree-days* as part of their name: heating degree-days, cooling degree-days, and growing degree-days. The first two are relative measures that allow us to evaluate the weather-produced needs and costs of heating and cooling. The third is a simple index used by farmers to estimate the maturity of crops.

Heating Degree-Days

Developed by heating engineers early in the twentieth century, **heating degree-days** represent a practical method for evaluating energy demand and consumption. It starts from the assumption that heating is not required in a building when the daily mean temperature is 65°F (18.3°C) or higher.* Simply, each degree of temperature below 65°F is counted as 1 heating degree-day. Therefore, heating degree-days are determined each day by subtracting the daily mean below 65°F from 65°F. Thus, a day with a mean temperature of 50°F has 15 heating degree-days (65 − 50 = 15), and one with an average temperature of 65°F or higher has none.

The amount of heat required to maintain a certain temperature in a building is proportional to the total heating degree-days. This linear relationship means that doubling the heating degree-days usually doubles the fuel consumption. Consequently, a fuel bill will generally be twice as high for a month with 1000 heating degree-days as for a month with just 500. When seasonal totals are compared for different places, we can estimate differences in seasonal fuel consumption (Table 2). For example, more than five times as much fuel is required to heat a building in Chicago (nearly 6500 total heating degree-days) than to heat a similar building in Los Angeles (almost 1300 heating degree-days). This statement is true, however, only if we assume that building construction and living habits in these areas are the same.

Each day, the previous day's accumulation is reported as well as the total thus far in the season. For reporting purposes the heating season is defined as the period from July 1 through June 30. These reports often include a compari-

son with the total up to this date last year or with the long-term average for this date or both, and so it is a relatively simple matter to judge whether the season thus far is above, below, or near normal.

Cooling Degree-Days

Just as fuel needs for heating can be estimated and compared by using heating degree-days, the amount of power required to cool a building can be estimated by using a similar index called the **cooling degree-day.** Because the 65°F base temperature is also used in calculating this index, cooling degree-days are determined each day by subtracting 65°F from the daily mean. Thus, if the mean temperature for a given day is 80°F, 15 cooling degree-days would be accumulated. Mean annual totals of cooling degree-days for selected cities are shown in Table 2. By comparing the totals for Baltimore and Miami, we can see that the fuel requirements for cooling a building in Miami are almost two and a half times as great as for a similar building in Baltimore. The "cooling season" is conventionally measured from January 1 through December 31. Therefore, when cooling degree-day totals are reported, the number represents the accumulation since January 1 of that year.

Although indices that are more sophisticated than heating and cooling degree-days have been proposed to take into account the effects of wind speed, solar radiation, and humidity, degree-days continue to be widely used.

Growing Degree-Days

Another practical application of temperature data is used in agriculture to determine the approximate date when crops will be ready for harvest. This simple index is called the **growing degree-day.**

The number of growing degree-days for a particular crop on any day is the difference between the daily mean temperature

---

*Because the National Weather Service and the news media in the United States still compute and report degree-day information in Fahrenheit degrees, we will use the Fahrenheit scale throughout this discussion.

TABLE 2 Average Annual Heating and Cooling Degree-Days for Selected Cities (1971–2000)[*]

City	Heating degree-days	Cooling degree-days
Anchorage, AK	10470	3
Baltimore, MD	3807	1774
Boston, MA	5630	777
Chicago, IL	6498	830
Denver, CO	6128	695
Detroit, MI	6422	736
Great Falls, MT	7828	288
International Falls, MN	10269	233
Las Vegas, NV	2239	3214
Los Angeles, CA	1274	679
Miami, FL	149	4361
New York City, NY	4754	1151
Phoenix, AZ	1125	4189
San Antonio, TX	1573	3038
Seattle, WA	4797	173

[*]*Source:* NOAA, National Climatic Data Center

and the base temperature of the crop, which is the minimum temperature required for it to grow. For example, the base temperature for sweet corn is 50°F and for peas it is 40°F. Thus, on a day when the mean temperature is 75°F, the number of growing degree-days for sweet corn is 25 and the number for peas is 35.

Starting with the onset of the growth season, the daily growing degree-day values are added. Thus, if 2000 growing degree-days are needed for that crop to mature, it should be ready to harvest when the accumulation reaches 2000 (Figure 26). Although many factors important to plant growth are not included in the index, such as moisture conditions and sunlight, this system nevertheless serves as a simple and widely used tool in determining approximate dates of crop maturity.

Temperature and Comfort

A more familiar use of temperature data relates to human perception of temperature. Television weather reports use indices that attempt to portray levels of human comfort and discomfort. Such indices are based on the fact that our sensation of temperature is often different from the actual air temperature recorded by a thermometer.

The human body is a heat generator that continually releases energy. Anything that influences the rate of heat loss from the body also influences our sensation of temperature, thereby affecting our feeling of comfort. Several factors control the thermal comfort of the human body, and certainly air temperature is a major one. Other environmental conditions are also significant, such as relative humidity, wind, and sunshine.

Because evaporation is a cooling process, the evaporation of perspiration from skin is a natural means of regulating body temperature. When the air is very humid, however, heat loss by evaporation is reduced. As a result, a hot and humid day feels warmer and more uncomfortable than a hot and dry day. This is the basis for a commonly used expression of summertime discomfort known as the *heat stress index* or simply the *heat index*.

Wind is another significant factor affecting the sensation of temperature. A cold and windy winter day may feel much colder than the air temperature indicates (Figure 27). Box 5 focuses on this frequently used wintertime application known as *windchill*.

FIGURE 26 Growing degree-days are used to determine the approximate date when crops will be ready for harvest. (Photo by Dennis MacDonald/PhotEdit)

FIGURE 27 Strong winds make winter days seem much colder. New Yorkers had to cope with frigid temperatures, strong winds, and lots of snow during this January blizzard in 1996. (Photo by Kaz Chiba Photography/Getty Images, Inc.-Liaison)

BOX 5 ▸ WINDCHILL: THE COOLING POWER OF MOVING AIR*

Most everyone is familiar with the wintertime cooling power of moving air. When the wind blows on a cold day, we realize that comfort would improve if the wind were to stop. A stiff breeze penetrates ordinary clothing and reduces its capacity to retain body heat while causing exposed parts of the body to chill rapidly. Not only is cooling by evaporation heightened in this situation but the wind is also acting to carry heat away from the body by constantly replacing warmer air next to the body with colder air.

In November 2001, the U.S. National Weather Service (NWS) and the Meteorological Services of Canada (MSC) implemented a new Wind Chill Temperature (WCT) index that was designed to more accurately calculate how the wind and cold feel on human skin (Figure H).

The index accounts for wind effects at face level and takes into account body heat–loss estimates. It was tested on human subjects in a chilled wind tunnel. The results of those trials were used to validate and improve the accuracy of the new formula.

The Wind Chill Chart includes a frostbite indicator that shows where temperature, wind speed, and exposure time will produce frostbite (Figure H). For example, a temperature of 0°F and a wind speed of 15 miles per hour will produce a windchill temperature of −19°F. Under these conditions, exposed skin can freeze in 30 minutes.

It is worth pointing out that in contrast to a cold and windy day, a calm and sunny day in winter feels *warmer* than the thermometer reading. In this situation the warm feeling is caused by the absorption of direct solar radiation by the body. The index does

not take into account any offsetting effect for windchill due to solar radiation. Such a factor may be added in the future.

It is important to remember that the windchill temperature is only an *estimate* of human discomfort. The degree of discomfort felt by different people will vary because it is influenced by many factors. Even if clothing is assumed to be the same, individuals vary widely in their responses because of such factors as age, physical condition, state of health, and level of activity. Nevertheless, as a relative measure, WCT is useful because it allows people to make more informed judgments regarding the potential harmful effects of wind and cold.

_____

*Based in part on material prepared by the U.S. National Weather Service.

FIGURE H Windchill chart. Fahrenheit temperatures are used because this is how the National Weather Service and the news media in the United States commonly report windchill information. The shaded areas on the chart indicate frostbite danger. Each shaded zone shows how long a person can be exposed before frostbite develops. (After NOAA, National Weather Service)

Chapter Summary

- Temperature is one of the basic elements of weather and climate. The *daily mean temperature* is determined by averaging the 24 hourly readings or by adding the maximum and minimum temperatures for a 24-hour period and dividing by two. The *daily temperature range* is computed by finding the difference between the maximum and minimum temperatures. Other temperature data involving longer periods include the *monthly mean temperature* (the sum of the daily means for each day of the month divided by the number of days in the month), the *annual mean temperature* (the average of the twelve monthly mean temperatures), and the *annual temperature range* (the difference between the warmest and coldest monthly mean temperatures).

- The *controls of temperature*—those factors that cause temperature to vary from place to place—are (1) differential heating of land and water; (2) ocean currents; (3) altitude; (4) geographic position; and (5) cloud cover and albedo.

- On maps illustrating the world distribution of temperature, *isotherms*, lines that connect points of equal temperature, generally trend east and west and show a decrease in temperature poleward. Moreover, the isotherms illustrate a latitudinal shifting of temperatures caused by the seasonal migration of the Sun's vertical rays and also reveal the presence of ocean currents. The north-south migration of isotherms is more pronounced over the continents because the temperatures do not fluctuate as much over water.

- Annual temperature range is small near the equator and increases with an increase in latitude. Outside the tropics, annual temperature range also increases with an increase in continentality.
- The primary control of the daily cycle of air temperature is Earth's rotation. However, the magnitude of these changes is variable and influenced by locational factors, local weather conditions, or both.
- As a consequence of the mechanism by which Earth's atmosphere is heated, the months of the highest and lowest temperatures do not coincide with the periods of maximum and minimum incoming solar radiation. In the Northern Hemisphere the greatest intensity of solar radiation occurs at the time of the summer solstice, yet the months of July and August are generally the warmest of the year. Conversely, in the Northern Hemisphere a minimum of solar energy is received in December at the time of the winter solstice, but January and February are usually colder.
- *Thermometers* measure temperature either mechanically or electrically. Most *mechanical thermometers* are based on the ability of a substance to expand when heated and contract when cooled. One type of mechanical thermometer, the liquid-in-glass thermometer, includes maximum thermometers, which use mercury, and minimum thermometers, which contain a liquid of low density, such as alcohol. A bimetal strip mechanical thermometer is frequently used in a thermograph, an instrument that continuously records temperature. *Electrical thermometers* use a thermistor (a thermal resistor) to measure temperature.

- Temperature scales use reference points, called *fixed points*. Three common temperature scales are (1) the *Fahrenheit scale*, which is defined by using the ice point (32°) and steam point (212°); (2) the *Celsius scale*, a decimal scale on which the melting point of ice is set at 0° and the boiling point of water at 100°; and (3) the *Kelvin* or *absolute scale*, where the zero point represents the temperature at which all molecular motion is presumed to cease (called *absolute zero*), the ice point is set at 273, and the steam point at 373.
- Three common applications of temperature data are (1) *heating degree-days,* where each degree of temperature below 65°F is counted as one heating degree day; (2) *cooling degree-days,* which are determined by subtracting 65°F from the daily mean; and (3) *growing degree-days,* which are determined from the difference between the daily mean temperature and the base temperature of the crop, the minimum temperature required for it to grow.
- One familiar use of temperature data relates to human perception of temperature. The *heat stress index* (or *heat index*), a commonly used expression of summertime discomfort, links humidity and temperature to determine the thermal comfort of the human body. *Windchill,* a typical wintertime index, uses both wind and air temperature to calculate the human sensation of temperature.

Vocabulary Review

absolute zero	daily mean temperature	isotherm	specific heat
annual mean temperature	daily temperature range	Kelvin or absolute scale	steam point
annual temperature range	Fahrenheit scale	liquid-in-glass	temperature gradient
bimetal strip	fixed points	thermometer	thermistor
Celsius scale	growing degree-days	maximum thermometer	thermograph
controls of temperature	heating degree-days	minimum thermometer	thermometers
cooling degree-day	ice point	monthly mean temperature	

Review Questions

1. How are the following temperature data calculated: daily mean, daily range, monthly mean, annual mean, and annual range?

2. What are isotherms and what is their purpose?

3. Why are summertime maximum temperatures so high in Death Valley, California? (See Box 1.)

4. a. State the relationship between the heating and cooling of land versus water.
   b. List and explain the factors that cause the difference between the heating and cooling of land and water.
   c. We are studying the atmosphere, so why are we concerned with the heating characteristics at Earth's surface?

5. How does the annual temperature range near the equator compare with the annual temperature ranges in the middle to high latitudes? Explain.

6. Three cities are at the same latitude (about 45° N). One city is located along a windward coast, another in the center of the continent, and the third along a leeward coast. Compare the annual temperature ranges of these cities.

7. Quito, Ecuador, is on the equator and is not a coastal city. It has an annual mean temperature of only 13°C. What is the likely cause for this low annual mean temperature?

8. How does the daily march of temperature on a completely overcast day compare with that on a cloudless, sunny day? Explain your answer.

9. Examine Figure 13 and explain why Yangon's monthly mean temperature for April is higher than the July monthly mean.

10. Answer the following questions about world temperature distribution (you may wish to refer to the January and July isotherm maps).

    a. Isotherms generally trend east–west. Why?
    b. Isotherms bend (poleward, equatorward) over continents in summer. Underline the correct answer and explain.
    c. Isotherms shift north and south from season to season. Why?
    d. Where do isotherms shift most, over land or water? Explain.

    e. How do isotherms show ocean currents? How can you tell if the current is warm or cold?
    f. Why are the isotherms more irregular in the Northern Hemisphere than in the Southern Hemisphere?

11. Which area on Earth experiences the highest annual temperature range? (Refer to Figure 16). Why is the annual range so high in this region?

12. Although the intensity of incoming solar radiation is greatest at local noon, the warmest part of the day is most often midafternoon. Why? Use Figure 19 to explain your answer.

13. List at least three factors that contribute to the urban heat island. (See Box 4.)

14. The magnitude of the daily temperature range can vary significantly from place to place and from time to time. List and describe at least three factors that might cause such variations.

15. Describe how each of the following thermometers works: liquid-in-glass, maximum, minimum, bimetal strip, and thermistor.

16. What is a thermograph? Which type of mechanical thermometer is commonly used in the construction of a thermograph?

17. In addition to having an accurate thermometer, which other factors must be considered to obtain a meaningful air temperature reading?

18. a. What is meant by the terms *steam point* and *ice point*?
    b. What values are given these points on each of the three temperature scales presented in this chapter?

19. Why is it not possible to have a negative value when using the Kelvin temperature scale?

20. When heating and cooling degree-day totals for different places are examined to compare fuel consumption, what important assumption is made?

21. How are growing degree-days calculated? For what purpose is this index used?

Problems

1. If you were asked to identify the coldest city in the United States (or any other designated region), what statistics could be used? Can you list at least three different ways of selecting the coldest city?

2. Examine the number of hurricane-related deaths in Figure C. Be sure to read the entire caption. If Hurricane Katrina had *not* occurred, what number would have been plotted on the graph for hurricane fatalities?

3. Refer to the thermograph record in Figure 17. Determine the maximum and minimum temperature for each day of the week. Use these data to calculate the daily mean and daily range for each day.

4. By referring to the world maps of temperature distribution for January and July (Figures 14 and 15), determine the approximate January mean, July mean, and annual temperature range for a place located at 60° north latitude, 80° east longitude, and a place located at 60° south latitude, 80° east longitude.

5. Referring to Figure H in Box 5, determine windchill temperatures under the following circumstances:
   a. Temperature = 5°F, wind speed = 15 mph.
   b. Temperature = 5°F, wind speed = 30 mph.

6. The mean temperature is 55°F on a particular day. The following day the mean drops to 45°F. Calculate the number of heating degree-days for each day. How much more fuel would be needed to heat a building on the second day compared with the first day?

7. Use the appropriate formula to convert the following temperatures:

$$20°C = \underline{\quad} °F$$
$$-25°C = \underline{\quad} K$$
$$59°F = \underline{\quad} °C$$

Atmospheric Science Online

The Atmosphere 11e website uses the resources and flexibility of the Internet to aid in your study of the topics in this chapter. Written and developed by meteorology instructors, this site will help improve your understanding of meteorology. Visit **www.mygeoscience.com** in order to:

- **Review** key chapter concepts

- **Read** with links to the eBook and to chapter-specific web resources
- **Visualize** and comprehend challenging topics using learning activities in *GEODe: Atmosphere*
- **Test yourself** with online quizzes

GEODe: Atmosphere

GEODe: Atmosphere makes studying more effective by reinforcing key concepts using animation, video, narration, interactive exercises, and practice quizzes. Available at **www.mygeoscience.com**.

Moisture and Atmospheric Stability

From Chapter 4 of *The Atmosphere: An Introduction to Meteorology*, Eleventh Edition, Frederick K. Lutgens, Edward J. Tarbuck, Dennis Tasa. Copyright © 2010 by Pearson Education, Inc. Published by Pearson Prentice Hall. All rights reserved.

Moisture and Atmospheric Stability

Clouds over Antelope Island along the south shore of Utah's Great Salt Lake. (Photo by Scott T. Smith/CORBIS)

W ater vapor is an odorless, colorless gas that mixes freely with the other gases of the atmosphere. Unlike oxygen and nitrogen—the two most abundant components of the atmosphere—water can change from one state of matter to another (solid, liquid, or gas) at the temperatures and pressures experienced on Earth. By comparison, nitrogen will not condense to a liquid unless its temperature is lowered to −196°C (−371°F). Because of this unique property, water freely leaves the oceans as a gas and returns again as a liquid.

As you observe day-to-day weather changes, you might ask: Why is it generally more humid in the summer than in the winter? Why do clouds form on some occasions but not on others? Why do some clouds look thin and harmless, whereas others form gray and ominous towers? Answers to these questions involve the role of water vapor in the atmosphere, the central theme of this chapter.

Movement of Water Through the Atmosphere

Water is everywhere on Earth—in the oceans, glaciers, rivers, lakes, the air, soil, and in living tissue (Figure 1). The vast majority of the water on or close to Earth's surface (over 97 percent) is salt-water found in the oceans. Much of the remaining three percent is locked-up in the ice sheets of Antarctica and Greenland. Only a meager 0.001 percent is found in the atmosphere, most of which is in the form of water vapor.

The increasing demands on this finite resource have led scientists to focus on the continuous exchange of water among the oceans, the atmosphere, and the continents (Figure 2). This unending circulation of Earth's water supply has come to be called the **hydrologic cycle**. The hydrologic cycle is a gigantic system powered by energy from the Sun in which the atmosphere provides the vital link between the oceans and continents. Water from the oceans and, to a much lesser extent,

FIGURE 1   Steam fog over a lake in Maine. (Photo by Sara Gray/Getty Image Inc.-Stone Allstock)

FIGURE 2 Earth's water balance. About 320,000 cubic kilometers of water are evaporated annually from the oceans, whereas evaporation from the land (including lakes and streams) contributes 60,000 cubic kilometers of water. Of this total of 380,000 cubic kilometers of water, about 284,000 cubic kilometers fall back to the ocean, and the remaining 96,000 cubic kilometers fall on Earth's land surface. Because 60,000 cubic kilometers of water leave the land through evaporation and transpiration, 36,000 cubic kilometers of water remain to erode the land during the journey back to the oceans.

from the continents, evaporates into the atmosphere. Winds transport this moisture-laden air, often over great distances.

The process of cloud formation eventually results in precipitation. The precipitation that falls into the ocean has ended its cycle and is ready to begin another. A portion of the water that falls on the continents soaks into the ground, some of it moving downward, then laterally, and finally seeping into lakes and streams or directly into the ocean. Much of the water that soaks in or runs off eventually finds its way back to the atmosphere. In addition to evaporation from the soil, lakes, and streams, some water that infiltrates the ground is absorbed by plants through their roots. They then release it into the atmosphere, a process called **transpiration**. Although transpiration is an important process in some regions, most water vapor enters the atmosphere through evaporation.

Figure 2 not only shows Earth's hydrologic cycle but also its *water balance*. The water balance is a quantitative view of the hydrologic cycle. Although the amount of water vapor in the air is just a tiny fraction of Earth's total water supply, the absolute quantities that are cycled through the atmosphere in a year are

immense, some 380,000 cubic kilometers (91,000 cubic miles). This is enough to cover Earth's surface uniformly to a depth of about 1 meter (3.3 feet). Estimates show that over North America almost six times more water is carried within the moving currents of air than is transported by all the continent's rivers.

Because the total amount of water vapor in the entire global atmosphere remains about the same, the average annual precipitation over Earth must be equal to the quantity of water evaporated. In other words, all of the water vapor that enters the atmosphere must eventually leave. However, for the continents, precipitation exceeds evaporation. Conversely, over the oceans, evaporation exceeds precipitation. Because the level of the world ocean is consistent, runoff from land areas must balance the deficit of precipitation over the oceans.

In summary, the hydrologic cycle depicts the continuous movement of water from the oceans to the atmosphere, from the atmosphere to the land, and from the land back to the sea. The movement of water through the cycle holds the key to the distribution of moisture over the surface of our planet and is intricately related to all atmospheric phenomena.

BOX 1 ▶ WATER: A UNIQUE SUBSTANCE

Water is the only *liquid* found at Earth's surface in large quantities. Water has several unusual properties that set it apart from other substances, for instance: 1) water is readily converted from one state of matter to another (solid, liquid, gas); 2) water's solid phase, ice, is less dense than liquid water; and 3) water has an unusually high heat capacity. All of these properties influence Earth's weather and climate and are favorable to life as we know it.

These unusual properties are largely a consequence of water's ability to form hydrogen bonds. To better grasp the nature of hydrogen bonds, let's examine a water molecule. A water molecule (H_2O) consists of two hydrogen atoms that are strongly bonded to an oxygen atom. Because oxygen atoms have a greater affinity for the bonding electrons (negatively charged subatomic particles) than do hydrogen atoms, the oxygen end of a water molecule acquires a partial negative charge. For the same reason, both hydrogen atoms on a water molecule acquire a partial positive charge. Because oppositely charged particles attract, a hydrogen atom on one water molecule is attracted to an oxygen atom on another water molecule. Thus, *hydrogen bonding* in water is an attractive force that exists between a hydrogen atom in one water molecule and an oxygen atom of any other water molecule.

Hydrogen bonds are what hold water molecules together to form the solid we call *ice*. In ice, hydrogen bonds produce a rigid

hexagonal network as shown in Figure A. The resulting molecular configuration is very open (lots of empty space), which accounts for ice being less dense than liquid water. It is important to note that the attractive forces between hydrogen and oxygen that form water molecules (H_2O) are much stronger than the hydrogen bonds that form ice. Thus, when ice is heated, it is only the hydrogen bonds that are broken.

When ice melts, some of the hydrogen bonds (but not all) are broken. This allows for the more compact arrangement shown in Figure B. Consequently, the liquid phase

FIGURE A Illustration of the crystalline structure of ice. Water molecules are joined together by hydrogen bonds (shown with solid lines) that connect a hydrogen atom on one water molecule with an oxygen atom on another. Oxygen atoms are represented by red spheres and hydrogen atoms by small blue spheres. For simplicity the three-dimensional nature of ice has not been illustrated.

of water is denser than the solid phase. Should water's temperature rise, more hydrogen bonds will break, and the liquid will become even denser, until it reaches 4°C (39°F) when maximum density is achieved. At higher temperatures water gradually becomes less dense because of increased molecular motion—just like most other substances. However, even at higher temperatures, liquid water has significant hydrogen bonding that tends to form clusters of water molecules that are free to move relative to each other. These clusters continually break up and are replaced by new ones.

As a body of water freezes, ice forms on top because ice is less dense than the water beneath it (Figure C). This has far-reaching effects, both for our daily weather and for

FIGURE B Water in the liquid state consists of clusters of water molecules joined together by hydrogen bonds. As these clusters move about, they continually break up and are replaced by new ones.

Water's Changes of State

  Moisture and Cloud Formation
THE ATMOSPHERE ▶ Water's Changes of State

Water is the only substance that exists in the atmosphere as a solid (ice), liquid, and gas (water vapor). It is made of hydrogen and oxygen atoms that are bonded together to form water molecules (H_2O). In all three states of matter (even ice) these molecules are in constant motion—the higher the temperature, the more vigorous the movement. The chief difference among liquid water, ice, and water vapor is the arrangement of the water molecules.

Ice, Liquid Water, and Water Vapor

Ice is composed of water molecules that have low kinetic energies (motion) and are held together by mutual molecular attractions (Box 1). Here the molecules form a tight, orderly network as shown in Figure 3. As a consequence, the water

molecules in ice are not free to move relative to each other but rather vibrate about fixed sites. When ice is heated, the molecules oscillate more rapidly. When the rate of molecular movement increases sufficiently, the bonds between some of the water molecules are broken, resulting in melting.

In the liquid state, water molecules are still tightly packed but are moving fast enough that they are able to easily slide past one another. As a result, liquid water is fluid and will take the shape of its container.

As liquid water gains heat from its environment, some of the molecules will acquire enough energy to break the remaining molecular attractions and escape from the surface, becoming water vapor. Water-vapor molecules are widely spaced compared to liquid water and exhibit very energetic random motion. What distinguishes a gas from a liquid is its compressibility (and expandability). For example, you can easily put more and more air into a tire and increase its volume only slightly. However, don't try to put 10 gallons of gasoline into a five-gallon can.

aquatic life. When ice forms on a water body, it insulates the underlying liquid and limits further freezing. If a water body froze from the bottom, imagine the consequences. Many lakes would freeze solid during the winter, killing the aquatic life. In addition, deep bodies of water, such as the Arctic Ocean, would never be ice-covered. This would alter Earth's heat budget, which in turn would modify global atmospheric and oceanic circulations.

Water's heat capacity is also related to hydrogen bonding. When water is heated, some of the energy is used to break hydrogen bonds rather than to increase molecular motion. (Recall that an increase in average molecular motion corresponds to an increase in temperature.) Thus, under similar conditions, water heats up and cools down more slowly than most common substances. Large water bodies tend to moderate temperatures by remaining warmer than adjacent landmasses in winter and remaining cooler in summer.

Hydrogen bonds are also broken as water evaporates. Thus, water molecules need "extra energy" to give them the motion needed to break the molecular attractions and escape the surface of the liquid to become a gas. (When liquids evaporate, the energy absorbed by the gas molecules is called *latent heat of vaporization*.) Water vapor molecules contain an unusually large amount of "stored energy," which is an important factor influencing weather and cli-

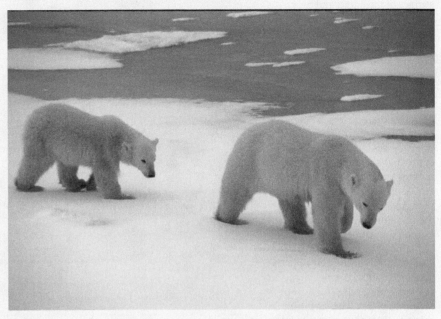

FIGURE C As a body of water freezes, ice forms on top because ice is less dense than liquid water. This is a very unique property, the solid forms of most other substances are denser than the liquid forms. (Photo Steven Morello)

mate. When water vapor condenses in the atmosphere, this energy is released, warming the surrounding air and giving it buoyancy. If the moisture content of air is high, this process can spur the development of thun-

derstorms and contribute to hurricane formation in the tropics.

To summarize, when water changes state, it does not turn into a different substance; only the distances and interactions among the water molecules changes.

Latent Heat

Whenever water changes state, heat is exchanged between water and its surroundings. When water evaporates, heat is absorbed (see Figure 3). Meteorologists often measure heat energy in calories. One **calorie** is the amount of heat required to raise the temperature of 1 gram of water 1°C (1.8°F). Thus, when 10 calories of heat are absorbed by 1 gram of water, the molecules vibrate faster and a 10°C (18°F) temperature rise occurs.

Under certain conditions, heat may be added to a substance without an accompanying rise in temperature. For example, when a glass of ice water is warmed, the temperature of the ice-water mixture remains a constant 0°C (32°F) until all the ice has melted. If adding heat does not raise the temperature, where does this energy go? In this case, the added

energy went to break the molecular attractions that bind water molecules into a crystalline structure.

Because the heat used to melt ice does not produce a temperature change, it is referred to as **latent heat**. (Latent means *hidden*, like the latent fingerprints hidden at a crime scene.) This energy can be thought of as being stored in liquid water, and it is not released to its surroundings as heat until the liquid returns to the solid state.

It requires 80 calories to melt one gram of ice, an amount referred to as *latent heat of melting*. *Freezing*, the reverse process, releases these 80 calories per gram to the environment as *latent heat of fusion*.

Evaporation and Condensation We saw that heat is absorbed when ice is converted to liquid water. Heat is also absorbed during **evaporation**, the process of converting a liquid to a gas (vapor). The energy absorbed by water molecules during evaporation is used to give them the motion needed to escape the surface of the liquid and become a gas. This energy is referred to as the **latent heat of vaporization** and varies from about 600 calories per gram for water at 0°C to 540 calories per gram at 100°C. (Notice from Figure 3 that it takes much more energy to evaporate 1 gram of water than it does to melt the same amount of ice.) During the process of evaporation, it is the higher-temperature (faster-moving) molecules that escape the surface. As a result, the average molecular motion (temperature) of the remaining water is reduced—hence, the common expression "Evaporation is a cooling process." You have undoubtedly experienced this cooling effect on stepping dripping wet from a swimming pool or bathtub. In this situation the energy used to evaporate water comes from your skin—hence, you feel cool.

Condensation, the reverse process, occurs when water vapor changes to the liquid state. During condensation, water-vapor molecules release energy (**latent heat of condensation**) in an amount equivalent to

FIGURE 3 Change of state always involves an exchange of heat. The amounts are expressed in calories and are shown here for the change of 1 gram of water from one state of matter to another.

what was absorbed during evaporation. When condensation occurs in the atmosphere, it results in the formation of such phenomena as fog and clouds (Figure 4).

FIGURE 4 Condensation of water vapor generates phenomena such as clouds and fog. (Photo by Jeremy Walker/Getty Image Inc.-Stone Allstock)

As you will see, latent heat plays an important role in many atmospheric processes. In particular, when water vapor condenses to form cloud droplets, latent heat of condensation is released, warming the surrounding air and giving it buoyancy. When the moisture content of air is high, this process can spur the growth of towering storm clouds. Furthermore, the evaporation of water over the tropical oceans and the subsequent condensation at higher latitudes results in significant energy transfer from equatorial to more poleward locations.

Sublimation and Deposition   You are probably least familiar with the last two processes illustrated in Figure 3—sublimation and deposition. **Sublimation** is the conversion of a solid directly to a gas without passing through the liquid state. Examples you may have observed include the gradual shrinking of unused ice cubes in the freezer and the rapid conversion of dry ice (frozen carbon dioxide) to wispy clouds that quickly disappear.

Deposition refers to the reverse process, the conversion of a vapor directly to a solid. This change occurs, for example, when water vapor is deposited as ice on solid objects such as grass or windows (Figure 5). These deposits are called *white frost* or *hoar frost* and are frequently referred to simply as *frost*. A household example of the process of deposition is the "frost" that accumulates in a freezer. As shown in Figure 3, deposition releases an amount of energy equal to the total amount released by condensation and freezing.

Humidity: Water Vapor in the Air

GE⬤De **Moisture and Cloud Formation**
THE ATMOSPHERE   ▶ Humidity: Water Vapor in the Air

Water vapor constitutes only a small fraction of the atmosphere, varying from as little as one-tenth of 1 percent up to about 4 percent by volume. But the importance of water in the air is far greater than these small percentages would indicate. Indeed, scientists agree that *water vapor* is the most important gas in the atmosphere when it comes to understanding atmospheric processes.

Humidity is the general term used to describe the amount of water vapor in the air (Figure 6). Meteorologists employ several methods to express the water-vapor content of the air, including (1) absolute humidity, (2) mixing ratio, (3) vapor pressure, (4) relative humidity, and (5) dew point. Two of these methods, *absolute humidity* and *mixing ratio*, are similar in that both are expressed as the quantity of water vapor contained in a specific amount of air.

Absolute humidity is *the mass of water vapor in a given volume of air* (usually as grams per cubic meter).

$$\text{Absolute humidity} = \frac{\text{mass of water vapor (grams)}}{\text{volume of air (cubic meters)}}$$

As air moves from one place to another, changes in pressure and temperature cause changes in its volume. When such volume changes occur, the absolute humidity also changes, even if no water vapor is added or removed. Consequently, it is

FIGURE 5   White frost on a window pane. (Photo by Stockxpert/Jupiter Images Unlimited)

FIGURE 6   Meteorologists use several methods to express the water-vapor content of air.

difficult to monitor the water-vapor content of a moving mass of air if absolute humidity is the index being used. Therefore, meteorologists generally prefer to employ mixing ratio to express the water-vapor content of air.

The **mixing ratio** is *the mass of water vapor in a unit of air compared to the remaining mass of dry air.*

$$\text{mixing ratio} = \frac{\text{mass of water vapor (grams)}}{\text{mass of dry air (kilograms)}}$$

Because it is measured in units of mass (usually grams per kilogram), the mixing ratio is not affected by changes in pressure or temperature. (Figure 7).*

Neither the absolute humidity nor the mixing ratio, however, can be easily determined by direct sampling. Therefore, other methods are also used to express the moisture content of the air. These include vapor pressure, relative humidity, and dew point.

Vapor Pressure and Saturation

Another measure of the moisture content of the air is obtained from the pressure exerted by water vapor. To understand how water vapor exerts pressure, imagine a closed flask containing

---

*Another commonly used expression is "specific humidity," which is the mass of water vapor in a unit mass of air, including the water vapor. Because the amount of water vapor in the air rarely exceeds a few percent of the total mass of the air, the specific humidity of air is equivalent to its mixing ratio for all practical purposes.

FIGURE 7 Comparison of absolute humidity and mixing ratio for a rising parcel of air. Note that the mixing ratio is not affected by changes in pressure as the parcel of air rises and expands.

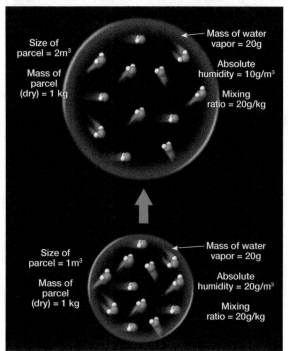

pure water and overlain by dry air, as shown in Figure 8a. Almost immediately some of the water molecules begin to leave the water surface and evaporate into the dry air above. The addition of water vapor into the air can be detected by a small increase in pressure (Figure 8b). This increase in pressure is the result of the motion of the water-vapor molecules that were added to the air through evaporation. In the atmosphere, this pressure is called **vapor pressure** and is defined as *that part of the total atmospheric pressure attributable to its water-vapor content.*

Initially, many more molecules will leave the water surface (evaporate) than will return (condense). However, as

FIGURE 8 The relationship between vapor pressure and saturation. (a) Initial conditions—dry air at 20°C with no observable vapor pressure. (b) Evaporation generates measurable vapor pressure. (c) As more and more molecules escape from the water surface, the steadily increasing vapor pressure forces more and more of these molecules to return to the liquid. Eventually, the number of water-vapor molecules returning to the surface will balance the number leaving. At that point the air is said to be saturated. (d) When the container is heated from 20° to 30°C, the rate of evaporation increases, causing the vapor pressure to increase until a new balance is reached.

more and more molecules evaporate from the water surface, the steadily increasing vapor pressure in the air above forces more and more water molecules to return to the liquid. Eventually a balance is reached in which the number of water molecules returning to the surface balances the number leaving. At that point the air is said to have reached an equilibrium called **saturation** (Figure 8c). When air is saturated, the pressure exerted by the motion of the water-vapor molecules is called the **saturation vapor pressure**.

Now suppose we were to disrupt the equilibrium by heating the water in our closed container, as illustrated in Figure 8d. The added energy would increase the rate at which the water molecules would evaporate from the surface. This in turn would cause the vapor pressure in the air above to increase until a new equilibrium was reached between evaporation and condensation. Thus, we conclude that the saturation vapor pressure is temperature-dependent, such that at higher temperatures it takes more water vapor to saturate air (Figure 9). The amount of water vapor required for the saturation of 1 kilogram (2.2 pounds) of dry air at various temperatures is shown in Table 1. Note that for every 10°C (18°F) increase in temperature, the amount of water vapor needed for saturation almost doubles. Thus, roughly four times more water vapor is needed to saturate 30°C (86°F) air than 10°C (50°F) air.

The atmosphere behaves in much the same manner as our closed container. In nature, gravity, rather than a lid, prevents water vapor (and other gases) from escaping into space. Also like our container, water molecules are constantly evaporating from liquid surfaces (such as lakes or cloud droplets) and other vapor molecules are arriving. However, in nature a balance is not always achieved. More often than not, more water molecules are leaving the surface of a water puddle than are arriving, causing what meteorologists call *net evaporation*. By contrast, during the formation of fog, more water molecules are condensing than are evaporating from the tiny fog droplets, resulting in *net condensation*.

What determines whether the rate of evaporation exceeds the rate of condensation (net evaporation) or vice versa? One of the major factors is the temperature of the surface water,

which in turn determines how much motion (kinetic energy) the water molecules possess. At higher temperatures the molecules have more energy and can more readily escape. Thus, under otherwise similar conditions, because hot water has more energy, it will evaporate faster than cold water.

The other major factor determining which will dominate, evaporation or condensation, is the vapor pressure in the air around the liquid. Recall from our example of a closed container that vapor pressure determines the rate at which the water molecules return to the surface (condense). When the air is dry (low vapor pressure), the rate at which water molecules return to the liquid phase is low. However, when the air around a liquid has reached the saturation vapor pressure, the rate of condensation will be equal to the rate of evaporation. Thus, at saturation there is neither a net condensation nor a net evaporation. Therefore, all else being equal, net evaporation is greater when the air is dry (low vapor pressure) than when the air is humid (high vapor pressure).

In addition to vapor pressure and temperature, other factors exist in nature that affect rates of evaporation and condensation. Although these factors are of minimal importance to most of the processes operating at Earth's surface, they are significant in the atmosphere where clouds and precipitation form.

TABLE 1	Saturation Mixing Ratio (at Sea-Level Pressure)
Temperature °C (°F)	Saturation mixing ratio g/kg
−40 (−40)	0.1
−30 (−22)	0.3
−20 (−4)	0.75
−10 (14)	2
0 (32)	3.5
5 (41)	5
10 (50)	7
15 (59)	10
20 (68)	14
25 (77)	20
30 (86)	26.5
35 (95)	35
40 (104)	47

FIGURE 9 The amount of water vapor required to saturate 1 kilogram of dry air at various temperatures.

Students Sometimes Ask . . .

Why do the sizes of snow piles seem to shrink a few days after a snowfall, even when the temperatures remain below freezing?

On clear, cold days following a snowfall, the air can be very dry. This fact, plus solar heating, causes the ice crystals to sublimate—turn from a solid to a gas. Thus, even without any appreciable melting, these accumulations of snow gradually get smaller.

Relative Humidity

Moisture and Cloud Formation
▸ Humidity: Water Vapor in the Air

The most familiar and, unfortunately, the most misunderstood term used to describe the moisture content of air is relative humidity. **Relative humidity** *is a ratio of the air's actual water-vapor content compared with the amount of water vapor required for saturation at that temperature (and pressure).* Thus, relative humidity indicates how near the air is to saturation rather than the actual quantity of water vapor in the air (Box 2).

To illustrate, we see from Table 1 that at 25°C, air is saturated when it contains 20 grams of water vapor per kilogram of air. Thus, if the air contains 10 grams per kilogram on a 25°C day, the relative humidity is expressed as 10/20, or 50 percent. Further, if air with a temperature of 25°C had a water-vapor content of 20 grams per kilogram, the relative humidity would be expressed as 20/20 or 100 percent. On those occasions when the relative humidity reaches 100 percent, the air is said to be saturated.

How Relative Humidity Changes

Because relative humidity is based on the air's water-vapor content, as well as the amount of moisture required for saturation, it can be changed in either of two ways. First, relative humidity can be changed by the addition or removal of water vapor. Second, because the amount of moisture required for saturation is a function of air temperature, relative humidity varies with temperature. (Recall that the saturation vapor pressure is temperature dependent, such that at higher temperatures, it takes more water vapor to saturate air than at lower temperatures.)

Adding or Subtracting Moisture Notice in Figure 10 that when water vapor is added to a parcel of air, its relative

---

BOX 2 ▸ DRY AIR AT 100 PERCENT RELATIVE HUMIDITY?

A common misconception relating to meteorology is the notion that air with a high relative humidity must have a greater water-vapor content than air with a lower relative humidity. Frequently, this is not the case (Figure D). To illustrate, let us compare a typical January day at International Falls, Minnesota, to one in the desert near Phoenix, Arizona. On this hypothetical day the temperature in International Falls is a cold −10°C (14°F) and the relative humidity is 100 percent. By referring to Table 1, we can see that saturated −10°C (14°F) air has a water-vapor content (mixing ratio) of 2 grams per kilogram (g/kg). By contrast, the desert air at Phoenix on this January day is a warm 25°C (77°F), and the relative humidity is just 20 percent. A look at Table 1 reveals that 25°C (77°F) air has a saturation mixing ratio of 20 g/kg. Therefore, with a relative humidity of 20 percent, the air at Phoenix has a water-vapor content of 4 g/kg (20 grams × 20 percent). Consequently, the "dry" air at Phoenix actually contains twice the water vapor as the "wet" air at International Falls.

This should make clear why places that are very cold are also very dry. The low water-vapor content of frigid air (even when saturated) helps to explain why many arctic areas receive only meager amounts of precipitation and are referred to as "polar deserts." This also helps us understand why people frequently experience dry skin and chapped lips during the winter months. The water vapor content of cold air is low, even when compared to some hot, arid regions.

FIGURE D Moisture content of hot air versus frigid air. Hot desert air with a low relative humidity generally has a higher water-vapor content than frigid air with a high relative humidity. (Top photo by Matt Duvall, bottom photo by E. J. Tarbuck)

humidity increases until saturation occurs (100 percent relative humidity). What if even more moisture is added to this parcel of saturated air? Does the relative humidity exceed 100 percent? Normally, this situation does not occur. Instead, the excess water vapor condenses to form liquid water.

You may have experienced such a situation while taking a hot shower. The water leaving the shower is composed of very energetic (hot) molecules, which means that the rate of evaporation is high. As long as you run the shower, the process of evaporation continually adds water vapor to the unsaturated air in the bathroom. Therefore, if you stay in a hot shower long enough, the air eventually becomes saturated and the excess water vapor condenses on the mirror, window, tile, and other surfaces in the room.

In nature, moisture is added to the air mainly via evaporation from the oceans. However, plants, soil, and smaller bodies of water do make substantial contributions. Unlike your shower, however, the processes that add water vapor to the air generally do not operate at rates fast enough to cause saturation to occur directly. One exception is when you exhale on a cold winter day and "see your breath." What is happening is the warm moist air from your lungs mixes with the cold outside air, which has a very low saturation vapor pressure. Your breath has enough moisture to saturate a small quantity of cold outside air and the result is a miniature "cloud." Almost as fast as the "cloud" forms, it mixes with more of the dry outside air and quickly evaporates.

Changes with Temperature The second condition that affects relative humidity is air temperature (Box 3). Examine

Figure 11 carefully. Note that in Figure 11a, when air at 20°C contains 7 grams of water vapor per kilogram, it has a relative humidity of 50 percent. This can be verified by referring to Table 1. Here we can see that at 20°C, air is saturated when it contains 14 grams of water vapor per kilogram of air. Because the air in Figure 11a contains 7 grams of water vapor, its relative humidity is 7/14 or 50 percent.

How does cooling affect relative humidity? When the flask in Figure 11a is cooled from 20° to 10°C, as shown in Figure 11b, the relative humidity increases from 50 to 100 percent. We can conclude from this that when the water-vapor content remains constant, a decrease in temperature results in an increase in relative humidity.

But there is no reason to assume that cooling would cease the moment the air reached saturation. What happens when the air is cooled below the temperature at which saturation occurs? Figure 11c illustrates this situation. Notice from Table 1 that when the flask is cooled to 0°C, the air is saturated at 3.5 grams of water vapor per kilogram of air. Because this flask originally contained 7 grams of water vapor, 3.5 grams of water vapor will condense to form liquid droplets that collect on the walls of the container. In the meantime, the relative humidity of the air inside remains at 100 percent. This raises an important concept. When air aloft is cooled below its saturation level, some of the water vapor condenses to form clouds. As clouds are made of liquid droplets, this moisture is no longer part of the water-vapor content of the air.

Let us return to Figure 11 and see what would happen should the flask in Figure 11a be heated to 35°C. From Table 1 we see that at 35°C, saturation occurs at 35 grams of water vapor per kilogram of air. Consequently, by heating the air from 20° to 35°C, the relative humidity would drop from 7/14 (50 percent) to 7/35 (20 percent).

We can summarize the effects of temperature on relative humidity as follows. When the water-vapor content of air remains at a constant level, a decrease in air temperature results in an increase in relative humidity, and an increase in temperature causes a decrease in relative humidity.

Natural Changes in Relative Humidity

In nature there are three major ways that air temperatures change (over relatively short time spans) to cause corresponding changes in relative humidity. These are:

1. Daily changes in temperatures (daylight versus nighttime temperatures).
2. Temperature changes that result as air moves horizontally from one location to another.

FIGURE 10 At a constant temperature (in this example it is 25°C) the relative humidity will increase as water vapor is added to the air. The saturation mixing ratio for air at 25°C is 20g/kg (see Table 1). As the water-vapor content in the flask increases, the relative humidity rises from 25 to 100 percent.

Temperature
25°C   25°C   25°C

1 kg air   1 kg air   1 kg air

5 grams H₂O vapor   10 grams H₂O vapor   20 grams H₂O vapor

Evaporation   Evaporation

1. Saturation mixing ratio at 25°C = 20 grams*
2. H₂O vapor content = 5 grams
3. Relative humidity = 5/20 = 25%
*See Table 1

1. Saturation mixing ratio at 25°C = 20 grams*
2. H₂O vapor content = 10 grams
3. Relative humidity = 10/20 = 50%

1. Saturation mixing ratio at 25°C = 20 grams*
2. H₂O vapor content = 20 grams
3. Relative humidity = 20/20 = 100%

(a) **Initial condition**   (b) **Addition of 5 grams of water vapor**   (c) **Addition of 10 grams of water vapor**

BOX 3 ▶ HUMIDIFIERS AND DEHUMIDIFIERS

In summer, stores sell *dehumidifiers*. As winter rolls around, these same merchants feature *humidifiers*. Why do you suppose so many homes are equipped with both a humidifier and a dehumidifier? The answer lies in the relationship between temperature and relative humidity. Recall that if the water-vapor content of air remains at a constant level, an increase in temperature lowers the relative humidity and a lowering of temperature increases the relative humidity.

During the summer months, warm, moist air frequently dominates the weather of the central and eastern United States. When hot and humid air enters a home, some of it circulates into the cool basement. As a result, the temperature of this air drops and its relative humidity increases. The result is a damp, musty-smelling basement. In response, the homeowner installs a dehumidifier to alleviate the problem. As air is drawn over the cold coils of the dehumidifier, water vapor condenses and collects in a bucket or flows down a drain. This process reduces the relative humidity and makes for a drier, more comfortable basement.

By contrast, during the winter months, outside air is cool and dry. When this air is drawn into the home, it is heated to room temperature. This process in turn causes the relative humidity to plunge, often to uncomfortably low levels of 40 percent or lower. Living with dry air can mean static electrical shocks, dry skin, sinus headaches, or even nose bleeds. Consequently, the homeowner may install a humidifier, which adds water to the air and increases the relative humidity to a more comfortable level.

---

3. Temperature changes caused as air moves vertically in the atmosphere.

The importance of the last two processes in creating weather will be discussed later. The effect of the typical daily temperature cycle on relative humidity is shown in Figure 12. Notice that during the warmer midday period, relative humidity reaches its lowest level, whereas the cooler evening hours are associated with higher relative humidities. In this example, the actual water-vapor content (mixing ratio) of the air remains unchanged; only the relative humidity varies. Now we can better understand why a high relative humidity does not necessarily indicate a high water-vapor content.

Despite the previous example, we still describe air having a low relative humidity as being "dry" and vice versa. The use of the word "dry" in this context indicates that the air is far from being saturated. Thus, the rate of evaporation on a dry day is generally higher than on a humid day.

In summary, relative humidity indicates how near the air is to being saturated, whereas the air's mixing ratio denotes the actual quantity of water vapor contained in that air.

Dew-Point Temperature

Moisture and Cloud Formation
▶ Humidity: Water Vapor in the Air

Another important measure of humidity is the dew-point temperature. The **dew-point temperature**, or simply the **dew point**, is the temperature to which

Students Sometimes Ask . . .

Why do my lips get chapped in the winter?

During the winter months, outside air is comparatively cool and dry. When this air is drawn into the home, it is heated, which causes the relative humidity to plunge. Unless your home is equipped with a humidifier, you are likely to experience chapped lips and dry skin at that time of year.

FIGURE 11 Relative humidity varies with temperature. When the water-vapor content (mixing ratio) remains constant, the relative humidity can be changed by increasing or decreasing the air temperature. In this example, when the temperature of the air in the flask was lowered from 20° to 10°C, the relative humidity increased from 50 to 100 percent. Further cooling (from 10° to 0°C) causes one-half of the water vapor to condense. In nature, cooling of air below its saturated mixing ratio generally causes condensation in the form of clouds, dew, or fog.

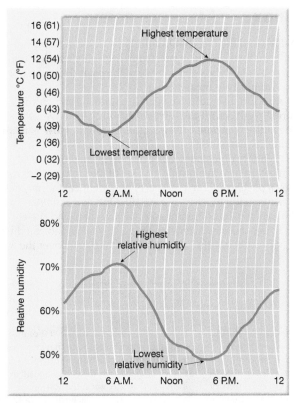

FIGURE 12 Typical daily variation in temperature and relative humidity during a spring day at Washington, D.C.

FIGURE 13 Condensation, or "dew," occurs when a cold drinking glass chills the surrounding layer of air to the dew-point temperature. (Photo by © Leonard Lessin/Peter Arnold)

air needs to be cooled to reach saturation. For example, in Figure 11 the unsaturated air in the flask had to be cooled to 10°C before saturation occurred. Therefore, 10°C is the dew-point temperature for this air. In nature, cooling below the dew point causes water vapor to condense, typically as dew, fog, or clouds (Figure 13). The term *dew point* stems from the fact that during nighttime hours, objects near the ground often cool below the dew-point temperature and become coated with dew.*

Unlike relative humidity, which is a measure of how near the air is to being saturated, dew-point temperature is a measure of the *actual moisture content* of a parcel of air. Because the dew-point temperature is directly related to the amount of water vapor in the air, and because it is easy to determine, it is one of the most useful measures of humidity.

Recall that the saturation vapor pressure is temperature-dependent and that for every 10°C (18°F) increase in temperature, the amount of water vapor needed for saturation doubles. Therefore, relatively cold *saturated air* (0°C or 32°F) contains about half the water vapor of *saturated air* having a temperature of 10°C (50°F) and roughly one-fourth that of hot *saturated air* with a temperature of 20°C (68°F). Because the dew point is the temperature at which saturation occurs, we

can conclude that high dew-point temperatures equate to moist air and low dew-point temperatures indicate dry air (Table 2). More precisely, based on what we have learned about vapor pressure and saturation, we can state that for every 10°C (18°F) increase in the dew-point temperature, air contains about twice as much water vapor. Therefore, we know that when the dew-point temperature is 25°C (77°F), air contains about twice the water vapor as when the dew point is 15°C (59°F) and four times that of air with a dew point of 5°C (41°F).

Because the dew-point temperature is a good measure of the amount of water vapor in the air, it is the measure of atmospheric moisture that appears on a variety of weather maps. Notice on the map in Figure 14 that much of the area near the warm Gulf of Mexico has dew-point temperatures that exceed 70°F (21°C). When the dew point exceeds 65°F (18°C), it is considered humid by most people, and air with a dew point 75°F (24°C) or higher is oppressive. Also notice in Figure 14 that although the Southeast is dominated by

---

*Normally we associate dew with grass. Because of transpiration by the blades of grass, the relative humidity on a calm night is much higher near the grass than a few inches above the surface. Consequently, dew forms on grass before it does on most other objects.

TABLE 2 Dew-Point Thresholds	
Dew-point temperature	
≤ 10°F	Significant snowfall is inhibited.
≥ 55°F	Minimum for severe thunderstorms to form.
≥ 65°F	Considered humid by most people.
≥ 70°F	Typical of the rainy tropics.
≥ 75°F	Considered oppressive by most.

humid conditions (dew points above 65°F), most of the remainder of the country is experiencing comparatively drier air.

Students Sometimes Ask . . .

Is frost just frozen dew?

Contrary to popular belief, frost is not frozen dew. Rather, white frost (*hoar frost*) forms on occasions when saturation occurs at a temperature of 0°C (32°F) or below (a temperature called the *frost point*). Thus, frost forms when water vapor changes directly from a gas into a solid (ice) without entering the liquid state. This process, called *deposition*, produces delicate patterns of ice crystals that often decorate windows during winter.

Humidity Measurement

Aside from the fact that humidity is important meteorologically, many of us are interested in humidity because it influences comfort (Box 4). Here we will look at the various ways that humidity is measured.

Absolute humidity and mixing ratio are difficult to measure directly, but if the relative humidity is known, they can be readily computed from a table or graph. How is relative humidity measured?

A variety of instruments, called **hygrometers**, can be used to measure relative humidity. One of the simplest hygrometers, a **psychrometer**, consists of two identical thermometers mounted side by side (Figure 15). One thermometer, called the *wet bulb*, has a thin muslin wick tied around the end.

To use the psychrometer, the cloth wick is saturated with water and a continuous current of air is passed over the wick,

---

BOX 4 ▶ ATMOSPHERIC HAZARD

Humidity and Heat Stress

During a heat wave in 1995 more than 500 heat-related fatalities occurred in the greater Chicago area. Although this was an exceptional event, the stress of high summer temperatures and exposure to the Sun claim about 175 American lives in an average year.

High humidity contributes significantly to the discomfort people feel during a heat wave. Why are hot, muggy days so uncomfortable? Humans, like other mammals, are warm-blooded creatures who maintain a constant body temperature regardless of the temperature of the environment. One of the ways the body prevents overheating is by perspiring or sweating. However, this process does little to cool the body unless the perspiration can evaporate. It is the cooling created by the evaporation of perspiration that reduces body temperature. Because high humidity retards evaporation, people are more uncomfortable on a hot and humid day than on a hot and dry day.

Generally, temperature and humidity are the most important elements influencing summertime human comfort. Several indices combine these factors to establish the level or degree of comfort or discomfort. One index widely used by the National Weather Service was developed by R. G. Steadman and is called the *heat stress index*, or simply the *heat index*. It is a measure of *apparent temperature*, the air temperature that an individual perceives. It indicates how "hot" an average person feels given various combinations of temperature and relative humidity (Table A).

For example, we can see from Table A that if the air temperature is 90°F and the

relative humidity is 60 percent, it should feel like 100°F. Note that as the relative humidity increases, the apparent temperature, and thus heat stress, increases as well. Further, when the relative humidity is low, the apparent temperature can have a value that is less than the actual air temperature.

To advise the public on the potential danger from heat stress, the National Weather Service uses the apparent temperature to determine the level of human discomfort, as shown in Table A. This method categorizes the impact that various apparent temperatures will have on the well-being of individuals. It is important to note that factors such as the length of exposure to direct sunlight, the wind speed, and the general health of the individual greatly affect the amount of stress a person will experience. Further, while a period of hot, humid weather in New Orleans might be tolerable, a similar event in Minneapolis, Minnesota, would tax that population. This is because hot and humid weather is more taxing on people who live where it is less common than it is on people who live where prolonged periods of heat and humidity are the rule.

Table A   Heat Index

Air Temperature (°F)	Relative Humidity (%)													With prolonged exposure and/or physical activity
	40	45	50	55	60	65	70	75	80	85	90	95	100	
110	136													**Extreme danger** Heat stroke or sunstroke highly likely
108	130	137												
106	124	130	137											
104	119	124	131	137										
102	114	119	124	130	137									**Danger** Sunstroke, muscle cramps, and/or heat exhaustion likely
100	109	114	118	124	129	136								
98	105	109	113	117	123	128	134							
96	101	104	108	112	116	121	126	132						
94	97	100	102	106	110	114	119	124	129	135				**Extreme caution** Sunstroke, muscle cramps, and/or heat exhaustion possible
92	94	96	99	101	105	108	112	116	121	126	131			
90	91	93	95	97	100	103	106	109	113	117	122	127	132	
88	88	89	91	93	95	98	100	103	106	110	113	117	121	
86	85	87	88	89	91	93	95	97	100	102	105	108	112	**Caution** Fatigue possible
84	83	84	85	86	88	89	90	92	94	96	98	100	103	
82	81	82	83	84	84	85	86	88	89	90	91	93	95	
80	80	80	81	81	82	82	83	84	84	85	86	86	87	

FIGURE 14 Surface map showing dew-point temperatures for September 15, 2005. Dew-point temperatures above 60°F dominate the southeastern United States, indicating that this region is blanketed with humid air.

either by swinging the instrument freely in the air or by fanning air past it (Figure 15c). As a result, water evaporates from the wick, absorbing heat energy from the thermometer to do so, and the temperature of the wet bulb drops. The amount of cooling that takes place is directly proportional to the dryness of the air. The drier the air, the greater the cooling. Therefore, the larger the difference between the wet- and dry-bulb temperatures, the lower the relative humidity; the smaller the difference, the higher the relative humidity. If the air is saturated, no evaporation will occur, and the two thermometers will have identical readings.

Using a psychrometer and the tables provided in the Appendix: Relative Humidity and Dew Point Tables, the relative humidity and the dew-point temperature can be determined. All that is required is to record the air (dry-bulb) temperature and calculate the difference between the dry- and wet-bulb readings. The difference is known as the *depression of the wet bulb*. Assume, for instance, that the dry-bulb temperature is 20°C and that the wet-bulb reading after swinging or fanning is 14°C. To determine the relative humidity, find the dry-bulb

FIGURE 15 Sling psychrometer. (a) Sling psychrometers use dry-bulb and wet-bulb thermometers to calculate both relative humidity and dew point. (b) The dry-bulb thermometer measures the current air temperature. The wet-bulb thermometer is covered with a cloth wick dipped in water. (c) As the instrument is spun, evaporation cooling causes the temperature of the wet-bulb thermometer to decrease. The amount of cooling that occurs is directly proportional to the dryness of the air. The temperature difference between the dry- and wet-bulb thermometers is used in conjunction with the tables in the Appendix: Relative Humidity and Dew Point Tables to determine relative humidity and dew point temperature. (Photo by E. J. Tarbuck)

Wet bulb — Dry bulb

Room temperature water

A.

B.

C.

temperature on the left-hand column of Table 1 of Appendix: Relative Humidity and Dew Point Tables and the depression of the wet bulb across the top. The relative humidity is found where the two meet. In this example, the relative humidity is 51 percent. The dew point can be determined in the same way, using Table 2. In this case, it would be 10°C.

Another instrument used for measuring relative humidity, the *hair hygrometer,* can be read directly without using tables. The hair hygrometer operates on the principle that hair changes length in proportion to changes in relative humidity. Hair lengthens as relative humidity increases and shrinks as relative humidity drops. People with naturally curly hair experience this phenomenon, for in humid weather their hair lengthens and hence becomes curlier. The hair hygrometer uses a bundle of hairs linked mechanically to an indicator that is calibrated between 0 and 100 percent. Thus, we need only glance at the dial to read directly the relative humidity. Unfortunately, the hair hygrometer is less accurate than the psychrometer. Furthermore, it requires frequent calibration and is slow in responding to changes in humidity, especially at low temperatures.

A different type of hygrometer is used in remote-sensing instrument packages, such as radiosondes, that transmit upper-air observations back to ground stations. The electric hygrometer contains an electrical conductor coated with a moisture-absorbing chemical. It works on the principle that electric current flow varies as the relative humidity varies. Most surface weather stations have converted from traditional hygrometers to electric hygrometers of the type used for upper-air observations.

Adiabatic Temperature Changes

 Moisture and Cloud Formation
▶ The Basics of Cloud Formation: Adiabatic Cooling

So far we have considered some basic properties of water vapor and how its variability in the atmosphere is measured. We are now ready to examine the critical role that water vapor plays in our daily weather.

Recall that condensation occurs when water vapor is cooled enough to change to a liquid. Condensation may produce dew, fog, or clouds. Although each type of condensation is different, all require saturated air to form. As indicated earlier, saturation occurs either when sufficient water vapor

is added to the air or, more commonly, when the air is cooled to its dew-point temperature.

Heat near Earth's surface is readily exchanged between the ground and the air above. As the ground loses heat in the evening (radiation cooling), dew may condense on the grass and fog may form in the air near the surface. Thus, surface cooling that occurs after sunset accounts for some condensation. However, cloud formation often takes place during the warmest part of the day. Clearly some other mechanism must operate aloft that cools air sufficiently to generate clouds.

The process that generates most clouds is easily visualized. Have you ever pumped up a bicycle tire with a hand pump and noticed that the pump barrel became very warm? When you applied energy to compress the air, the motion of the gas molecules increased and the temperature of the air rose. Conversely, if you allow air to escape from a bicycle tire, it expands; the gas molecules move less rapidly and the air cools. You have probably felt the cooling effect of the propellant gas expanding as you applied hair spray or spray deodorant.

The temperature changes just described, in which heat was neither added nor subtracted, are called **adiabatic temperature changes**. They result when air is compressed or allowed to expand. In summary, *when air is allowed to expand, it cools; when air is compressed, it warms.*

Adiabatic Cooling and Condensation

To simplify the following discussion, it helps if we imagine a volume of air enclosed in a thin elastic cover. Meteorologists call this imaginary volume of air a **parcel**. Typically, we consider a parcel to be a few hundred cubic meters in volume, and we assume that it acts independently of the surrounding air. It is also assumed that no heat is transferred into, or out of, the parcel. Although highly idealized, over short time spans, a parcel of air behaves in a manner much like an actual volume of air moving vertically in the atmosphere. In nature, sometimes the surrounding air infiltrates a vertically moving column of air, a process called **entrainment**. For the following discussion we will assume no mixing of this type is occurring.

Any time a parcel of air moves upward, it passes through regions of successively lower pressure. As a result, ascending air expands and it cools adiabatically. Unsaturated air cools at a constant rate of 10°C for every 1000 meters of ascent (5.5°F per 1000 feet). Conversely, descending air comes under increasing pressure and is compressed and heated 10°C for every 1000 meters of descent (Figure 16). This rate of cooling or heating applies only to vertically moving unsaturated air and is known as the **dry adiabatic rate** ("dry" because the air is unsaturated).

If a parcel of air rises high enough, it will eventually cool to its dew point. Here the process of condensation begins. The altitude at which a parcel reaches saturation and cloud formation begins is called the **lifting condensation level**. At the lifting condensation level an important thing happens: The latent heat that was absorbed by the water vapor when it evaporated is liberated. Although the parcel will continue to cool adiabatically, the release of this latent heat slows the rate of cooling. In other words, when a parcel of air ascends

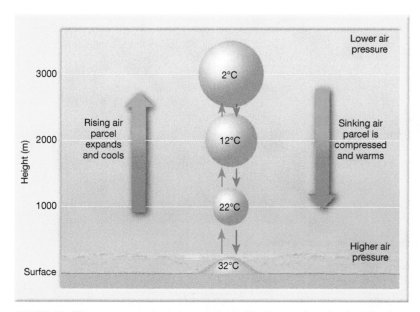

FIGURE 16 Whenever an unsaturated parcel of air is lifted it expands and cools at the *dry adiabatic rate* of 10°C per 1000 meters. Conversely, when air sinks, it is compressed and heats at the same rate.

above the lifting condensation level, the rate of cooling is reduced because the release of latent heat partially offsets the cooling due to expansion. This slower rate of cooling caused by the release of latent heat is called the **wet adiabatic rate** of cooling ("wet" because the air is saturated).

Because the amount of latent heat released depends on the quantity of moisture present in the air (generally between

FIGURE 17 Rising air expands and cools at the dry adiabatic rate of 10°C per 1000 meters until the air reaches the dew point and condensation (cloud formation) begins. As air continues to rise, the latent heat released by condensation reduces the rate of cooling. The wet adiabatic rate is therefore always less than the dry adiabatic rate.

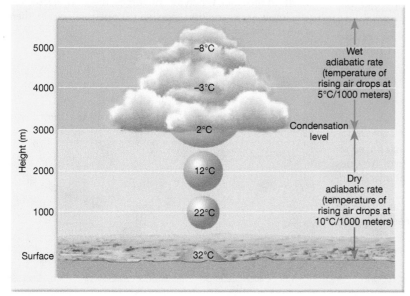

0 and 4 percent), the wet adiabatic rate varies from 5°C per 1000 meters for air with a high moisture content to 9°C per 1000 meters for air with a low moisture content. Figure 17 illustrates the role of adiabatic cooling in the formation of clouds. Note that from the surface up to the lifting condensation level, the air cools at the faster, dry adiabatic rate. The slower, wet adiabatic rate commences at the point where condensation begins.

Processes That Lift Air

 Moisture and Cloud Formation
THE ATMOSPHERE ▸ **Processes That Lift Air**

To review, when air rises, it expands and cools adiabatically. If air is lifted sufficiently, it will eventually cool to its dew-point temperature, saturation will occur, and clouds will develop. But why does air rise on some occasions and not on others?

It turns out that in general the tendency is for air to resist vertical movement. Therefore, air located near the surface tends to stay near the surface, and air aloft tends to remain aloft. Exceptions to this rule, as we shall see, include conditions in the atmosphere that give air sufficient buoyancy to rise without the aid of outside forces. In many situations, however, when you see clouds forming, there is some mechanical phenomenon at work that forces the air to rise (at least initially).

We will look at four mechanisms that cause air to rise. These are:

1. *Orographic lifting*—air is forced to rise over a mountainous barrier.
2. *Frontal wedging*—warmer, less dense air, is forced over cooler, denser air.
3. *Convergence*—a pile-up of horizontal air flow results in upward movement.
4. *Localized convective lifting*—unequal surface heating causes localized pockets of air to rise because of their buoyancy.

Orographic Lifting

Orographic lifting occurs when elevated terrains, such as mountains, act as barriers to the flow of air (Figure 18). As air ascends a mountain slope, adiabatic cooling often

FIGURE 18 Orographic lifting and rainshadow deserts. (a) Orographic lifting occurs where air is forced over a topographic barrier. (b) The arid conditions in the Great Basin of the western United States can be partially attributed to the adjacent Sierra Nevada Range, which orographically removes the moisture from the air originating over the Pacific. (Photo by James E. Patterson/James Patterson Collection)

generates clouds and copious precipitation. In fact, many of the rainiest places in the world are located on windward mountain slopes (Box 5).

In addition to providing lift, mountains remove additional moisture in other ways. By slowing the horizontal flow of air, they cause convergence and retard the passage of storm systems. Moreover, the irregular topography of mountains enhances the differential heating that causes some localized convective lifting. These combined effects account for the generally higher precipitation associated with mountainous regions compared with surrounding lowlands.

By the time air reaches the leeward side of a mountain, much of its moisture has been lost. If the air descends, it warms adiabatically, making condensation and precipitation even less likely. As shown in Figure 18(a), the result can be a **rain shadow desert** (Box 6). The Great Basin Desert of the western United States lies only a few hundred kilometers from the Pacific Ocean, but it is effectively cut off from the ocean's moisture by the imposing Sierra Nevada (Figure 18b). The Gobi Desert of Mongolia, the Takla Makan of China, and the Patagonia Desert of Argentina are other examples of deserts that exist because they are on the leeward sides of mountains.

Frontal Wedging

If orographic lifting were the only mechanism that forced air aloft, the relatively flat central portion of North America would be an expansive desert instead of the nation's breadbasket. Fortunately, this is not the case.

In central North America, masses of warm and cold air collide producing a **front**. Here the cooler, denser air acts as a barrier over which the warmer, less dense air rises. This process, called **frontal wedging**, is illustrated in Figure 19.

It should be noted that weather-producing fronts are associated with storm systems called *middle-latitude cyclones*.

Convergence

We saw that the collision of contrasting air masses forces air to rise. In a more general sense, whenever air in the lower troposphere flows together, lifting results. This phenomenon is called **convergence**. When air flows in from more than one direction, it must go somewhere. As it cannot go down, it goes up (Figure 20). This, of course, leads to adiabatic cooling and possibly cloud formation.

Convergence can also occur whenever an obstacle slows or restricts horizontal air flow (wind). We saw earlier that mountains slow winds and cause convergence. Further, when air moves from a relatively smooth surface, such as the ocean, onto an irregular landscape its speed is reduced. The result is a pileup of air (convergence). This is similar to what happens when people leave a well-attended sporting event and pileup results at the exits. When air converges, the air molecules do not simply squeeze closer together (like people); rather, there is a net upward flow.

FIGURE 19 Frontal wedging. Colder, denser air acts as a barrier over which warmer, less dense air rises.

BOX 5 ▶ PRECIPITATION RECORDS AND MOUNTAINOUS TERRAIN

Many of the rainiest places in the world are located on windward mountain slopes. Typically, these rainy areas occur because the mountains act as a barrier to the general circulation. Thus, the prevailing winds are forced to ascend the sloping terrain, thereby generating clouds and often abundant precipitation. A station at Mount Waialeale, Hawaii, for example, records the highest average annual rainfall in the world, some 1234 centimeters (486 inches). The station is located on the windward (northeast) coast of the island of Kauai at an elevation of 1569 meters (5148 feet). Incredibly, only 31 kilometers (19 miles) away lies sunny Barking Sands, with annual precipitation that averages less than 50 centimeters (20 inches).

The greatest recorded rainfall for a single 12-month period occurred at Cherrapunji, India, where an astounding 2647 centimeters (1042 inches), over 86 feet, fell. Cherrapunji, which is located at an elevation of 1293 meters (4309 feet), lies just north of the Bay of Bengal in an ideal location to receive the full effect of India's wet summer monsoon. Most of this rainfall occurred in the summer, particularly during the month of July, when a record 930 centimeters (366 inches) fell. For comparison, 10 times more rain fell in a single month at Cherrapunji, India, than falls in an average year at Chicago.

Because mountains can be sites of abundant precipitation, they are frequently very important sources of water. This is true for many dry locations in the western United States. Here the snow pack, which accumulates high in the mountains during the winter, is a major source of water for the summer season when precipitation is light and demand is great (Figure E). Reservoirs in the Sierra Nevada, for example, accumulate and store spring runoff, which is then delivered to cities such as Los Angeles by way of an extensive network of canals. The record for greatest annual snowfall in the United States goes to the Mount Baker ski area north of Seattle, Washington, where 2896 centimeters (1140 inches) of snow were measured during the winter of 1998–1999.

FIGURE E Heavy snow pack along Trail Ridge Road, in Colorado's Rocky Mountain National Park. (Photo by Henry Lansford)

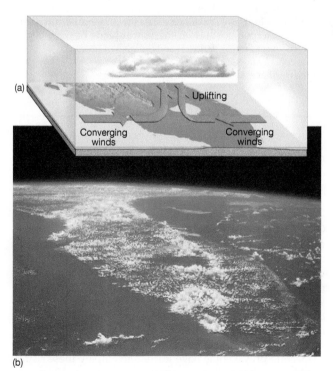

FIGURE 20 Convergence. (a) When surface air converges, the column of air increases in height to allow for the decreased area it occupies. (b) Southern Florida viewed from the space shuttle. On warm days, airflow from the Atlantic Ocean and the Gulf of Mexico converge over the Florida peninsula generating many mid-afternoon thunderstorms. (Photo by NASA/Media Services)

BOX 6 ▶ OROGRAPHIC EFFECTS: WINDWARD PRECIPITATION AND LEEWARD RAIN SHADOWS

A good way to see the role that orographic lifting plays in the development of windward precipitation and leeward rain shadows is to examine a simplified hypothetical situation. In Figure F, prevailing winds force warm, moist air over a 3000-meter-high mountain range. As the unsaturated air ascends the windward side of the range, it cools at the rate of 10°C per 1000 meters (dry adiabatic rate) until it reaches the dew-point temperature of 20°C. Because the dew-point temperature is reached at 1000 meters, we can say that this height represents the lifting condensation level and the height of the cloud base. Notice in Figure F that above the lifting condensation level, latent heat is released, which results in a slower rate of cooling, called the *wet adiabatic rate*.

From the cloud base to the top of the mountain, water vapor within the rising air is condensing to form more and more cloud droplets. As a result, the windward side of the mountain range experiences abundant precipitation.

For simplicity, we will assume that the air that was forced to the top of the mountain is cooler than the surrounding air and hence begins to flow down the leeward slope of the mountain. As the air descends, it is compressed and *heated* at the dry adiabatic rate (Figure F). Upon reaching the base of the mountain range, the temperature of the descending air has risen to 40°C, or 10°C warmer than the temperature at the base of the mountain on the windward side. The higher temperature on the leeward side is the result of the latent heat that was released during condensation as the air ascended the windward slope of the mountain range.

FIGURE F Orographic lifting and the formation of rain shadow deserts.

Two reasons account for the rain shadow commonly observed on leeward mountain slopes. First, water is extracted from air in the form of precipitation on the windward side. Second, the air on the leeward side is warmer than the air on the windward side. (Recall that whenever the temperature of air rises, the relative humidity drops.)

It should be emphasized that the hypothetical example provided here is only a rough approximation of conditions in the natural world. Most often, only a small percentage (sometimes none) of the moisture that condenses to form clouds actually falls as precipitation. Nevertheless, warmer and

dryer conditions are the rule on the leeward side of a mountainous barrier as compared to the rainier, windward side.

A classic example of windward precipitation and leeward rain shadows is found in western Washington State. As moist Pacific air flows inland over the Olympic and Cascade mountains, orographic precipitation is abundant (Figure G). On the other hand, precipitation data for Sequim and Yakima indicate the presence of rain shadows on the leeward side of these highlands.

The Florida peninsula provides an excellent example of the role that convergence can play in initiating cloud development and precipitation. On warm days, the airflow is from the ocean to the land along both coasts of Florida. This leads to a pileup of air along the coasts and general convergence over the peninsula. This pattern of air movement and the uplift that results is aided by intense solar heating of the land. The result is that the peninsula of Florida experiences the greatest frequency of mid-afternoon thunderstorms in the United States (Figure 20b).

More important, convergence as a mechanism of forceful lifting is a major contributor to the weather associated with middle-latitude cyclones and hurricanes. The low-level horizontal airflow associated with these systems is inward and upward around their centers. These important weather producers will be covered in more detail later, but for now

remember that convergence near the surface results in a general upward flow.

Localized Convective Lifting

On warm summer days, unequal heating of Earth's surface may cause pockets of air to be warmed more than the surrounding air (Figure 21). For instance, air above a paved parking lot will be warmed more than the air above an adjacent wooded park. Consequently, the parcel of air above the parking lot, which is warmer (less dense) than the surrounding air, will be buoyed upward. These rising parcels of warmer air are called *thermals*. Birds such as hawks and eagles use these thermals to carry them to great heights where they can gaze down on unsuspecting prey. People have learned to employ these rising parcels using hang gliders as a way to "fly" (Figure 22).

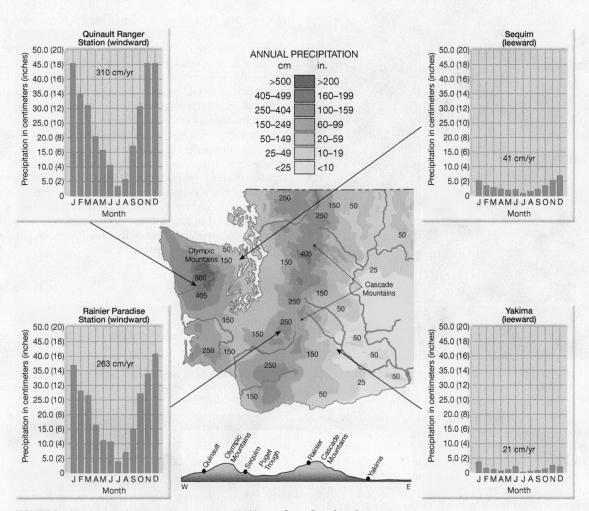

FIGURE G Distribution of precipitation in western Washington State. Data from four stations provide examples of wetter windward locations and drier leeward rain shadows. (After Robert W. Christopherson).

FIGURE 21 Localized convective lifting. Unequal heating of Earth's surface causes pockets of air to be warmed more than the surrounding air. These buoyant parcels of hot air rise, producing thermals, and if they reach the condensation level, clouds form.

FIGURE 22 Hang gliders use rising parcels of air called thermals to lift their crafts. (Photo by Bill Ross/CORBIS)

The phenomenon that produces rising thermals is called **localized convective lifting**. When these warm parcels of air rise above the lifting condensation level, clouds form, which on occasion produce mid-afternoon rain showers. The height of clouds produced in this fashion is somewhat limited, for instability caused solely by unequal surface heating is confined to, at most, the first few kilometers of the atmosphere. Also, the accompanying rains, although occasionally heavy, are of short duration and widely scattered.

Although localized convective lifting by itself is not a major producer of precipitation, the added buoyancy that results from surface heating contributes significantly to the lifting initiated by the other mechanisms. It should also be remembered that while the other mechanisms force air to rise, convective lifting occurs because the air is warmer (less dense) than the surrounding air and rises for the same reasons as a hot air balloon.

The Critical Weathermaker: Atmospheric Stability

GE◯De
THE ATMOSPHERE

Moisture and Cloud Formation
▸ The Critical Weathermaker: Atmospheric Stability

When air rises, it cools and eventually produces clouds. Why do clouds vary so much in size, and why does the resulting precipitation vary so much? The answers are closely related to the *stability* of the air.

Recall that a parcel of air can be thought of as having a thin flexible cover that allows it to expand but prevents it from mixing with the surrounding air (picture a hot-air balloon). If this parcel were forced to rise, its temperature would decrease because of expansion. By comparing the parcel's temperature to that of the surrounding air, we can determine its stability. If the parcel were *cooler* than the surrounding environment, it would be more dense; and if allowed to do so, it would sink to its original position. Air of this type, called **stable air**, resists vertical movement.

If, however, our imaginary rising parcel were *warmer* and hence less dense than the surrounding air, it would continue to rise until it reached an altitude where its temperature equaled that of its surroundings. This is exactly how a hot-air balloon works, rising as long as it is warmer and less dense than the surrounding air (Figure 23). This type of air is classified as **unstable air**. In summary, stability is a property of air that describes its tendency to remain in its original position (stable), or to rise (unstable).

Types of Stability

The stability of the atmosphere is determined by measuring the air temperature at various heights. Recall that this measure is called the *environmental lapse rate*. Do not confuse the

FIGURE 23 As long as air is warmer than its surroundings, it will rise. Hot-air balloons rise up through the atmosphere for this reason. (Photo by Steve Vidler/Superstock)

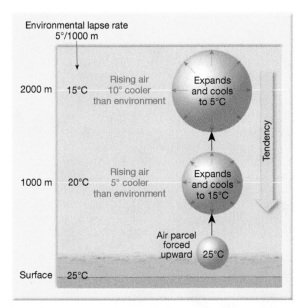

Environmental lapse rate
5°/1000 m

FIGURE 24 In a stable atmosphere, as an unsaturated parcel of air is lifted, it expands and cools at the dry adiabatic rate of 10°C per 1000 meters. Because the temperature of the rising parcel of air is lower than that of the surrounding environment, it will be heavier and, if allowed to do so, will sink to its original position.

environmental lapse rate with adiabatic temperature changes. The environmental lapse rate is the actual temperature of the atmosphere, as determined from observations made by radiosondes and aircraft. Adiabatic temperature changes are changes in temperature that a parcel of air would experience if it moved vertically through the atmosphere.

To illustrate how the stability of the atmosphere is determined, consider a situation in which the prevailing environmental lapse rate is 5°C per 1000 meters (Figure 24). Under this condition, when the air at the surface has a temperature of 25°C, the air at 1000 meters will be 5°C cooler, or 20°C, whereas the air at 2000 meters will have a temperature of 15°C, and so forth.

Examine Figure 24 and note that the air at the surface appears to be less dense than the air at 1000 meters, for it is 5°C warmer. However, if the air near the surface were to rise to 1000 meters, it would expand and cool at the dry adiabatic rate of 1°C per 100 meters. Therefore, on reaching 1000 meters, the temperature of the rising parcel would have dropped from 25°C to 15°C, a total of 10°C. Being 5°C cooler than its environment, it would be more dense and would tend to sink to its original position. Thus, we say that the air near the surface is *potentially cooler* than the air aloft and therefore it will not rise on its own.

By similar reasoning, if the air at 1000 meters subsided, adiabatic heating would increase its temperature 10°C by the time it reached the surface, making it warmer than the surrounding air; thus, its buoyancy would cause it to return to its original position. The air just described is stable and resists vertical movement.

With that background, we will now look at three fundamental conditions of the atmosphere: absolute stability, absolute instability, and conditional instability.

Absolute Stability Stated quantitatively, **absolute stability** prevails when *the environmental lapse rate is less than the wet adiabatic rate.* Figure 25 depicts this situation by using an environmental lapse rate of 5°C per 1000 meters and a wet adiabatic rate of 6°C per 1000 meters. Note that at 1000 meters the temperature of the surrounding air is 15°C and that the rising parcel of air has cooled by expansion to 10°C and so is the denser air. Even if this stable air were forced above the condensation level, it would remain cooler and denser than its environment and would have a tendency to return to the surface.

The most stable conditions occur when the temperature in a layer of air actually increases with altitude. When such a reversal occurs, a *temperature inversion* exists. Many circumstances can create temperature inversions. Temperature inversions frequently occur on clear nights as a result of radiation cooling at Earth's surface. Under these conditions an inversion is created because the ground and the air next to it will cool more rapidly than the air aloft.

Temperature inversions also occur in winter when warm air from the Gulf of Mexico invades the cold, snow-covered surface of the midcontinent. Anytime warmer air overlies cooler air, the resulting layer is extremely stable and resists appreciable vertical mixing. Because of this, temperature inversions are responsible for trapping pollutants in a narrow zone near Earth's surface.

Absolute Instability At the other extreme, a layer of air is said to exhibit **absolute instability** when *the environmental lapse rate is greater than the dry adiabatic rate.* As shown in Figure 26, the ascending parcel of air is always warmer than its environment and will continue to rise because of its own buoyancy. Absolute instability occurs most often during the warmest months and on clear days when solar heating is intense. Under these conditions the lowermost layer of the atmosphere is heated to a much higher temperature than the air aloft. This results in a steep environmental lapse rate and a very unstable atmosphere.

Instability produced mainly by strong surface heating is generally confined to the first few kilometers of the atmosphere. Above this height the environmental lapse rate assumes a more "normal" value. Stated another way, the temperature drops more slowly with altitude, creating a more stable temperature regime. Consequently, clouds produced by surface heating lack great vertical height and thus rarely produce violent weather.

Conditional Instability A more common type of atmospheric instability is called **conditional instability**. This situation prevails when *moist air has an environmental lapse rate between the dry and wet adiabatic rates* (between about 5° and 10°C per 1000 meters). Simply stated, the atmosphere is said

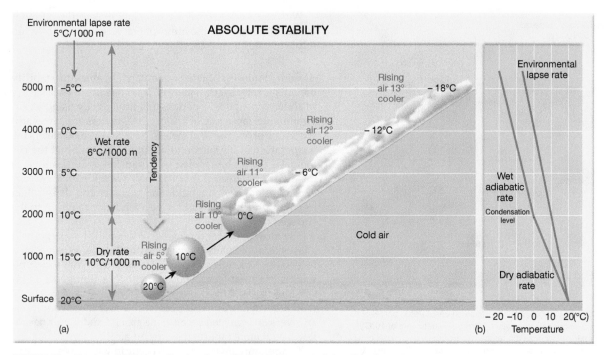

FIGURE 25 *Absolute stability* prevails when the environmental lapse rate is less than the wet adiabatic rate. (a) The rising parcel of air is always cooler and heavier than the surrounding air, producing stability. (b) Graphic representation of the conditions shown in part (a).

FIGURE 26 Illustration of *absolute instability* that develops when solar heating causes the lowermost layer of the atmosphere to be warmed to a higher temperature than the air aloft. The result is a steep environmental lapse rate that renders the atmosphere unstable. (b) Graphic representation of the conditions shown in part (a).

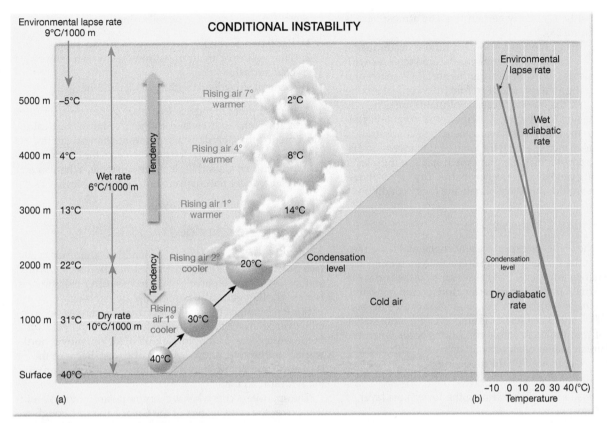

FIGURE 27 Illustration of *conditional instability,* where warm air is forced to rise along a frontal boundary. Note that the environmental lapse rate of 9°C per 1000 meters lies between the dry and wet adiabatic rates. (a) The parcel of air is cooler than the surrounding air up to nearly 3000 meters, where its tendency is to sink toward the surface (stable). Above this level, however, the parcel is warmer than its environment and will rise because of its own buoyancy (unstable). Thus, when conditionally unstable air is forced to rise, the result can be towering cumulus clouds. (b) Graphic representation of the conditions shown in part (a).

to be conditionally unstable when it is *stable* with respect to an *unsaturated* parcel of air, but *unstable* with respect to a *saturated* parcel of air. Notice in Figure 27 that the rising parcel of air is cooler than the surrounding air for the first 4000 meters. With the release of latent heat above the lifting condensation level, the parcel becomes warmer than the surrounding air. From this point along its ascent, the parcel will continue to rise without an outside force.

Thus, conditional instability depends on whether or not the rising air is saturated. The word "conditional" is used because the air must be forced upward before it reaches the level where it becomes unstable and rises on its own.

In summary, the stability of air is determined by measuring the temperature of the atmosphere at various heights (environmental lapse rate). In simple terms, a column of air is deemed unstable when the air near the bottom of this layer is significantly warmer (less dense) than the air aloft, indicating a steep environmental lapse rate. Under these conditions, the air actually turns over because the warm air below rises and displaces the colder air aloft. Conversely, the air is considered to be stable when the temperature decreases

gradually with increasing altitude. The most stable conditions occur during a temperature inversion when the temperature actually increases with height. Under these conditions, there is very little vertical air movement.

Stability and Daily Weather

From the previous discussion, we can conclude that stable air resists vertical movement and that unstable air ascends freely because of its own buoyancy. How do these facts manifest themselves in our daily weather?

When stable air is forced aloft, the clouds that form are widespread and have little vertical thickness compared with their horizontal dimension. Precipitation, if any, is light to moderate. In contrast, clouds associated with unstable air are towering and are usually accompanied by heavy precipitation. Thus, we can conclude that on a dreary and overcast day with light drizzle, stable air was forced aloft. Conversely, on a day when cauliflower-shaped clouds appear to be growing as if bubbles of hot air were surging upward, we can be relatively certain that the atmosphere is unstable (Figure 28).

As noted earlier, the most stable conditions occur during a temperature inversion when temperature increases with height. In this situation, the air near the surface is cooler and heavier than the air aloft, and therefore little vertical mixing occurs between the layers. Because pollutants are generally added to the air from below, a temperature inversion confines them to the lowermost layer, where their concentration will continue to increase until the temperature inversion dissipates. Widespread fog is another sign of stability. If the layer containing fog were mixing freely with the "dry" layer above, evaporation would quickly eliminate the foggy condition.

How Stability Changes

Recall that the higher (steeper) the environmental lapse rate, the more rapidly the temperature drops with increasing altitude. Therefore, any factor that causes air near the surface to become warmed in relation to the air aloft increases instability. The opposite is also true; any factor that causes the surface air to be chilled results in the air becoming more stable. Also recall that the most stable conditions occur when the temperature in a layer of air actually increases with altitude.

Instability is enhanced by the following:

1. Intense solar heating warming the lowermost layer of the atmosphere.
2. The heating of an air mass from below as it passes over a warm surface.
3. General upward movement of air caused by processes such as orographic lifting, frontal wedging, and convergence.
4. Radiation cooling from cloud tops.

Stability is enhanced by the following:

1. Radiation cooling of Earth's surface after sunset.
2. The cooling of an air mass from below as it traverses a cold surface.
3. General subsidence within an air column.

Note that most processes that alter stability result from temperature changes caused by horizontal or vertical air movement, although daily temperature changes are important too. In general, any factor that increases the environmental lapse rate renders the air more unstable, whereas any factor that reduces the environmental lapse rate increases the air's stability.

Temperature Changes and Stability

As stated earlier, on a clear day when there is abundant surface heating, the lower atmosphere often becomes warmed sufficiently to cause parcels of air to rise. After the Sun sets, surface cooling generally renders the air stable again.

Similar changes in stability occur as air moves horizontally over a surface having markedly different temperatures. In the winter, warm air from the Gulf of Mexico moves northward over the cold, snow-covered Midwest. Because the air is cooled from below, it becomes more stable, often producing widespread fog.

The opposite occurs when wintertime polar air moves southward over the open waters of the Great Lakes. Although we would die of hypothermia in a few minutes if we fell into these cold waters (perhaps 5°C or 41°F), compared to the frigid air temperatures, these waters are warm. Recall from our discussion of vapor pressure that the temperature of the water surface and the vapor pressure of the surrounding air determine the rate at which water will evaporate. Because the water of the Great Lakes is comparatively warm and because the polar air is dry (low vapor pressure) the rate of evaporation will be high. The moisture and heat added to the frigid polar air from the water below are enough to make it unstable and generate the clouds that produce heavy snowfalls on the downwind shores of these lakes (called "lake-effect snows").

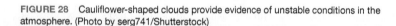

FIGURE 28 Cauliflower-shaped clouds provide evidence of unstable conditions in the atmosphere. (Photo by serg741/Shutterstock)

Radiation Cooling from Clouds On a smaller scale the loss of heat by radiation from cloud tops during evening hours adds to their instability and growth. Unlike air, which is a poor radiator of heat, cloud droplets emit energy to space nearly as well as does Earth's surface. Towering clouds that owe their growth to surface heating lose that source of energy at sunset. After sunset, however, radiation cooling at their tops steepens the lapse rate near the top of the cloud and can lead to additional upward flow of warmer parcels from below. This process is believed responsible for producing nocturnal thunderstorms from clouds whose growth prematurely ceased at sunset.

Vertical Air Movement and Stability

Vertical movements of air also influence stability. When there is a general downward airflow, called **subsidence**, the upper portion of the subsiding layer is heated by compression, more so than the lower portion. Usually the air near the surface is not involved in the subsidence and so its temperature remains unchanged. The net effect is to stabilize the air, for the air aloft is warmed in relation to the surface air. The warming effect of a few hundred meters of subsidence is enough to evaporate the clouds found in any layer of the atmosphere. Thus, one sign of subsiding air is a deep blue, cloudless sky. Subsidence can also produce a temperature inversion aloft. The most intense and prolonged temperature inversions and associated air pollution episodes are caused by subsidence.

Upward movement of air generally enhances instability, particularly when the lower portion of the rising layer has a higher moisture content than the upper portion, which is usually the situation. As the air moves upward, the lower portion becomes saturated first and cools at the lesser wet adiabatic rate. The net effect is to increase the lapse rate within the rising layer. This process is especially important in producing the instability associated with thunderstorms. In addition, recall that conditionally unstable air can become unstable if lifted sufficiently.

In summary, the role of stability in determining our daily weather cannot be overemphasized. The air's stability, or lack of it, determines to a large degree whether clouds develop and produce precipitation and whether that precipitation will come as a gentle shower or a violent downpour. In general, when stable air is forced aloft, the associated clouds have little vertical thickness, and precipitation, if any, is light. In contrast, clouds associated with unstable air are towering and are frequently accompanied by heavy precipitation.

Chapter Summary

- The unending circulation of Earth's water supply is called the *hydrologic cycle* (or water cycle). The cycle illustrates the continuous movement of water from the oceans to the atmosphere, from the atmosphere to the land, and from the land back to the sea.

- *Water vapor*, an odorless, colorless gas, can change from one state of matter (solid, liquid, or gas) to another at the temperatures and pressures experienced on Earth. The heat energy involved in the change of state of water is often measured in *calories*. The processes involved in changes of state include *evaporation* (liquid to gas), *condensation* (gas to liquid), *melting* (solid to liquid), *freezing* (liquid to solid), *sublimation* (solid to gas), and *deposition* (gas to solid). During each change, *latent* (hidden, or stored) *heat* energy is either absorbed or released.

- *Humidity* is the general term used to describe the amount of water vapor in the air. The methods used to express humidity quantitatively include (1) *absolute humidity*, the mass of water vapor in a given volume of air, (2) *mixing ratio*, the mass of water vapor in a unit of air compared to the remaining mass of dry air, (3) *vapor pressure*, that part of the total atmospheric pressure attributable to its water-vapor content, (4) *relative humidity*, the ratio of the air's actual water-vapor content compared with the amount of water vapor required for saturation at that temperature, and (5) *dew point*, the temperature to which a parcel of air would need to be cooled to reach saturation. When air is *saturated*, the pressure exerted by the water vapor, called the *saturation vapor pressure*, produces a balance between the number of water molecules leaving the surface of the water

and the number returning. Because the saturation vapor pressure is temperature-dependent, at higher temperatures more water vapor is required for saturation to occur.

- Relative humidity can be changed in two ways: (1) by changing the amount of moisture in the air or (2) by changing the air's temperature. Adding moisture to the air while keeping the temperature constant increases the relative humidity. Removing moisture lowers the relative humidity. When the water vapor content of air remains at a constant level, a decrease in air temperature results in an increase in relative humidity, and an increase in temperature causes a decrease in relative humidity. In nature there are three major ways that air temperatures change to cause corresponding changes in relative humidity: (1) daily (daylight versus nighttime) changes in temperature, (2) temperature changes that result as air moves horizontally from one location to another, and (3) changes caused as air moves vertically in the atmosphere.

- An important concept related to relative humidity is the *dew-point temperature* (or simply *dew point*), which is the temperature to which a parcel of air would need to be cooled to reach saturation. Unlike relative humidity, which is a measure of how near the air is to being saturated, dew-point temperature is a measure of the air's actual moisture content. High dew-point temperatures equate to moist air, and low dew-point temperatures indicate dry air. Because the dew-point temperature is a good measure of the amount of water vapor in the air, it is the measure of atmospheric moisture that appears on daily weather maps.

- A variety of instruments, called *hygrometers,* can be used to measure relative humidity. One of the simplest hygrometers, a *psychrometer,* consists of two identical thermometers mounted side by side. One thermometer, called the wet-bulb thermometer, has a thin muslin wick tied around the bulb. After spinning or fanning air past the instrument and noting the difference between the dry- and wet-bulb readings (known as the depression of the wet bulb), tables are consulted to determine the relative humidity. A second instrument, the *hair hygrometer,* can be read directly without using tables.

- When air is allowed to expand, it cools. When air is compressed, it warms. Temperature changes produced in this manner, in which heat is neither added nor subtracted, are called *adiabatic temperature changes.* The rate of cooling or warming of vertically moving unsaturated ("dry") air is 10°C for every 1000 meters (5.5°F per 1000 feet), the *dry adiabatic rate.* At the *lifting condensation level* (the altitude where a rising parcel of air has reached saturation and cloud formation begins), latent heat is released, and the rate of cooling is reduced. The slower rate of cooling, called the *wet adiabatic rate* of cooling ("wet" because the air is saturated) varies from 5°C per 1000 meters for air, with a high-moisture content to 9°C per 1000 meters for air with a low-moisture content.

- When air rises, it expands and cools adiabatically. If air is lifted sufficiently high, it will eventually cool to its dew-point temperature, and clouds will develop. Four mechanisms that cause air to rise are (1) *orographic lifting,* where air is forced to rise over a mountainous barrier, (2) *Frontal wedging,* where warmer, less dense air is forced over cooler, denser air along a *front,* (3) *convergence,* a pile-up of horizontal airflow resulting in an upward flow, and (4) *localized convective lifting,* where unequal surface heating causes localized pockets of air to rise because of their buoyancy.

- When air rises, it cools and can eventually produce clouds. *Stable air* resists vertical movement, whereas *unstable air* rises because of its buoyancy. The stability of air is determined by knowing the *environmental lapse rate,* the temperature of the atmosphere at various heights. The three fundamental conditions of the atmosphere are (1) *absolute stability,* when the environmental lapse rate is less than the wet adiabatic rate, (2) *absolute instability,* when the environmental lapse rate is greater than the dry adiabatic rate, and (3) *conditional instability,* when moist air has an environmental lapse rate between the dry and wet adiabatic rates. In general, when stable air is forced aloft, the associated clouds have little vertical thickness, and precipitation, if any, is light. In contrast, clouds associated with unstable air are towering and frequently accompanied by heavy rain.

- Any factor that causes air near the surface to become warmed in relation to the air aloft increases the air's instability. The opposite is also true; any factor that causes the surface air to be chilled results in the air becoming more stable. Most processes that alter atmospheric stability result from temperature changes caused by horizontal or vertical air movements, although daily temperature changes are important too. Changes in stability occur as air moves horizontally over a surface having a markedly different temperature than the air. Furthermore, *subsidence* (a general downward airflow) generally stabilizes the air, while upward air movement enhances instability.

Vocabulary Review

absolute humidity	dew point	latent heat	relative humidity
absolute instability	dew-point temperature	latent heat of condensation	saturation
absolute stability	dry adiabatic rate	latent heat of vaporization	saturation vapor pressure
adiabatic temperature changes	entrainment	lifting condensation level	stable air
calorie	evaporation	localized convective lifting	sublimation
condensation	front	mixing ratio	subsidence
conditional instability	frontal wedging	orographic lifting	transpiration
convergence	humidity	parcel	unstable air
deposition)	hydrologic cycle	psychrometer	vapor pressure
	hygrometer	rain shadow desert	wet adiabatic rate

Review Questions

1. Describe the movement of water through the hydrologic cycle.

2. The quantity of water lost to evaporation over the oceans is not equaled by precipitation. Why, then, does the sea level not drop?

3. Summarize the processes by which water changes from one state to another. Indicate whether heat is absorbed or liberated.

4. After reviewing Table 1, write a generalization relating temperature and the amount of water vapor needed to saturate the air.

5. How do absolute humidity and mixing ratio differ? What do they have in common? How is relative humidity different from absolute humidity and the mixing ratio?

6. Refer to Figure 12 and then answer the following questions.
   a. When is relative humidity highest during a typical day? When is it lowest?
   b. At what time of day would dew most likely form?
   c. Write a generalization relating changes in air temperature to changes in relative humidity.

7. If the temperature remains unchanged, and if the mixing ratio decreases, how will relative humidity change?

8. How much more water vapor does a mass of air having a dew-point temperature of 24°C (75°F) contain than air having a dew-point temperature of 4°C (39°F)?

9. Explain the principle of both the psychrometer and the hair hygrometer.

10. What are the disadvantages of the hair hygrometer? Does this instrument have any advantages over the psychrometer?

11. What name is given to the processes whereby the temperature of the air changes without the addition or subtraction of heat?

12. At what rate does unsaturated air cool when it rises through the atmosphere?

13. Why does air expand as it moves upward through the atmosphere?

14. Explain why air warms whenever it sinks.

15. Why does the adiabatic rate of cooling change when condensation begins? Why is the wet adiabatic rate not a constant figure?

16. The contents of an aerosol can are under very high pressure. When you push the nozzle on such a can, the spray feels cold. Explain.

17. How do orographic lifting and frontal wedging act to force air to rise?

18. Explain why the Great Basin area of the western United States is dry. What term is applied to such a situation?

19. How is localized convective lifting different from the other three processes that cause air to rise?

20. How does stable air differ from unstable air?

21. Explain the difference between the environmental lapse rate and adiabatic cooling.

22. How is the stability of air determined?

23. Write a statement relating the environmental lapse rate to stability.

24. What weather conditions would lead you to believe that air is unstable?

25. List four ways instability can be enhanced.

26. List three ways stability can be enhanced.

Problems

1. Using Table 1, answer the following:
   a. If a parcel of air at 25°C contains 10 grams of water vapor per kilogram of air, what is its relative humidity?
   b. If a parcel of air at 35°C contains 5 grams of water vapor per kilogram of air, what is its relative humidity?
   c. If a parcel of air at 15°C contains 5 grams of water vapor per kilogram of air, what is its relative humidity?
   d. If the temperature of this same parcel of air dropped to 5°C, how would its relative humidity change?
   e. If 20°C air contains 7 grams of water vapor per kilogram of air, what is its dew point?

2. Using the standard tables (Appendix: Relative Humidity and Dew Point Tables, Tables 1 and 2), determine the relative humidity and dew-point temperature if the dry-bulb thermometer reads 22°C and the wet-bulb thermometer reads 16°C. How would the relative humidity and dew point change if the wet-bulb reading were 19°C?

3. If unsaturated air at 20°C were to rise, what would its temperature be at a height of 500 meters? If the dew-point temperature at the lifting condensation level were 11°C, at what elevation would clouds begin to form?

4. Using Figure 29, answer the following. (*Hint:* Read Box 6.)

   a. What is the elevation of the cloud base?
   b. What is the temperature of the ascending air when it reaches the top of the mountain?
   c. What is the dew-point temperature of the rising air at the top of the mountain? (Assume 100 percent relative humidity.)
   d. Estimate the amount of water vapor that must have condensed (in grams per kilogram) as the air moved from the cloud base to the top of the mountain.
   e. What will the temperature of the air be if it descends to point B? (Assume that the moisture that condensed fell as precipitation on the windward side of the mountain.)
   f. What is the approximate capacity of the air to hold water vapor at point B?
   g. Assuming that no moisture was added or subtracted from the air as it traveled downslope, estimate the relative humidity at point B.
   h. What is the *approximate* relative humidity at point A? (Use the dew-point temperature at the condensation level for the surface dew point.)
   i. Give *two* reasons for the difference in relative humidity between points A and B.
   j. Needles, California, is situated on the dry leeward side of a mountain range similar to the position of point B. What term describes this situation?

5. If a lake is ice covered, what is the temperature of the water at the bottom of the lake? (*Hint:* See Box 1.)

FIGURE 29 Orographic lifting problem.

Temperature at Point A = 24°C
Dew point at condensation level = 11°C
Dry adiabatic rate = 1°C/100 m
Wet adiabatic rate = 0.5°C/100 m

Atmospheric Science Online

The Atmosphere 11e website uses the resources and flexibility of the Internet to aid in your study of the topics in this chapter. Written and developed by meteorology instructors, this site will help improve your understanding of meteorology. Visit **www.mygeoscience.com** in order to:

• **Review** key chapter concepts

• **Read** with links to the eBook and to chapter-specific web resources

• **Visualize** and comprehend challenging topics using learning activities in *GEODe: Atmosphere*

• **Test yourself** with online quizzes

GEODe: Atmosphere

GEODe: Atmosphere makes studying more effective by reinforcing key concepts using animation, video, narration, interactive exercises, and practice quizzes. Available at **www.mygeoscience.com**.

Forms of Condensation *and* Precipitation

From Chapter 5 of *The Atmosphere: An Introduction to Meteorology*, Eleventh Edition, Frederick K. Lutgens, Edward J. Tarbuck, Dennis Tasa. Copyright © 2010 by Pearson Education, Inc. Published by Pearson Prentice Hall. All rights reserved.

Forms of Condensation *and* Precipitation

Cumulonimbus clouds are often associated with thunderstorms and severe weather. (Photo by Bruno Burklin/Photex/CORBIS)

Clouds, fog, rain, snow, and sleet are among the most observable weather phenomena (Figure 1). This chapter will provide a basic understanding of each. In addition to learning the basic scheme for classifying and naming clouds, you will learn that the formation of an average raindrop involves complex processes requiring water from roughly a million cloud droplets. Can scientists make rain by triggering these processes? Can modern weather-modification technology increase the precipitation that falls from a cloud? Can we control weather events such as fog and frost?

Cloud Formation

Clouds can be defined as *visible aggregate of minute droplets of water, or tiny crystals of ice, or a mixture of both.* In addition to being prominent and sometimes spectacular features in the sky, clouds are of continual interest to meteorologists because they provide a visible indication of what is going on in the atmosphere.

Condensation Aloft

Clouds are a form of condensation produced when water vapor condenses in the atmosphere. Clearly the most important cloud-forming process is *adiabatic cooling*. To review, any time a parcel of air ascends, it passes through regions of successively lower pressure. As a result, rising air expands and cools adiabatically. At a height called the *lifting condensation level*, the ascending parcel has cooled to its dew-point temperature, and further ascent (cooling) causes condensation.

As you learned earlier, condensation occurs when water vapor changes to a liquid. The result of this process may be dew, fog, or clouds. Although each type of condensation is somewhat different, they all form when two conditions are met. First, for any form of condensation to occur, the air must be *saturated* (or nearly so). Saturation occurs most often when air is cooled to its dew point. (Condensation may also occur when sufficient water vapor is added to a layer of the atmosphere.) Second, there generally must be a *surface* on which the water vapor can condense. When dew forms, objects at or near the ground, like blades of grass, serve this purpose.

When condensation occurs aloft, tiny particles known as **cloud condensation nuclei** serve as surfaces on which water vapor condenses. Nuclei are important because, if they are absent, a relative humidity well in excess of 100 percent is necessary to produce cloud droplets. (At very low temperatures—low kinetic energies—water molecules will "stick together" in tiny clusters without the presence of condensation nuclei.) Cloud condensation nuclei include microscopic dust,

FIGURE 1   People caught in a downpour. (Photo by Mary Fulton/Getty Images, Inc. — Liaison)

smoke, and salt particles, all of which are profuse in the lower atmosphere. Consequently, in the troposphere the relative humidity seldom exceeds 100 percent.

Growth of Cloud Droplets

Particles that are the most effective sites for condensation are called **hygroscopic (*water-seeking*) nuclei.** Some familiar food items, such as crackers and cereals, are hygroscopic, which is why they quickly absorb moisture when exposed to humid air and become stale.

Over the ocean, salt particles are released into the atmosphere when sea spray evaporates. Because salt is hygroscopic, water droplets begin to form around sea salt particles at relative humidities less than 100 percent. As a result, the cloud droplets that form on salt are generally much larger than those that grow on **hydrophobic (*water-repelling*) nuclei.** Although hydrophobic particles are not efficient condensation nuclei, cloud droplets will form on them whenever the relative humidity reaches 100 percent.

Dust storms, volcanic eruptions, and pollen are major sources of cloud condensation nuclei on land. In addition, hygroscopic nuclei are introduced into the atmosphere as a by-product of combustion (burning) from such sources as forest fires, automobiles, and coal-burning furnaces. Because cloud condensation nuclei have a wide range of affinities for water, cloud droplets of various sizes often coexist in the same cloud. This fact has important consequences for the formation of precipitation.

Initially, the growth of cloud droplets is rapid. However, the rate of growth quickly diminishes because the available water vapor is consumed by the large number of competing droplets. The result is the formation of a cloud consisting of billions of tiny water droplets, all so small that they remain suspended in air. Even in very moist air, the growth of cloud droplets by additional condensation is quite slow. Furthermore, the immense size difference between cloud droplets and raindrops (it takes about a million cloud droplets to form a single raindrop) suggests that condensation alone is not responsible for the formation of drops (or ice crystals) large enough to fall to the ground without evaporating. We will investigate this idea later when we examine the processes that generate precipitation.

Students Sometimes Ask . . .

What is the driest place on Earth?

The record for the lowest average annual precipitation belongs to Arica, Chile, which receives 0.03 inch of rainfall per year. Over a span of 59 years this region in South America received a total of less than 2 inches of precipitation.

Cloud Classification

 Forms of Condensation and Precipitation
THE ATMOSPHERE ▶ **Classifying Clouds**

Anyone who observes clouds finds a bewildering variety of these white and gray masses streaming across the sky. Once the basic classification scheme for clouds is known, however, most of the confusion vanishes.

Prior to the beginning of the nineteenth century, there were no generally accepted names for clouds. In 1803 Luke Howard, an English naturalist, published a cloud classification that met with great success and subsequently served as the basis of our present-day system.

Clouds are classified on the basis of two criteria: *form* and *height* (Figure 2). Three basic cloud forms are recognized:

- **Cirrus** clouds are high, white, and thin. They are separated or detached and form delicate veil-like patches or extended wispy fibers and often have a feathery appearance. (*Cirrus* is a Latin word meaning "curl" or "filament.")
- **Cumulus** clouds consist of globular individual cloud masses. Normally they exhibit a flat base and appear as rising domes or towers. Such clouds are frequently described as having a cauliflower-like structure.
- **Stratus** clouds are best described as sheets or layers (strata) that cover much or all of the sky. Although there may be minor breaks, there are no distinct individual cloud units.

All clouds have one of these three basic forms or combinations or modifications of them.

Looking at the second aspect of cloud classification—height—three levels are recognized: high, middle, and low. **High clouds** normally have bases above 6000 meters (20,000 feet); **middle clouds** generally occupy heights from 2000 to 6000 meters; **low clouds** form below 2000 meters (6500 feet). These altitudes are not hard and fast. They vary somewhat by season of the year and by latitude. At high (poleward) latitudes or during cold winter months, high clouds generally occur at lower altitudes. Further, some clouds extend vertically to span more than one height range. These are called **clouds of vertical development.**

Definite weather patterns can be associated with specific clouds or combinations of clouds, so it is important to become familiar with cloud characteristics.

Ten basic cloud types are recognized internationally. We describe them below and summarize them in Table 1.

High Clouds

Three cloud types make up the family of high clouds (above 6000 meters/20,000 feet). They are *cirrus, cirrostratus,* and *cirrocumulus.* Because of the low temperatures and small quantities of water vapor present at high altitudes, all high

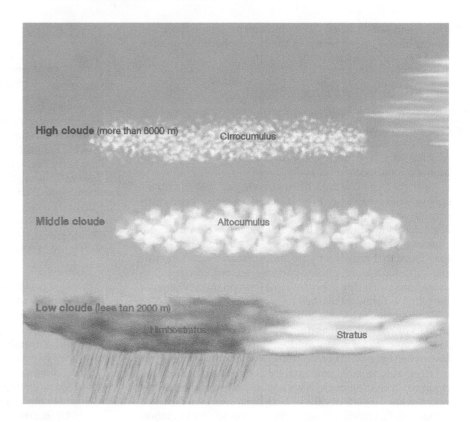

FIGURE 2 Classification of clouds according to height and form. (After Ward's Natural Science Establishment, Inc., Rochester, N.Y.)

clouds are thin and white and made up primarily of ice crystals (Box 1).

Cirrus are detached clouds composed of white, delicate, icy filaments. Winds aloft often cause these fibrous ice trails to bend or curl. As shown in Figure 3a, cirrus clouds with hooked filaments are called "mares' tails".

Cirrostratus is a transparent, whiteish cloud veil of fibrous or sometimes smooth appearance that may cover much or all of the sky. This cloud is easily recognized when it produces a halo around the Sun or Moon (Figure 3b). On occasions, cirrostratus may be so thin and transparent that the clouds are barely discernible. With the approach of a warm

Cloud family and height	Cloud type	Characteristics
High clouds—above 6000 m (20,000 ft)	Cirrus (Ci)	Thin, delicate, fibrous, ice-crystal clouds. Sometimes appear as hooked filaments called "mares' tails" (cirrus uncinus; Figure 3a).
	Cirrostratus (Cs)	Thin sheet of white, ice-crystal clouds that may give the sky a milky look. Sometimes produces halos around the Sun and Moon (Figure 3b).
	Cirrocumulus (Cc)	Thin, white, ice-crystal clouds. In the form of ripples or waves, or globular masses all in a row. May produce a "mackerel sky." Least common of high clouds (Figure 3c).
Middle clouds—2000–6000 m (6500 to 20,000 ft)	Altocumulus (Ac)	White to gray clouds often made up of separate globules; "sheepback" clouds (Figure 4a).
	Altostratus (As)	Stratified veil of clouds that is generally thin and may produce very light precipitation. When thin, the Sun or Moon may be visible as a "bright spot," but no halos are produced (Figure 4b).
Low clouds—below 2000 m (6500 ft)	Stratus (St)	Low uniform layer resembling fog but not resting on the ground. May produce drizzle.
	Stratocumulus (Sc)	Soft, gray clouds in globular patches or rolls. Rolls may join together to make a continuous cloud.
	Nimbostratus (Ns)	Amorphous layer of dark gray clouds. One of the chief precipitation producing clouds (Figure 5).
Clouds of vertical development	Cumulus (Cu)	Dense, billowy clouds often characterized by flat bases. May occur as isolated clouds or closely packed (Figure 6).
	Cumulonimbus (Cb)	Towering cloud, sometimes spreading out on top to form an "anvil head." Associated with heavy rainfall, thunder, lightning, hail, and tornadoes (Figure 7).

TABLE 1 Basic Cloud Types

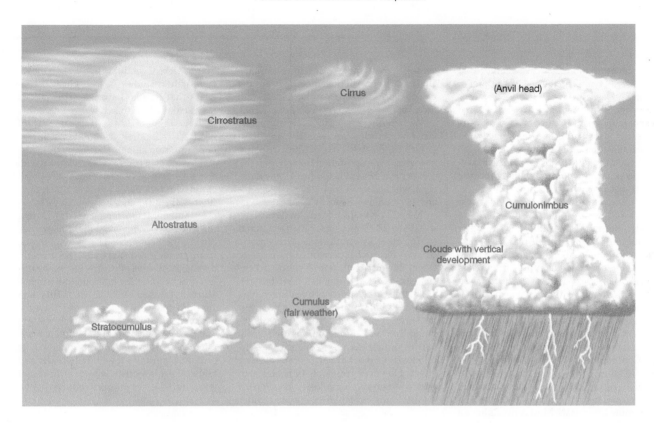

front, cirrostratus clouds generally thicken and grade into middle-level altostratus clouds.

Cirrocumulus clouds appear as white patches composed of very small cells or ripples (Figure 3c). Most often the masses that make up these clouds have an apparent width similar to that of the Sun. Furthermore, these small globules, which may be merged or separate, are often arranged in a regular pattern. This pattern is commonly called "mackerel sky" because of the similarity to the pattern formed by fish scales.

High clouds generally are not precipitation makers. However, when cirrus clouds give way to cirrocumulus clouds that cover even more of the sky, they may warn of impending stormy weather. The following mariner's saying is based on this observation: *Mackerel scales and mares' tails make lofty ships carry low sails.*

Middle Clouds

Clouds that appear in the middle altitude range (2000 to 6000 meters/6500 to 20,000 feet) have the prefix *alto* as part of their name. There are two types: *altocumulus* and *altostratus*.

Altocumulus tend to form in large patches composed of rounded masses or rolls that may or may not merge (Figure 4a). Because they are generally composed of water droplets rather than ice crystals, the individual cells usually have a more distinct outline. Altocumulus are most easily confused with two other cloud types: cirrocumulus (which are smaller and less dense) and stratocumulus (which are larger).

Altostratus is the name given to a formless layer of grayish clouds covering all or a large portion of the sky. Generally, the Sun is visible through these clouds as a bright spot, but with the edge of its disc not discernible (Figure 4b). However, unlike cirrostratus clouds, altostratus do not produce halos. Infrequent precipitation in the form of light snow or drizzle may accompany these clouds. Altostratus clouds are commonly associated with warm fronts. As the front approaches, the clouds thicken into a dark gray layer of nimbostratus that is capable of producing copious rainfall.

Low Clouds

There are three members of the family of low clouds (below 2000 meters/6500 feet): *stratus, stratocumulus,* and *nimbostratus.*

Stratus is a uniform layer that frequently covers much of the sky and, on occasion, may produce light precipitation. When stratus clouds develop a scalloped bottom that appears as long parallel rolls or broken globular patches, they are called *stratocumulus* clouds.

Nimbostratus clouds derive their name from the Latin *nimbus,* "rain cloud," and *stratus,* "to cover with a layer" (Figure 5). As the name implies, nimbostratus clouds are one of the chief precipitation producers. Nimbostratus clouds form in association with stable conditions. We might not expect clouds to grow or persist in stable air, yet cloud growth of this type is common when air is forced to rise, as along a front or near the center of a cyclone where converging winds cause air to ascend. Such forced ascent of stable air leads to

BOX 1 ▶ AIRCRAFT CONTRAILS AND CLOUDINESS

You have undoubtedly seen a *contrail* (from *con*densation *trail*), in the wake of an aircraft flying on a clear day (Figure A). Contrails are produced by jet aircraft engines that expel large quantities of hot, moist air. As this air mixes with the frigid air aloft, a streamlined cloud is produced. Because it often takes a few seconds for sufficient cooling to occur, the contrail usually forms a short distance behind the aircraft.

Why do contrails occur on some occasions and not on others? Contrails form under the same conditions as any other cloud that is, when the air reaches saturation and condensation nuclei exist in sufficient numbers. Most contrails form when the exhaust gases add sufficient water vapor to the air to cause saturation. Further, it has been demonstrated that the exhaust gases of aircraft engines supply abundant sulfate molecules that serve as nuclei to promote the development of contrails.

Contrails typically form above 9 kilometers (6 miles) where air temperatures are a frigid $-50°C$ ($-58°F$) or colder. Thus, it is not surprising that contrails are composed of minute ice crystals. Most contrails have a very short life span. Once formed, these streamlined clouds mix with surrounding cold, dry air and ultimately evaporate. However, if the air aloft is near saturation,

contrails may survive for long periods. Under these conditions, the upper airflow usually spreads the streamlike clouds into broad bands of clouds called *contrail cirrus.*

With the increase in air traffic during the last few decades, an overall increase in cloudiness has been recorded, particularly near major transportation hubs (Figure B). This is most evident in the American Southwest, where aircraft contrails persist in otherwise cloudless or mostly clear skies.

In addition to the added cloud cover associated with increasing levels of jet aircraft traffic, other less noticeable effects are of concern. Research is currently under way to assess the impact of contrail-produced cirrus clouds on the planet s heat budget. High, thin clouds are effective transmitters of solar radiation (most radiation reaches the surface) but are good absorbers of outgoing infrared radiation emitted from Earth s surface. As a consequence, high cirrus clouds tend to have an overall warming effect. However, research indicates that most contrails differ markedly from typical cirrus clouds, which are generated under

quite different conditions. Although the results of these studies are inconclusive, it appears that human-induced cirrus clouds may actually lead to surface cooling rather than warming. Additional research is still needed to accurately determine the impact of contrails on climate change.

One effect of contrails that is known with some certainty is how these artificial clouds impact daily temperature ranges (that is, the difference between daily maximum and minimum temperatures). During the three-day commercial flight hiatus following the September 11 terrorist attacks, contrails all but disappeared. As a result, during these days of clearer skies, the differences between the high and low temperatures increased by $2°F$ ($1.1°C$). This data supports the view that contrails reduce the transfer of both incoming solar radiation and outgoing terrestrial radiation. Consequently, cities located near major air-traffic centers experience lower daily highs and higher daily lows than would be the case if jet aircraft did not produce contrails.

FIGURE B · This photograph, taken through the window of the International Space Station, shows contrails over the Rhone Valley in eastern France. It is estimated that these "artificial clouds" cover 0.1 percent of the planet's surface, and the percentages are far higher in some places, such as southern California and part of Europe, as illustrated here. (Photo courtesy of NASA).

FIGURE A Aircraft contrails. Condensation trails produced by jet aircraft often spread out to form broad bands of cirrus clouds. (Photo by J. F. Towers/CORBIS/Stock Market)

(a)

(b)

(c)

FIGURE 3 Three basic cloud types make up the family of high clouds: (a) cirrus, (b) cirrostratus, and (c) cirrocumulus. (Photos (a) and (c) by E. J. Tarbuck, (b) by A. and J. Verkaik/CORBIS/Stock Market)

the formation of a stratified cloud layer that is large horizontally compared to its thickness. Precipitation associated with nimbostratus clouds is generally light to moderate but of long duration and widespread.

Clouds of Vertical Development

Some clouds do not fit into any one of the three height categories. Such clouds have their bases in the low height range and extend upward into the middle or high altitudes; they are referred to as *clouds of vertical development*. Vertically developed clouds are all closely related and are associated with unstable air. There are two types, *cumulus* and *cumulonimbus*.

Cumulus clouds are individual masses that develop into vertical domes or towers, the tops of which often resemble cauliflower. Cumulus clouds most often form on clear days when unequal surface heating causes parcels of air to rise convectively above the lifting condensation level (Figure 6). This level is often apparent to an observer because the flat cloud bottoms define it.

On days when cumulus clouds are present, we usually notice an increase in cloudiness into the afternoon as solar heating intensifies. Furthermore, because small cumulus clouds (*cumulus humilis*) rarely produce appreciable precipitation, and because they form on "sunny" days, they are often called "fair-weather clouds."

Although cumulus clouds are associated with fair weather, they may, under the proper circumstances, grow dramatically in height. Once upward movement is triggered, acceleration is powerful, and clouds with great vertical extent are formed.

(a)

(b)

FIGURE 4 Two forms of clouds are generated in the middle-altitude range. (a) Altocumulus tend to form in patches composed of rolls or rounded masses. (b) Altostratus occur as grayish sheets covering a large portion of the sky. When visible, the Sun appears as a bright spot through these clouds. (Photos by E. J. Tarbuck)

As the cumulus enlarges, its top leaves the low height range, and it is called a *cumulus congestus*. Finally, when the cloud becomes even more towering and rain begins to fall, it becomes a cumulonimbus.

Cumulonimbus are dark, dense, billowy clouds of considerable vertical extent in the form of huge towers (Figure 7). In its later stages of development, the upper part of a cumulonimbus turns to ice and appears fibrous. Furthermore, the tops of these clouds frequently spread out in the shape of an anvil. Cumulonimbus towers extend from a few hundred meters above the surface upward to 12 kilometers (7 miles) or, on rare occasions, 20 kilometers (12 miles). These huge towers produce heavy precipitation with accompanying lightning and thunder and occasionally hail.

Cloud Varieties

In addition to the names given to the 10 basic cloud types, adjectives may also be used to describe variations of a particular cloud type. For example, the term *uncinus*, meaning "hook-shaped," is applied to streaks of cirrus clouds that are shaped like a comma resting on its side. Cirrus uncinus are often precursors of bad weather.

When stratus or cumulus clouds appear to be broken into smaller pieces, the adjective *fractus* may be used in their description. In addition, some clouds have rounded protuberances on their bottom surface, not unlike the udders of cows. When these structures are present, the term *mammatus* can be applied. This configuration is sometimes associated with stormy weather and cumulonimbus clouds.

Lens-shaped clouds are referred to as *lenticular*. They are common in areas that have rugged or mountainous

FIGURE 5 Nimbostratus clouds are one of the chief precipitation producers. These dark gray layers often exhibit a ragged-appearing base. (Photo by E. J. Tarbuck)

topography, where they are called *lenticular altocumulus* (Figure 8a). Although lenticular clouds can form whenever the airflow undulates sharply in the vertical, they most frequently form on the lee side of mountains. As air passes

FIGURE 6 Cumulus clouds. These small, white, billowy clouds generally form on sunny days and, therefore, are often called "fair weather clouds." (Photo by E. J. Tarbuck)

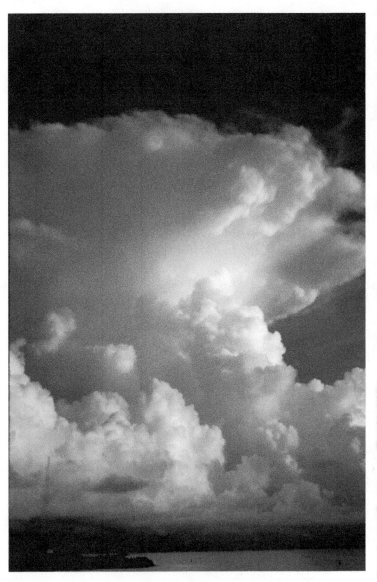

FIGURE 7 Cumulonimbus clouds. These dense, billowy clouds have great vertical extent and can produce heavy precipitation. (Photo by Doug Millar/Science Source/Photo Researchers, Inc.)

over mountainous terrain, a wave pattern develops, as shown in Figure 8b. Clouds form where the wavy flow causes air to ascend, whereas areas with descending air are cloud-free.

Students Sometimes Ask . . .

How much water is found in a cloud?

That depends a lot on the size of the cloud. Let's consider a modest sized cumulonimbus cloud that is roughly 3000 meters (about 2 miles) in width and depth and 10,000 meters high. If our hypothetical cloud contains an average of 0.5 cubic centimeter of liquid per cubic meter, it would contain 45 billion cubic centimeters of water ($3000 \times 3000 \times 10,000 \times 0.5$). That equates to 13 million gallons—enough to fill a small pond.

(a)

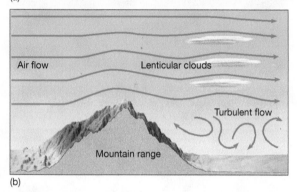

(b)

FIGURE 8 Lenticular clouds. (a) These lens-shaped clouds are relatively common in mountainous areas. (Photo by Dennis Tasa) (b) This diagram depicts the formation of lenticular clouds in the turbulent flow that develops in the lee of a mountain range.

Types of Fog

 GEODe THE ATMOSPHERE Forms of Condensation and Precipitation
▶ Types of Fog

Fog is generally considered an atmospheric hazard. When it is light, visibility is reduced to 2 or 3 kilometers (1 or 2 miles). When it is dense, visibility may be cut to a few dozen meters or less, making travel by any mode not only difficult but dangerous. Official weather stations report fog only when the visibility is reduced to 1 kilometer or less. Although arbitrary, this figure does permit a more objective criterion for comparing fog frequencies at different locations.

Fog is defined as *a cloud with its base at or very near the ground*. Physically, there is basically no difference between a fog and a cloud; their appearance and structure are the same. The essential difference is the method and place of formation. Clouds result when air rises and cools adiabatically. Fog results from cooling or by the addition of enough water vapor to cause saturation. Let us look at fogs, first those formed by cooling and then those formed by the addition of water vapor.

Fogs Formed by Cooling

When the temperature of a layer of air in contact with the ground falls below its dew point, condensation produces fog. Depending upon the prevailing conditions, the ground may become shrouded in radiation fog, advection fog, or upslope fog.

Radiation Fog As the name implies, **radiation fog** results from radiation cooling of the ground and adjacent air. It is a nighttime phenomenon requiring clear skies and a fairly high relative humidity. Under these circumstances, the ground and the air immediately above it will cool rapidly. Because the relative humidity is high, just a small amount of cooling will lower the temperature to the dew point. If the air is calm, the fog may be patchy and less than a meter deep. For radiation fog to be more extensive vertically, a light breeze of 3 to 5 kilometers (2 to 3 miles) per hour is necessary. Then the light wind creates enough turbulence to carry the fog upward 10 to 30 meters (30 to 100 feet) without dispersing it.

Because the air containing the fog is relatively cold and dense, it drains downslope in hilly terrain. As a result, radiation fog is thickest in valleys, whereas the surrounding hills are clear (Figure 9). Normally these fogs dissipate within one to three hours after sunrise. Often the fog is said to "lift."

FIGURE 9 Satellite image of dense fog in California's San Joaquin Valley on November 20, 2002. This early morning radiation fog was responsible for several car accidents in the region, including a 14-car pileup. The white areas to the east of the fog are the snow-capped Sierra Nevadas. (NASA image)

However, it does not rise. Instead, the Sun warms the ground, which in turn heats the lowest layer of air first. Consequently, the fog evaporates from the bottom up, giving the impression of lifting. The last vestiges of radiation fog may appear to be a low stratus cloud layer.

In the eastern United States, radiation fog may also form when the skies clear after a rainfall. In these situations, the air near the surface is close to saturation and only a small amount of radiation cooling is needed to promote condensation. Radiation fog of this type often occurs around sunset and can make driving hazardous.

Advection Fog When warm and moist air is blown over a cold surface, it becomes chilled by contact and, to a certain extent, by mixing with the cold air created by the cold surface below. If cooling is sufficient, the result will be a blanket of fog called **advection fog.** The term *advection* refers to air moving horizontally. Therefore, advection fogs are a consequence of air giving up heat to the surface below during horizontal movement. A classic example is the frequent advection fog around San Francisco's Golden Gate Bridge (Figure 10).

A certain amount of turbulence is needed for proper development of advection fog. Thus, winds between 10 and 30 kilometers (6 and 18 miles) per hour are usually associated with it. Not only does the turbulence facilitate cooling through a thicker layer of air but it also carries the fog to greater heights.

Unlike radiation fogs, advection fogs are often thick (300 to 600 meters deep) and persistent.

Examples of such fogs are common. The foggiest location in the United States is Cape Disappointment, Washington. The name is indeed appropriate because the station averages 2552 hours (106 days) of fog each year. The fog experienced at Cape Disappointment, as well as that at other West Coast locations during the summer and early autumn, is produced when warm, moist air from the Pacific Ocean moves over the cold California Current. It is then carried onshore by westerly winds or a local sea breeze.

Advection fog is also a common wintertime phenomenon along the Gulf and Atlantic coasts. Here, comparatively warm, moist air from the Gulf of Mexico and Atlantic moves over cold and occasionally snow-covered surfaces to produce widespread foggy conditions. These fogs are frequently thick and produce hazardous driving conditions.

Upslope Fog As its name implies, **upslope fog** is created when relatively humid air moves up a gradual sloping plain or, in some cases, up the steep slopes of a mountain. Because of the upward movement, air expands and cools adiabatically (this is the only type of fog that forms adiabatically). If the dew point is reached, an extensive layer of fog may form.

It is easy to visualize how upslope fog might form in mountainous terrain. However, in the United States upslope

FIGURE 10 Advection fog rolling into San Francisco Bay. (Photo by Ed Pritchard/Getty Images Inc.-Stone Allstock)

fog also occurs in the Great Plains. Here, when humid Gulf air moves westward from the Mississippi River toward the Rocky Mountains, it gradually glides upslope. (Recall that Denver, Colorado, is called the "mile-high city," and the Gulf of Mexico is at sea level.) Air flowing "up" the Great Plains expands and cools adiabatically by as much as 12°C (22°F). The result can be an extensive upslope fog in the western plains.

Fogs Formed by Evaporation

When saturation occurs primarily because of the addition of water vapor, the resulting fogs are called *evaporation fogs*. Two types of evaporation fogs are recognized: steam fog and frontal (precipitation) fog.

Steam Fog   When cool air moves over warm water, enough moisture may evaporate from the water surface to saturate the air immediately above. As the rising water vapor meets the cold air, it condenses and rises with the air that is being warmed from below. Because the rising air looks like the "steam" that forms above a hot cup of coffee, the phenomenon is called **steam fog** (Figure 11). It is a fairly common occurrence over lakes and rivers on clear, crisp mornings in the fall when the waters are still relatively warm while the air is rather cold. Steam fog is often shallow, for as it rises, the water droplets evaporate as they mix with the unsaturated air above.

Steam fogs can be dense, however. During the winter, cold arctic air pours off the continents and ice shelves onto the comparatively warm open ocean. The temperature contrast between the warm ocean and cold air has been known to exceed 30°C (54°F). The result is an intense steam fog produced as the rising water vapor saturates a large volume of air. Because of its source and appearance, this type of steam fog is given the name *arctic sea smoke*.

Frontal Fog   When frontal wedging occurs, warm air is lifted over colder air. If the resulting clouds yield rain, and the cold

FIGURE 11   Steam fog rising from Sparks Lake near Bend, Oregon. (Photo by Warren Morgan/CORBIS)

Students Sometimes Ask . . .

Why do I see my breath on cold mornings?

On cold days when you "see your breath," you are actually creating steam fog. The moist air that you exhale saturates a small volume of cold air, causing tiny droplets to form. Like most steam fogs, the droplets quickly evaporate as the "fog" mixes with the unsaturated air around it.

air below is near the dew point, enough rain can evaporate to produce fog. A fog formed in this manner is called **frontal or precipitation fog.** The result is a more or less continuous zone of condensed water droplets reaching from the ground up through the clouds.

In summary, both steam fog and frontal fog result from the addition of moisture to a layer of air. As you saw, the air is usually cool or cold and already near saturation. Thus, only a relatively modest amount of evaporation is necessary to produce saturated conditions and fog.

The frequency of dense fog varies considerably from place to place (Figure 12). As might be expected, fog incidence is highest in coastal areas, especially where cold currents prevail, as along the Pacific and New England coasts. Relatively high frequencies are also found in the Great Lakes region and in the humid Appalachian Mountains of the East. In contrast, fogs are rare in the interior of the continent, especially in the arid and semiarid areas of the West.

Dew and Frost

Clouds and fog are the most conspicuous and meteorologically important forms of condensation. Dew and white frost must be considered minor by comparison. These common forms of condensation generally result from radiation cooling on clear, cool nights.

Dew is the condensation of water vapor on objects that have radiated sufficient heat to lower their temperature below the dew point of the surrounding air. Because different objects radiate heat at different rates, dew may form on some surfaces but not on others. An automobile, for example, may be covered with dew shortly after sunset, whereas the concrete driveway surrounding the car remains free of condensation throughout the night.

Dew is a common sight on lawns in the early morning. In fact, the grass will frequently have a coating of dew when nothing else does. Dew is more frequent on grass because the transpiration of water vapor by the blades raises the relative humidity to higher levels directly above the grass. Therefore, only modest radiation cooling may be necessary to bring about saturation and condensation.

Although dew is an unimportant source of moisture in humid areas, plant life in some arid regions depends on it for survival. In parts of Israel, for example, dew may supply as much as 55 millimeters (2.17 inches) of water annually.

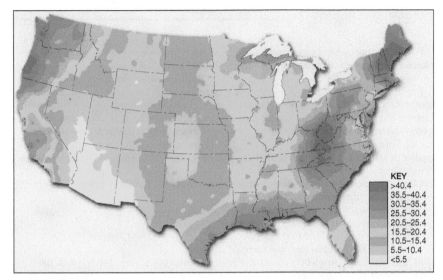

FIGURE 12 Map showing average number of days per year with heavy fog. Notice that the frequency of dense fog varies considerably from place to place. Coastal areas, particularly the Pacific Northwest and New England where cold currents prevail, have high occurrences of dense fog.

Further, this moisture is available mainly during the dry summer months when plants are experiencing the greatest stress.

Contrary to popular belief, white frost is not frozen dew. Rather, **white frost** (*hoar frost*) forms when the dew point of the air is below freezing. Thus, frost forms when water vapor changes directly from a gas into a solid (ice), without entering the liquid state. This process, called *deposition*, produces delicate patterns of ice crystals that frequently decorate windows in northern winters.

How Precipitation Forms

GE●De   Forms of Condensation and Precipitation
THE ATMOSPHERE   ▶ How Precipitation Forms

Although all clouds contain water, why do some produce precipitation and others drift placidly overhead? This seemingly simple question perplexed meteorologists for many years. Before examining the processes that generate precipitation, we need to examine a couple of facts.

First, cloud droplets are very tiny, 20 micrometers (0.02 millimeter) in diameter (Figure 13). (One micrometer equals 0.001 millimeter.) For comparison, a human hair is about 75 micrometers in diameter. The small size of cloud droplets results mainly because condensation nuclei are usually very abundant and the available water is distributed among numerous droplets rather than concentrated into fewer large droplets.

Second, because of their small size, the rate at which cloud droplets fall is incredibly slow (Box 2). An average cloud droplet falling from a cloud base at 1000 meters would require several hours to reach the ground. However, it would never complete its journey. This cloud droplet would evaporate before it fell a few meters from the cloud base into the unsaturated air below.

How large must a droplet grow in order to fall as precipitation? A typical raindrop has a diameter of about 2000 micrometers (2 millimeters), or 100 times that of the average cloud droplet having a diameter of 20 micrometers (0.02 millimeter). However, as shown in Box 2, the *volume* of a typical raindrop is a million times that of a cloud droplet. Thus, for precipitation to form, cloud droplets must grow in volume by roughly 1 million times. You might suspect that additional condensation creates drops large enough to survive the descent to the surface. However, clouds consist of many billions of tiny cloud droplets that all compete for the available water. Thus, condensation provides an inefficient means of raindrop formation.

Two processes are responsible for the formation of precipitation: the Bergeron process and the collision–coalescence process.

Precipitation from Cold Clouds: The Bergeron Process

You have probably watched a TV documentary in which mountain climbers brave intense cold and ferocious snowstorms as they scale an ice-covered peak. Although it is hard to imagine, very similar conditions exist in the upper portions of towering cumulonimbus clouds, even on sweltering summer days. (In fact, in the upper troposphere where

FIGURE 13 Comparative diameters of particles involved in condensation and precipitation processes.

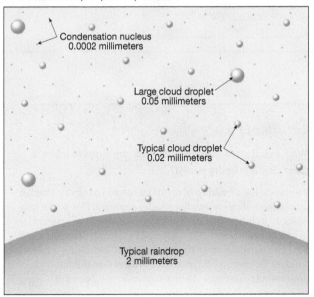

Condensation nucleus
0.0002 millimeters

Large cloud droplet
0.05 millimeters

Typical cloud droplet
0.02 millimeters

Typical raindrop
2 millimeters

BOX 2 ▶ FORCES ACTING ON CLOUD DROPLETS AND RAINDROPS

Gregory J. Carbone*

Two opposing forces act on cloud droplets *gravity* and *friction*. Gravitational force pulls a water droplet toward Earth s surface and is equal to the mass of the droplet times gravitational acceleration (gravitational force = droplet mass $\times$ 9.8 m/s^2). Because 1 cubic centimeter ($1\ cm^3$) of volume equals 1 gram of mass, we can substitute volume for mass in the above equation and say that the gravitational force of a droplet increases with its volume. Assuming the droplet is a sphere, its volume is calculated as follows:

$$Volume = \frac{4}{3}\pi r^3$$

As a droplet falls, it encounters air resistance, or frictional force. The magnitude of this force depends on the size of the drop s bottom that is, the surface area resisting the fall (Figure C). Again, assuming the droplet is spherical, frictional force will change with the area of a circle:

$$Area = \pi r^2$$

FIGURE C Raindrops and friction.

Raindrop

Surface area encountering friction

Frictional drag increases as a droplet accelerates, because a faster droplet encounters more air molecules.

Eventually, frictional and gravitational forces balance, and the droplet no longer accelerates but falls at a constant speed. This speed is referred to as the droplet s *terminal velocity.* Terminal velocity depends on size. Smaller droplets have a lower terminal velocity than do larger droplets, because as droplet radius increases, gravitational force increases to the third power and frictional force increases to the second power. Consequently, larger droplets accelerate to higher speeds before reaching terminal velocity. (Refer to Table 3 to find the terminal velocity of different-sized droplets.)

The terminal velocity of individual droplets is important because it determines the probability that a droplet will reach Earth without evaporating or being carried in updrafts. In fact, it is possible to estimate the maximum fall distance before evaporation for droplets of various size. Table A shows such values assuming a barometric pressure of 900 mb, temperature of 5¡C, and relative humidity equal to 90 percent. Note that droplets with a radius less than $100\ \mu m$ (micrometers) are unlikely to reach Earth s

surface because cloud bases are typically higher than their maximum fall distance.

Because most cloud droplets are too small to reach the surface, precipitation requires processes that cause droplet growth. But condensation is a very slow growth process. Consider a typical cloud droplet of 10-μm radius. To grow to the size of a typical raindrop ($1000\ \mu m$, or 100 times its original size), the cloud droplet must increase its volume by 1 million times:

$$Volume_{10\ \mu m} = \frac{4}{3} \times \pi \times (10\ \mu m)^3$$
$$= 4,189\ \mu m^3$$
$$Volume_{100\ \mu m} = \frac{4}{3} \times \pi \times (1000\ \mu m)^3$$
$$4,189,000,000\ \mu m^3 / 4,189\ \mu m^3$$
$$= 1,000,000$$

Clearly, condensation provides an inefficient means of cloud droplet growth, thus emphasizing the importance of other mechanisms, such as the collision—coalescence and Bergeron process.

_____
*Professor Carbone is a faculty member in the Department of Geography at the University of South Carolina.

TABLE A Maximum Fall Distance Before Evaporation	
Drop diameter (μm)	Maximum fall distance (m)
2500	280,000
1000	42,000
100	150
10	0.033
0	0.0000033

Students Sometimes Ask . . .

Why does it often seem like the roads are slippery when it rains after a long dry period?

It appears that a buildup of debris on roads during dry weather causes more slippery conditions after a rainfall. One recent traffic study indicates that if it rains today, there will be no increase in risk of fatal crashes if it also rained yesterday. However, if it has been two days since the last rain, then the risk for a deadly accident increases by 3.7 percent. Furthermore, if it has been 21 days since the last rain, the risk increases by 9.2 percent.

Precipitation from Cold Clouds: The Bergeron Process

You have probably watched a TV documentary in which mountain climbers brave intense cold and ferocious snowstorms as they scale an ice-covered peak. Although it is hard to imagine, very similar conditions exist in the upper portions of towering cumulonimbus clouds, even on sweltering summer days. (In fact, in the upper troposphere where commercial aircraft cruise, the temperature typically approaches $-50¡C\ (-58¡F)$ or lower.) It turns out that the frigid conditions high in the troposphere provide an ideal environment to initiate precipitation. In fact, in the middle latitudes much of the rain that falls begins with the birth of snowflakes

BOX 3 ▶ SCIENCE AND SERENDIPITY*

Serendipity is defined by Nobel Laureate Irving Langmuir as the art of profiting from unexpected occurrences. In other words, if you are observing something and the entirely unexpected happens, and if you see in this accident a new and meaningful discovery, then you have experienced serendipity. Most nonscientists, some scientists, and, alas, many teachers are not aware that many of the great discoveries in science were serendipitous.

An excellent example of serendipity in science occurred when Tor Bergeron, the great Swedish meteorologist, discovered the importance of ice crystals in the initiation of precipitation in supercooled clouds. Bergeron s discovery occurred when he spent several weeks at a health resort at an altitude of 430 meters (1400 feet) on a hill near Oslo. During his stay, Bergeron noted that this hill was often fogged in by a layer of supercooled clouds. As he walked along a narrow road in the fir forest along the hillside, he noticed that the fog did not enter the road tunnel at temperatures below $-5°C$, but did enter it when the temperature was warmer than $0°C$. (Profiles of the hill, trees, and fog for the two temperature regimes is shown in Figure D.)

Bergeron immediately concluded that at temperatures below about $-5°C$ the branches of the firs acted as freezing nuclei upon which some of the supercooled droplets crystallized. Once the ice crystals developed, they grew rapidly at the expense of the remaining water droplets (Figure D). The result was the growth of ice crystals

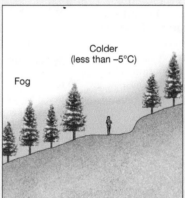

FIGURE D Distribution of fog when the temperature is above freezing and when the temperature falls below $-5°C$.

(rime) on the branches of the firs accompanied by a clearing-off between the trees and along the road-tunnel.

From this experience, Bergeron realized that if ice crystals somehow were to appear in the midst of a cloud of supercooled droplets, they would grow rapidly as water molecules diffused toward them from the evaporating cloud droplets. This rapid growth forms snow crystals that, depending on the air temperature beneath the cloud, fall to the ground as snow or rain. Bergeron had thus discovered one way that minuscule cloud droplets can grow large enough to fall as precipitation (see the section entitled Precipitation from Cold Clouds: The Bergeron Process).

Serendipity influences the entire realm of science. Can we conclude that anyone who makes observations will necessarily make a major discovery? Not at all. A perceptive and inquiring mind is required, a mind that has been searching for order in a labyrinth of facts. As Langmuir said, the unexpected occurrence is not enough; you must know how to profit from it. Louis Pasteur observed that in the field of observation, chance favors only the prepared mind. The discoverer of vitamin C, Nobel Laureate Albert Szent-Gyorgyi, remarked that discoveries are made by those who see what everybody else has seen, and think what nobody else has thought. Serendipity is at the heart of science itself.

---

*Based on material prepared by Duncan C. Blanchard.

---

high in the cloud tops, where temperatures are considerably below freezing. Often even low clouds are cold enough to trigger precipitation.

The process that generates much of the precipitation in the middle latitudes is named the **Bergeron process** for its discoverer, the highly respected Swedish meteorologist, Tor Bergeron (Box 3). The Bergeron process, which involves ice-crystal growth, depends on the coexistence of water vapor, liquid cloud droplets, and ice crystals. To understand just how this mechanism operates, we must first examine two important properties of water. First, *cloud droplets do not freeze at $0°C$ as expected.* In fact, pure water suspended in air does not freeze until it reaches a temperature of nearly $-40°C$ ($-40°F$). Water in the liquid state below $0°C$ ($32°F$) is referred to as **supercooled.** Supercooled water will readily freeze if it impacts an object, which explains why airplanes collect ice when they pass through a liquid cloud made up of supercooled droplets. This also explains why the stuff we call *freezing rain*

or *glaze* falls as a liquid but then turns to a sheet of ice when it strikes the pavement or a tree branch.

In addition, supercooled droplets will freeze on contact with solid particles that have a crystal form closely resembling that of ice (silver iodide is an example). These materials are called **freezing nuclei.** The need for freezing nuclei to initiate the freezing process is similar to the requirement for condensation nuclei in the process of condensation.

In contrast to condensation nuclei, however, freezing nuclei are sparse in the atmosphere and do not generally become active until the temperature reaches $-10°C$ ($14°F$) or below. Thus, at temperatures between 0 and $-10°C$, clouds consist mainly of supercooled water droplets. Between -10 and $-20°C$, liquid droplets coexist with ice crystals, and below $-20°C$ ($-4°F$), clouds are generally composed entirely of ice crystals for example, high altitude cirrus clouds.

This brings us to a second important property of water. *The saturation vapor pressure above ice crystals is somewhat lower than above supercooled liquid droplets.* This occurs because ice

TABLE 2 Relative Humidity with Respect to Ice when Relative Humidity with Respect to Water is 100 percent		
	Relative humidity with respect to:	
Temperature (°C)	Water	Ice
0	100%	100%
−5	100%	105%
−10	100%	110%
−15	100%	115%
−20	100%	121%

rapid to generate crystals large enough to fall. During their descent, these crystals enlarge as they intercept cloud drops that freeze on them. Air movement will sometimes break up these delicate crystals, and the fragments will serve as freezing nuclei for other liquid droplets. A chain reaction develops and produces many snow crystals, which, by accretion, will form into larger masses called snowflakes. Large snowflakes may consist of 10 to 30 individual crystals.

In summary, the Bergeron process can produce precipitation throughout the year in the middle latitudes, provided at least the upper portions of clouds are cold enough to generate ice crystals. The type of precipitation (snow, sleet, rain, or freezing rain) that reaches the ground depends on the temperature profile in the lower few kilometers of the atmosphere. When the surface temperature is above 4°C (39°F), snowflakes usually melt before they reach the ground and continue their descent as rain. Even on a hot summer day a heavy downpour may have begun as a snowstorm high in the clouds overhead.

With these facts in mind, we can now explain how the Bergeron process produces precipitation. Visualize a cloud at a temperature of −10°C (14°F), where each ice crystal is surrounded by many thousands of liquid droplets (Figure 14). Because the air was initially saturated (100 percent) with respect to liquid water, it will be supersaturated (over 100 percent) with respect to the newly formed ice crystals. As a result of this supersaturated condition, the ice crystals collect more water molecules than they lose by sublimation. Thus, continued evaporation from the liquid drops provides a source of water vapor to feed the growth of ice crystals (Figure 14).

Because the level of supersaturation with respect to ice can be great, the growth of snow crystals is generally sufficiently

Precipitation from Warm Clouds: The Collision–Coalescence Process

A few decades ago meteorologists believed that the Bergeron process was responsible for the formation of most precipitation except for light drizzle. Later it was discovered that copious rainfall is often associated with clouds located well below the freezing level (called *warm clouds*), especially in the tropics. Clearly, a second mechanism also must trigger precipitation. Researchers discovered the **collision–coalescence process.**

Research has shown that clouds made entirely of liquid droplets must contain some droplets larger than 20 micrometers (0.02 millimeters) if precipitation is to form. These large droplets form when "giant" condensation nuclei are present, or when hygroscopic particles exist (such as sea salt). Recall that hygroscopic particles begin to remove water vapor from the air at relative humidities under 100 percent. Because the rate at which drops fall is size-dependent, these "giant" droplets fall most rapidly. (Table 3 summarizes drop size and falling velocities.)

As the larger droplets fall through a cloud, they collide with the smaller, slower droplets and coalesce (see Box 2). Becoming larger in the process, they fall even more rapidly (or, in an updraft, they rise more slowly) and increase their chances of collision and rate of growth (Figure 15a). After collecting the equivalent of a million or so cloud droplets, they are large enough to fall to the surface without evaporating.

Because of the huge number of collisions required for growth to raindrop size, clouds that have great vertical thickness and contain large cloud droplets have the best chance of producing precipitation. Updrafts

FIGURE 14 The Bergeron process. Ice crystals grow at the expense of cloud droplets until they are large enough to fall. The size of these particles has been greatly exaggerated.

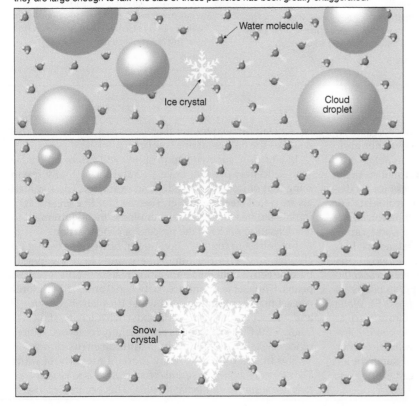

TABLE 3	Fall Velocity of Water Drops		
Types	Diameter (millimeters)	Fall velocity (km/hr)	(mi/hr)
Small cloud droplets	0.01	0.01	0.006
Typical cloud droplets	0.02	0.04	0.03
Large cloud droplets	0.05	0.3	0.2
Drizzle drops	0.5	7	4
Typical rain drops	2.0	23	14
Large rain drops	5.0	33	20
Data from Smithsonian Meteorological Tables.			

also aid this process because they allow the droplets to traverse the cloud repeatedly, colliding with more droplets.

As raindrops grow in size, their fall velocity increases. This in turn increases the frictional resistance of the air, which causes the drop's "bottom" to flatten out (Figure 15b). As the drop approaches 4 millimeters in diameter, it develops a depression as shown in Figure 15c. Raindrops can grow to a maximum of 5 millimeters when they fall at the rate of 33 kilometers (20 miles) per hour. At this size and speed, the water's surface tension, which holds the drop together, is surpassed by the frictional drag of the air. At this point the depression grows almost explosively, forming a donutlike ring that immediately breaks apart. The resulting breakup of a large raindrop produces numerous smaller drops that begin anew the task of sweeping up cloud droplets (Figure 15d).

The collision–coalescence process is not that simple, however. First, as the larger droplets descend, they produce an airstream around them similar to that produced by an automobile when driven rapidly down the highway. The airstream repels objects, especially small ones. If an automobile is driven at night and we use the bugs that fill the air on a summer evening as being like cloud droplets, it is easy to visualize how most cloud droplets, which are tiny, are swept aside. The larger the cloud droplet (or bug), the better chance it will have of colliding with the giant droplet (or car).

Next, collision does not guarantee coalescence. Experimentation has indicated that the presence of atmospheric electricity may be the key to what holds these droplets together once they collide. If a droplet with a negative charge should collide with a positively charged droplet, their electrical attraction may bind them together.

From the preceding discussion, it should be apparent that the collision–coalescence mechanism is most efficient in environments where large cloud droplets are plentiful. It turns out that the air over the tropics, particularly the tropical oceans, is ideal. Here the air is very humid and relatively clean, so fewer condensation nuclei exist compared to the air over more populated regions. With fewer condensation nuclei to compete for available water vapor (which is plentiful), condensation is fast-paced and produces comparatively few large cloud droplets. Within developing cumulus clouds, the largest drops quickly gather smaller droplets to generate the warm afternoon showers associated with tropical climates.

In the middle latitudes the collision–coalescence process may contribute to the precipitation from a large cumulonimbus

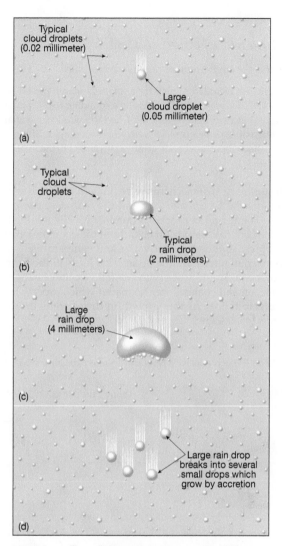

FIGURE 15 The collision–coalescence process. (a) Most cloud droplets are so small that the motion of the air keeps them suspended. Because large cloud droplets fall more rapidly than smaller droplets, they are able to sweep up the smaller ones in their path and grow. (b) As these drops increase in size, their fall velocity increases, resulting in increased air resistance, which causes the raindrop to flatten. (c) As the raindrop approaches 4 millimeters in size, it develops a depression in the bottom. (d) Finally, when the diameter exceeds about 5 millimeters, the depression grows upward almost explosively, forming a donutlike ring of water that immediately breaks into smaller drops. (Note that the drops are not drawn to scale—a typical raindrop has a volume equal to roughly 1 million cloud droplets.)

cloud by working in tandem with the Bergeron process—particularly during the hot, humid summer months. High in these towers the Bergeron process generates snow that melts as it passes below the freezing level. Melting generates relatively large drops with fast fall velocities. As these large drops descend, they overtake and coalesce with the slower and smaller cloud droplets that comprise much of the lower regions of the cloud. The result can be a heavy downpour.

In summary, two mechanisms are known to generate precipitation: the *Bergeron process* and the *collision–coalescence process*. The Bergeron process is dominant in the middle latitudes where cold clouds (or cold cloud tops) are the rule. In the tropics, abundant water vapor and comparatively few condensation nuclei are the norm. This leads to the formation of fewer, larger drops with fast fall velocities that grow by collision and coalescence. No matter which process initiates precipitation, further growth in drop size is through collision–coalescence.

Forms of Precipitation

 Forms of Condensation and Precipitation
THE ATMOSPHERE ▸ Forms of Precipitation

Because atmospheric conditions vary greatly both geographically and seasonally, several different forms of precipitation are possible (Figure 16). Rain and snow are the most common and familiar forms, but others listed in Table 4 are important as well. The occurrence of sleet, glaze, and hail is often associated with important weather events. Although limited in occurrence and sporadic in both time and space, these forms, especially glaze and hail, may on occasion cause considerable damage.

Rain

In meteorology the term **rain** is restricted to drops of water that fall from a cloud and have a diameter of at least 0.5 millimeter. (This excludes drizzle and mist, which have smaller droplets.) Most rain originates in either nimbostratus clouds

FIGURE 16 Four precipitation types and their temperature profiles.

TABLE 4	Types of Precipitation		
Type	Approximate size	State of water	Description
Mist	0.005 to 0.05 mm	Liquid	Droplets large enough to be felt on the face when air is moving 1 meter/second. Associated with stratus clouds.
Drizzle	Less than 0.5 mm	Liquid	Small uniform drops that fall from stratus clouds, generally for several hours.
Rain	0.5 to 5 mm	Liquid	Generally produced by nimbostratus or cumulonimbus clouds. When heavy, size can be highly variable from one place to another.
Sleet	0.5 to 5 mm	Solid	Small, spherical to lumpy ice particles that form when raindrops freeze while falling through a layer of subfreezing air. Because the ice particles are small, any damage is generally minor. Sleet can make travel hazardous.
Glaze	Layers 1 mm to 2 cm thick	Solid	Produced when supercooled raindrops freeze on contact with solid objects. Glaze can form a thick coating of ice having sufficient weight to seriously damage trees and power lines.
Rime	Variable accumulations	Solid	Deposits usually consisting of ice feathers that point into the wind. These delicate frostlike accumulations form as supercooled cloud or fog droplets encounter objects and freeze on contact.
Snow	1 mm to 2 cm	Solid	The crystalline nature of snow allows it to assume many shapes, including six sided crystals, plates, and needles. Produced in supercooled clouds where water vapor is deposited as ice crystals that remain frozen during their descent.
Hail	5 mm to 10 cm or larger	Solid	Precipitation in the form of hard, rounded pellets or irregular lumps of ice. Produced in large convective, cumulonimbus clouds, where frozen ice particles and supercooled water coexist.
Graupel	2 mm to 5 mm	Solid	Sometimes called "soft hail," graupel forms as rime collects on snow crystals to produce irregular masses of "soft" ice. Because these particles are softer than hailstones, they normally flatten out upon impact.

or in towering cumulonimbus clouds that are capable of producing unusually heavy rainfalls known as *cloudbursts*. No matter what the rainfall intensity is, the size of raindrops rarely exceeds about 5 millimeters. Larger drops cannot survive, because surface tension, which holds the drops together, is exceeded by the frictional drag of the air. Consequently, large raindrops regularly break apart into smaller ones.

Much of the world's rainfall begins as snow crystals or other solid forms such as hail or graupel, as shown in Figure 16a. Entering the warmer air below the cloud, these ice particles often melt and reach the ground as raindrops. In some parts of the world, particularly the subtropics, precipitation often forms in clouds that are warmer than 0°C (32°F). These rains frequently occur over the ocean where cloud condensation nuclei are not plentiful and those that do exist vary in size. Under such conditions, cloud droplets can grow rapidly by the collision–coalescence process to produce copious amounts of rain.

Fine, uniform drops of water having a diameter less than 0.5 millimeter are called *drizzle*. Drizzle and small raindrops generally are produced in stratus or nimbostratus clouds where precipitation may be continuous for several hours, or on rare occasions for days.

Precipitation containing the very smallest droplets able to reach the ground is called *mist*. Mist can be so fine that the tiny droplets appear to float and their impact is almost imperceptible.

As rain enters the unsaturated air below the cloud, it begins to evaporate. Depending on the humidity of the air and size of the drops, the rain may completely evaporate before reaching the ground. This phenomenon produces *virga*, which

appear as streaks of precipitation falling from a cloud that extend only part of the way to Earth's surface (Figure 17).

Snow

Snow is precipitation in the form of ice crystals (snowflakes) or, more often, aggregates of ice crystals (Figure 16b). The size, shape, and concentration of snowflakes depend to a great extent on the temperature at which they form.

Recall that at very low temperatures, the moisture content of air is small. The result is the generation of very light and fluffy snow made up of individual six-sided ice crystals (Figure 18). This is the "powder" that downhill skiers talk so much about. By contrast, at temperatures warmer than about

FIGURE 17 Virga, latin for "streak." In the arid west, rain frequently evaporates before reaching the ground. (Photo by Frank Zullo/Photo Researchers)

FIGURE 18   Computer-enhanced image of snow crystals. All snow crystals are six-sided, but they come in an infinite variety of forms. (Photo by Scott Camazine/Photo Researchers)

−5°C (23°F), the ice crystals join together into larger clumps consisting of tangled aggregates of crystals. Snowfalls consisting of these composite snowflakes are generally heavy and have a high moisture content, which makes them ideal for making snowballs. (For more on winter weather, see Box 4.)

Sleet and Glaze

Sleet is a wintertime phenomenon and refers to the fall of small particles of ice that are clear to translucent. Figures 5–16c and 5–19 show how sleet is produced: An above-freezing air layer must overlie a subfreezing layer near the ground. When the raindrops, which are often melted snow, leave the warmer air and encounter the colder air below, they freeze and reach the ground as small pellets of ice roughly the size of the raindrops from which they formed.

On some occasions, when the vertical distribution of temperatures is similar to that associated with the formation of sleet, **freezing rain** or **glaze** results instead. In such situations the subfreezing air near the ground is not thick enough to allow the raindrops to freeze (Figure 16d). The raindrops, however, do become

supercooled as they fall through the cold air and turn to ice. The result can be a thick coating of ice having sufficient weight to break tree limbs, to down power lines, and to make walking and driving extremely hazardous.

In January 1998 an ice storm of historic proportions caused enormous damage in New England and southeastern Canada. Here five days of freezing rain deposited a heavy layer of ice on all exposed surfaces from eastern Ontario to the Atlantic coast. The 8 centimeters (3 inches) of precipitation caused trees, power lines, and high-voltage towers to collapse, leaving over a million households without power—many for nearly a month following the storm (Figure 20).

At least 40 deaths were blamed on the storm, which caused damages in excess of $3 billion. Much of the damage was to the electrical grid, which one Canadian climatologist summed up this way: "What it took human beings a half-century to construct, took nature a matter of hours to knock down."

Hail

Hail is precipitation in the form of hard, rounded pellets or irregular lumps of ice. Large hailstones, when cut in half, often reveal nearly concentric shells of differing densities and degrees of opaqueness (Figure 21). The layers of ice accumulate as the hailstone travels up and down in a strong convective cloud.

Most hailstones have diameters between 1 centimeter (pea size) and 5 centimeters (golf ball size), although some can be as big as an orange or even bigger. Occasionally, hailstones weighing a pound or more have been reported. Many of these were probably composites of several stones frozen together.

The largest hailstone ever recorded in the United States fell during violent thunderstorms that pounded southeastern Nebraska on June 22, 2003. In the town of Aurora, a seven-inch (17.8-centimeter)-wide chunk of ice, almost as large as a volleyball, was recovered. However, this hailstone was not the heaviest hailstone ever measured. Apparently, a chunk of this stone was broken off when it hit the gutter of a house.

The heaviest hailstone in North America fell on Coffeyville, Kansas, in 1970. Having a 5.5 inch (14 centimeter) diameter,

FIGURE 19   Sleet forms when rain passes through a cold layer of air and freezes into ice pellets. This occurs most often in the winter when warm air is forced over a layer of subfreezing air.

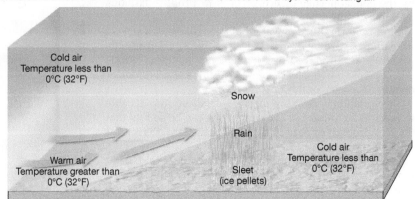

BOX 4 ▶ ATMOSPHERIC HAZARD

Worst Winter Weather

Extremes, whether they be the tallest building or the record low temperature for a location, fascinate us. When it comes to weather, some places take pride in claiming to have the worst winters on record. In fact, Fraser, Colorado, and International Falls, Minnesota, have both proclaimed themselves the "ice box of the nation." Although Fraser recorded the low temperature for the 48 contiguous states 23 times in 1989, its neighbor, Gunnison, Colorado, recorded the low temperature 62 times, far more than any other location.

Such facts do not impress the residents of Hibbing, Minnesota, where the temperature dropped to −38°C (−37°F) during the first week of March 1989. But this is mild stuff, say the old-timers in Parshall, North Dakota, where the temperature fell to −51°C (−60°F) on February 15, 1936. Not to be left out, Browning, Montana, holds the record for the most dramatic 24-hour temperature drop. Here the temperature plummeted 56°C (100°F), from a cool 7°C (44°F) to a frosty −49°C (−56°F) during a January evening in 1916.

Although impressive, the temperature extremes cited here represent only one aspect of winter weather. What about snowfall (Figure E)? Cooke City holds the seasonal snowfall record for Montana, with 1062 centimeters (418.1 inches) during the winter of 1977–1978. But what about cities like Sault Ste. Marie, Michigan, or Buffalo, New York? The winter snowfalls associated with the Great Lakes are legendary. Even larger snowfalls occur in many sparsely inhabited mountainous areas.

Try telling residents of the eastern United States that heavy snowfall by itself makes for the worst weather. A blizzard in March 1993 produced heavy snowfall along with hurricane-force winds and record low temperatures that immobilized much of the region from Alabama to the Maritime Provinces of eastern Canada. This event quickly earned the well-deserved title of Storm of the Century.

As we can see, determining which location has the worst winter weather depends on how you measure it. Most snowfall in a season? Longest cold spell? Coldest temperature? Most disruptive storm?

FIGURE E   Rochester, NY, was hit by blizzard conditions that left 24 inches of snow in 24 hours on March 4, 1999. (Photo by AP/Wide World Photos)

Here are the meanings of some common terms used by the National Weather Service for winter weather events.

Snow flurries Snow falling for short durations at intermittent periods and resulting in generally little or no accumulation.

Blowing snow Snow lifted from the surface by the wind and blown about to a degree that horizontal visibility is reduced.

Drifting snow Significant accumulations of falling or loose snow caused by strong wind.

Blizzard A winter storm characterized by winds of at least 56 kilometers (35 miles) per hour for at least three hours. The storm must also be accompanied by low temperatures and considerable falling and/or blowing snow that reduces visibility to a quarter of a mile or less.

Severe blizzard A storm with winds of at least 72 kilometers (45 miles) per hour, a great amount of falling or drifting snow, and temperatures −12°C (10°F) or lower.

Heavy snow warning A snowfall in which at least 4 inches in 12 hours or 6 inches in 24 hours is expected.

Freezing rain Rain falling in a liquid form through a shallow subfreezing layer of air near the ground. The rain (or drizzle) freezes on impact with the ground or other objects, resulting in a clear coating of ice known as *glaze*.

Sleet Also called *ice pellets*. Sleet is formed when raindrops or melted snowflakes freeze as they pass through a subfreezing layer of air near Earth's surface. Sleet does not stick to trees and wires, and it usually bounces when it hits the ground. An accumulation of sleet sometimes has the consistency of dry sand.

Travelers' advisory Issued to inform the public of hazardous driving conditions caused by snow, sleet, freezing precipitation, fog, wind, or dust.

Cold wave A rapid fall of temperature in a 24-hour period, usually signifying the beginning of a spell of very cold weather.

Windchill A measure of apparent temperature that uses the effects of wind and temperature on the human body by translating the cooling power of wind to a temperature under calm conditions. It is an approximation only for the human body and has no meaning for cars, buildings, or other objects.

FIGURE 20 Glaze forms when supercooled raindrops freeze on contact with objects. (a) In January 1998 an ice storm of historic proportions caused enormous damage in New England and southeastern Canada. Nearly five days of freezing rain (glaze) caused 40 deaths, more than $3 billion in damages and left millions of people without electricity—some for as long as a month. (Photo by Syracuse Newspapers/The Image Works) (b) A simplified weather map that includes selected temperatures (°F) and wind arrows, showing the conditions that produced this devastating ice storm. Cold arctic air from central Canada spread into New England and southeastern Canada causing nighttime temperatures to fall into the low 20s. Meanwhile, a persistent, mild, moist flow aloft was overriding the cold low-level air. The precipitation passed through the cold layer, turning it into freezing rain and creating havoc for residents in the area.

FIGURE 21 Hail. A cross section of the Coffeyville hailstone. This record-breaking hailstone fell over Coffeyville, Kansas, in 1970 and weighed 0.75 kilogram (1.67 pounds). (Photo courtesy of University Corporation for Atmospheric Research/National Science Foundation/Visual Communications NCAR)

Students Sometimes Ask . . .

What is the difference between a winter storm warning and a blizzard warning?

A winter storm warning is usually issued when heavy snow exceeding six inches in 12 hours or possible icing conditions are likely. It is interesting to note that in Upper Michigan and mountainous areas where snowfall is abundant, winter storm warnings are issued only if eight or more inches of snow is expected in 12 hours. By contrast, blizzard warnings are issued for periods when considerable falling or blowing snow is accompanied by winds of 35 or more miles per hour. Thus, a blizzard is a type of winter storm in which winds are the determining factor, not the amount of snowfall.

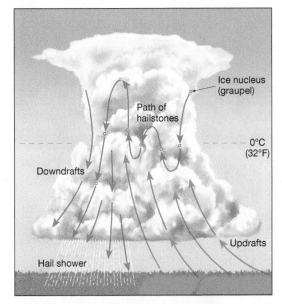

FIGURE 23 Growth of hailstones. Hailstones begin as small ice pellets that grow by adding supercooled water droplets as they move through a cloud. Strong updrafts may carry stones upward in several cycles, increasing the size of the hail by adding a new layer with each cycle. Eventually, the hailstones encounter a downdraft or grow too large to be supported by the updraft.

this hailstone weighed 1.67 pounds (766 grams). Even heavier hailstones have reportedly been recorded in Bangladesh, where a hailstorm in 1987 killed more than 90 people. It is estimated that large hailstones hit the ground at speeds exceeding 100 miles (160 kilometers) per hour.

The destructive effects of large hailstones are well known, especially to farmers whose crops have been devastated in a few minutes and to people whose windows, roofs, and cars have been damaged (Figure 22). In the United States, hail damage each year can run into the hundreds of millions of dollars. One of the costliest hailstorms to occur in North America took place on June 11, 1990, in Denver, Colorado. Total damage was estimated to exceed $625 million.

Hail is produced only in large cumulonimbus clouds where updrafts can sometimes reach speeds approaching 160

kilometers (100 miles) per hour, and where there is an abundant supply of supercooled water. Figure 23 shows the process. Hailstones begin as small embryonic ice pellets that grow by collecting supercooled droplets as they fall through the cloud. If they encounter a strong updraft, they may be carried upward again and begin the downward journey anew. Each trip through the supercooled portion of the cloud might be represented by an additional layer of ice. Hailstones can also form from a single descent through an updraft. Either way, the process continues until the hailstone encounters a downdraft or grows too heavy to remain suspended by the thunderstorm's updraft.

Hailstones may contain several layers that alternate between clear and milky ice. High in the clouds, rapid freezing of small, supercooled water droplets traps air bubbles, which cause the milky appearance. By contrast, the clear ice is produced in the lower and warmer regions of the clouds where colliding droplets wet the surface of the hailstones. As these droplets slowly freeze, they produce relatively bubble-free clear ice.

FIGURE 22 Hail damage at an auto dealership in Amarillo, Texas, following a storm in June 2004. (AP Photo)

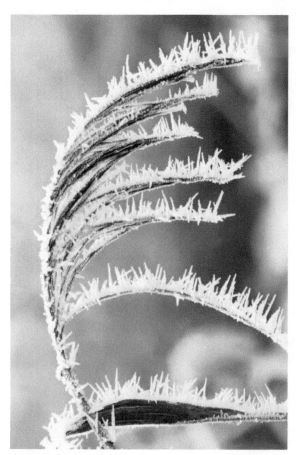

FIGURE 24 Rime consists of delicate ice crystals that form when supercooled fog or cloud droplets freeze on contact with objects. (Photo by John Cancalosi/Stock Boston)

Rime

Rime is a deposit of ice crystals formed by the freezing of supercooled fog or cloud droplets on objects whose surface temperature is below freezing. When rime forms on trees, it adorns them with its characteristic ice feathers, which can be spectacular to behold (Figure 24). In these situations, objects such as pine needles act as freezing nuclei, causing the supercooled droplets to freeze on contact. On occasions when the wind is blowing, only the windward surfaces of objects will accumulate the layer of rime.

Precipitation Measurement

The most common form of precipitation, rain, is probably the easiest to measure. Any open container that has a consistent cross section throughout can be a rain gauge (Figure 25a). In general practice, however, more sophisticated devices are used to measure small amounts of rainfall more accurately and to reduce loss from evaporation.

Standard Instruments

The **standard rain gauge** (Figure 25b) has a diameter of about 20 centimeters (8 inches) at the top. Once the water is caught, a funnel conducts the rain through a narrow opening into a cylindrical measuring tube that has a cross-sectional area only one-tenth as large as the receiver. Consequently, rainfall depth is magnified 10 times, which allows for accurate measurements to the nearest 0.025 centimeter (0.01 inch), and the nar-

FIGURE 25 Precipitation measurement. (a) The simplest gauge is any container left in the rain. However, these homemade devices are hard to read precisely. (b) The standard rain gauge increases the height of water collected by a factor of 10, allowing for accurate rainfall measurement to the nearest 0.025 centimeter (0.01 inch). Because the cross-sectional area of the measuring tube is only one-tenth as large as the collector, rainfall is magnified 10 times. (c) The tipping-bucket rain gauge contains two "buckets" that hold the equivalent of 0.025 centimeter (0.01 inch) of liquid precipitation. When one bucket fills, it tips and the other bucket takes its place. Each event is recorded as 0.01 inch of rainfall.

(a) **Simple rain gauge**

(b) **Standard rain gauge**

(c) **Tipping–bucket gauge**

row opening minimizes evaporation. When the amount of rain is less than 0.025 centimeter (0.01 inch), it is generally reported as being a **trace of precipitation.**

In addition to the standard rain gauge, several types of recording gauges are routinely used. These instruments not only record the amount of rain, but also its time of occurrence and intensity (amount per unit of time). Two of the most common gauges are the tipping-bucket gauge and the weighing gauge.

As can be seen in Figure 25c, the **tipping-bucket gauge** consists of two compartments, each one capable of holding 0.025 centimeter (0.01 inch) of rain, situated at the base of a funnel. When one "bucket" fills, it tips and empties its water. Meanwhile, the other "bucket" takes its place at the mouth of the funnel. Each time a compartment tips, an electrical circuit is closed and 0.025 centimeter (0.01 inch) of precipitation is automatically recorded on a graph.

The **weighing gauge,** as the name would indicate, works on a different principle. Precipitation is caught in a cylinder that rests on a spring balance. As the cylinder fills, the movement is transmitted to a pen that records the data.

Measuring Snowfall

When snow records are kept, two measurements are normally taken—depth and water equivalent. Usually, the depth of snow is measured with a calibrated stick. The actual measurement is not difficult, but choosing a representative spot can be. Even when winds are light or moderate, snow drifts freely. As a rule, it is best to take several measurements in an open place away from trees and obstructions and then average them. To obtain the water equivalent, samples may be melted and then weighed or measured as rain.

Sometimes large cylinders are used to collect snow. A major problem that hinders accurate measurement by snow gauges is the wind. Snow will blow around the top of the cylinder instead of falling into it. Therefore, the amount caught by the gauge is generally less than the actual fall. As is often the practice with rain gauges, shields designed to break up wind eddies are placed around the snow gauge to ensure a more accurate catch.

The quantity of water in a given volume of snow is not constant. A general ratio of 10 units of snow to 1 unit of water is often used when exact information is not available. You may have heard TV weathercasters use this ratio, saying, "Every 10 inches of snow equals 1 inch of rain." But the actual water content of snow may deviate widely from this figure. It may take as much as 30 centimeters of light and fluffy dry snow (30:1) or as little as 4 centimeters of wet snow (4:1) to produce 1 centimeter of water.

Measurement Errors

We tend to be unquestioning when we hear weather reports concerning the past day's events. However, unlike temperature and pressure, which tend to vary only slightly over a few dozen miles, precipitation on one side of the street can be significantly greater than on the other. Further, by its very nature precipitation is difficult to collect, and the techniques used have numerous potential sources for error.

When measuring rain, a certain amount goes unrecorded—some because it splashes out upon impact, and some "wets" the collection funnel and never makes it into the cylinder. Snow in particular is often underestimated by rain gauges. In addition, in certain climates, evaporation removes some of the precipitation before it is measured.

No matter which rain gauge is used, proper exposure is critical. Errors arise when gauges are located too close to buildings, trees, or other high objects that block obliquely falling rain. For best results, the instrument should be twice as far away from such obstructions as the objects are high. Another cause for error is wind. It has been shown that as wind speed strengthens, turbulence increases, and it becomes more difficult to collect a representative quantity of rain. To offset this effect, a windscreen is often placed around the instrument so that rain falls into the gauge and is not carried across it (Figure 26).

Studies have shown that in the United States, annual precipitation errors range between about 7 and 20 percent. Most often the precipitation is underestimated. In some high latitudes, percentage errors are thought to exceed 80 percent.

Precipitation Measurement by Weather Radar

Today's TV weathercasts show helpful maps, like the one in Figure 27, to depict precipitation patterns. The instrument that produces these images is the *weather radar.*

The development of radar has given meteorologists an important tool to probe storm systems that may be up to a few hundred kilometers away. All radar units have a transmitter that sends out short pulses of radio waves. The specific wavelengths that are used depend on the objects the user

FIGURE 26 This standard rain gauge is fitted with metal slats that serve as a windscreen to minimize the undercatch that results because of windy conditions. (Photo by Bobbé Christopherson)

FIGURE 27 Doppler radar display commonly seen on The Weather Channel and local TV weathercasts. Colors indicate different intensities of precipitation. Note the band of heavy precipitation extending from northerneastern Iowa to Milwaukee, Wisconsin.

wants to detect. When radar is used to monitor precipitation, wavelengths between 3 and 10 centimeters are employed.

These wavelengths can penetrate small cloud droplets but are reflected by larger raindrops, ice crystals, or hailstones. The reflected signal, called an *echo*, is received and displayed on a TV monitor. Because the echo is "brighter" when the precipitation is more intense, modern radar is able to depict not only the regional extent of the precipitation but also the rate of rainfall. Figure 27 is a typical radar display in which colors show precipitation intensity. Weather radar can also measure the rate and direction of storm movement.

Intentional Weather Modification

Intentional weather modification is deliberate human intervention to influence atmospheric processes that constitute the weather—that is, to alter the weather for human purposes.

Students Sometimes Ask . . .

What places in the United States receive the most snowfall?

Despite the impressive lake-effect snowstorms recorded in cities such as Buffalo and Rochester, New York, the greatest accumulations of snow generally occur in the mountainous regions of the western United States. The record for a single season goes to Mount Baker ski area north of Seattle, Washington, where 2896 centimeters (1140 inches) of snow fell during the winter of 1998–1999.

This desire to change the weather is nothing new. From earliest recorded times people have used prayer, wizardry, dances, and even black magic in attempts to alter the weather.

During the American Civil War, rainfall seemed to increase following some battles, leading to experiments in which cannons were fired into clouds to trigger more rain. These experiments and many others proved unsuccessful. However, by the nineteenth century, smudge pots, sprinklers, and wind machines were used successfully to fight frost.

Weather-modification strategies fall into three broad categories. The first employs energy to forcefully alter the weather. Examples are the use of intense heat sources or the mechanical mixing of air (such as by helicopters) to disperse fog at some airports.

The second category involves modifying land and water surfaces to change their natural interaction with the lower atmosphere. One often discussed but untried example is the blanketing of a land area with a dark substance. The additional solar energy absorbed by this dark surface would warm the layer of air near the surface and encourage the development of updrafts that might aid cloud formation.

The third category involves triggering, intensifying, or redirecting atmospheric processes. The seeding of clouds with agents such as dry ice (frozen carbon dioxide) and silver iodide to stimulate precipitation is the primary example. Because **cloud seeding** sometimes seems to show promising results and is a relatively inexpensive technique, it has been a primary focus of modern weather-modification technology.

Cloud Seeding

The first breakthrough in weather modification came in 1946 when Vincent J. Schaefer discovered that dry ice, dropped into a supercooled cloud, spurred the growth of ice crystals. Recall that once ice crystals form in a supercooled cloud, they grow larger at the expense of the remaining liquid cloud droplets and, on reaching a sufficient size, fall as precipitation.

Later it was learned that silver iodide could also be used for cloud seeding. The similarity in the structure of silver iodide crystals and ice crystals accounts for silver iodide's ability to initiate ice crystal growth. Thus, unlike dry ice, which simply chills the air, silver iodide crystals act as freezing nuclei. Because silver iodide can be more easily delivered to clouds from burners on the ground or from aircraft, it is a better alternative than dry ice (Figure 28).

If cloud seeding is to trigger precipitation, certain atmospheric conditions must exist. Clouds must be present, for

FIGURE 28 Cloud seeding using silver iodide flares is one way that freezing nuclei are supplied to clouds. (Courtesy of University Corporation for Atmospheric Research/National Science Foundation/National Center for Atmospheric Research)

seeding cannot create clouds. Also, a portion of the cloud must be supercooled—it must be made of liquid droplets below 0°C (32°F) in temperature.

One type of cloud seeding assumes that cold cumulus clouds are deficient in freezing nuclei and that adding them will stimulate precipitation. The object is to produce just enough ice crystals so they will grow large enough (via the Bergeron process) to fall as precipitation. Overseeding will simply produce billions of ice crystals that are too tiny to fall.

Seeding of winter clouds that form along mountain barriers (orographic clouds) has been tried repeatedly. These clouds are thought to be good candidates for seeding because only a small percentage of the water that condenses in cold orographic clouds actually falls as precipitation. The idea is to increase the winter snowpack, which melts and runs off during warmer months and is collected in reservoirs for irrigation and hydroelectric power generation. Since 1977 Colorado's Vail and Beaver Creek ski areas have used this method to increase winter snows.

In recent years the seeding of warm convective clouds with hygroscopic (water-seeking) particles has received renewed attention. The interest in this technique arose when it was discovered that a pollution-belching paper mill near Nelspruit, South Africa, seemed to be triggering precipitation. Flying through clouds near the paper mill, research aircraft collected samples of the particulate matter emitted from the mill. It turned out that the mill was emitting tiny salt crystals (potassium chloride and sodium chloride), which rose with updrafts into the clouds. Because these salts attract moisture, they quickly form large cloud droplets, which grow into raindrops by the collision–coalescence process. Ongoing experiments being conducted over the arid landscape of northern Mexico are attempting to duplicate this process by seeding clouds using flares mounted on airplanes that spread hygroscopic salts. Although the results of these studies are promising, conclusive evidence that such seeding can increase rainfall over economically significant areas is not yet available.

More than two dozen countries around the globe have weather modification programs, mainly rainfall enhancement.

China appears to have the greatest number of projects, including efforts in cloud dispersal. Other projects are aimed at bringing drought relief and hail suppression to a large part of central China.

In the United States, over 50 weather modification projects are currently underway in 10 states. Some of the most promising results come from western Texas, where researchers estimate a 10 percent increase in rainfall from silver iodide–seeded clouds compared to unseeded ones.

In summary, researchers are gaining confidence that precipitation can be enhanced by seeding supercooled clouds. Further, the use of large hygroscopic particles to seed warm convective clouds appears to hold promise, although the processes involved are poorly understood. However, because these studies have been limited in scope, the economic viability of cloud seeding remains uncertain. The major outcome of the last five decades of cloud-seeding experimentation has been the sobering realization that even the simplest weather events are exceedingly complex and not yet fully understood.

Fog and Cloud Dispersal

One of the most successful applications of cloud seeding involves spreading dry ice, particles of solid carbon dioxide at temperatures of −78°C (−108°F), into layers of supercooled fog or stratus clouds to disperse them and thereby improve visibility. Airports, harbors, and foggy stretches of interstate highway are obvious candidates. Such applications trigger a transformation in cloud composition from supercooled water droplets to ice crystals. The ice crystals then settle out, leaving an opening in the cloud or fog (Figure 29). Initially the ice crystals are too small to fall to the ground, but as the Bergeron process proceeds and they grow at the expense of the

FIGURE 29 Effects produced by seeding a cloud deck with dry ice. Within one hour a hole developed over the seeded area. (Photo courtesy of E. J. Tarbuck)

remaining water droplets, and as turbulent air disperses them, they can grow large enough to produce a snow shower. The snowfall is light, and visibility almost always improves. Often a large hole is opened in the stratus clouds or super-cooled fog.

The U.S. Air Force has practiced this technology for many years at airbases, and commercial airlines have used this method at selected foggy airports in the western United States. The possibility of opening large holes in winter clouds to increase the solar radiation reaching the ground in northerly locations has been discussed, but little experimentation has followed.

Unfortunately, most fog does not consist of supercooled water droplets. The more common "warm fogs" are more expensive to combat because seeding will not diminish them. Successful attempts at dispersing warm fogs have involved mixing drier, warmer air from above into the fog, or heating the air. When the layer of fog is very shallow, helicopters have been used. By flying just above the fog, the helicopter creates a strong downdraft that forces drier air toward the surface, where it mixes with the saturated foggy air.

At some airports where warm fogs are common, it has become more usual to heat the air and thus evaporate the fog. A sophisticated thermal fog-dissipation system, called Turboclair, was installed in 1970 at Orly Airport in Paris. It uses eight jet engines in underground chambers along the upwind edge of the runway. Although expensive to install, the system is capable of improving visibility for about 900 meters along the approach and landing zones.

Hail Suppression

Each year hail storms inflict an average of $500 million in property damage and crop loss in the United States alone (Figure 30). Occasionally, a single severe hailstorm can produce damages that exceed that amount. Examples include large hailstorms that occurred in Germany, 1984, Canada, 1991 and Australia, 1999. As a result, some of history's more interesting efforts at weather modification have focused on hail suppression.

Farmers who are desperate to find ways to save their crops have long believed that strong noises—explosions, cannon shots, or ringing church bells—can help reduce the amount of hail that is produced during a thunderstorm. In Europe it was common practice for village priests to ring church bells to shield nearby farms from hail. Although this practice was banned in 1780 due to the number of bell ringers killed by lightning, it is still employed in a few locations in Italy.

In 1880, a new hypothesis of hail formation sparked renewed interest in hail suppression. This untested proposal suggested that hailstones form in cold moist clouds during calm conditions. (We now know that large hailstones form in clouds with strong vertical air currents.) In this environment the pointed ends of tiny ice needles were thought to collect around a central embryo to form a spherical ice pellet. Once a layer was complete, another layer of ice crystals was added,

FIGURE 30   Hail damage to a soybean field north of Sioux Falls, South Dakota. (AP/Wide World Photos)

which explains the layered structure of hailstones. It was also believed that the migration of the tiny crystals toward the embryo would not take place if there was chaos in the environment.

This incorrect hypothesis of hail formation led to the development of the first "anti-hail cannons" in the 1890s. These hail cannons were vertical muzzle-loading mortars that resembled huge megaphones. The one shown in Figure 31 weighed 9000 kilograms (10 tons), was 9 meters (30 feet) tall, and pivoted in all directions. When fired, the cannons produced a loud whistling noise and a large smoke ring that rose to a height of about 300 meters. The noise from the cannons was thought to disrupt the development of large hailstones.

During a two-year test of hail cannons near the town of Windisch-Feistritz, Austria, no hail was observed. At the same time, nearby provinces suffered severe hail damage. From this unscientific study it was concluded that hail cannons were effective. Use of these devices spread to other areas in Europe where crops of great value frequently experienced hail losses. Soon much of Europe acquired "cannon fever," and by 1899 over 2000 cannons were in use in Italy alone. However, the anti-hail cannons proved to be ineffective, and the practice was largely abandoned in the early twentieth century.

FIGURE 31 Around 1900, cannons like this fired smoke particles into thunderstorms to prevent the formation of hail. However, hail shooting proved to be ineffective, and the practice was abandoned after a decade. (Photo courtesy of J. Loreena Ivens, Illinois State Water Survey)

With the disappearance of anti-hail cannons, came the introduction of anti-hail rockets, which used dynamite to prevent the formation of hail. Because these rockets exploded several thousand feet above the ground they soon came into conflict with civil aviation regulations. These restrictions caused farmers to look for other alternatives. Interestingly, in 1972 a French company began producing a modern version of the anti-hail cannon, and today several small companies still manufacture these devices. In the United States they can be found in scattered sites in Colorado, Texas, and California. A Japanese auto manufacturer has installed anti-hail cannons to protect new cars at a plant located in Mississippi.

Modern attempts at hail suppression have employed various methods of cloud seeding using silver iodide crystals to disrupt the growth of hailstones. The process requires seeding, or dispersing, millions of silver iodide crystals into developing storm clouds. The tiny crystals, which act as freezing nuclei, cause a large number of the cloud's supercooled water droplets to crystallize. Thus, seeding produces millions of tiny ice crystals which all compete for the available supercooled water droplets. The limited supply of water inhibits the ice crystals from growing into hailstones large enough to be destructive.

In an effort to verify the effectiveness of cloud seeding, the U.S. government established the National Hail Research Experiment in northeastern Colorado. This experiment included several randomized cloud seeding experiments. An analysis of the data collected after three years revealed no statistically significant difference in the occurrence of hail between the seeded and non-seeded clouds, so the planned five-year experiment was abandoned. Nevertheless, cloud seeding is still employed today in many locations, including Colorado.

Frost Prevention

Frost, the fruit grower's plight, occurs when the air temperature falls to 0°C (32°F) or below. Thus, frost conditions are dependent on temperature and need not be accompanied by deposits of ice crystals (called *white frost*), which only form if the air becomes saturated.

A frost hazard is produced by two conditions: when a cold air mass moves into a region or when sufficient radiation cooling occurs on a clear night. Frost associated with an invasion of cold air is characterized by low daytime temperatures and long periods of freezing conditions that inflict widespread crop damage. By contrast, frost induced by radiation cooling is strictly a nighttime phenomenon that tends to be confined to low-lying areas. Obviously, the latter phenomenon is much easier to combat.

Several methods of frost prevention are being used with varying success. They either conserve heat (reduce the heat lost at night) or add heat to warm the lowermost layer of air.

Heat-conservation methods include covering plants with insulating material, such as paper or cloth, or generating particles that, when suspended in air, reduce the rate of radiation cooling. *Smudge fires,* which produce dense black smoke, have been used to fill the air with carbon particles. Generally, this method has proved unsatisfactory. In addition to polluting the air, the carbon particles impede daytime warming by reducing the solar radiation that can reach the surface.

Warming methods employ water sprinklers, air-mixing techniques, and/or orchard heaters. Sprinklers (Figure 32a) add heat in two ways: first, from the warmth of the water and, more important, from the latent heat of fusion released when the water freezes. As long as an ice-water mixture remains on the plants, the latent heat released will keep the temperature from dropping below 0°C (32°F).

Air mixing works best when the air temperature 15 meters (50 feet) above the ground is at least 5°C (9°F) warmer than the surface temperature. By using a wind machine, the warmer air aloft is mixed with the colder surface air (Figure 32b).

Orchard heaters probably produce the most successful results (Figure 33). However, because as many as 30 to 40 heaters per acre are required, fuel cost can be significant.

(a)

(b)

FIGURE 32   Two common frost-prevention methods. (a) Sprinklers distribute water, which releases latent heat as it freezes on citrus. (b) Wind machines mix warmer air aloft with cooler surface air. (Photos by (a) Bruce Borich/Silver Image Photo Agency, Inc. and (b) na3/ZUMAPress/Newscom)

FIGURE 33   Orchard heaters used to prevent frost damage to pear trees, Hood River, Oregon. (Photo by Bruce Hands/The Image Works)

Understanding the Role of Clouds in the Climate System

Views of Earth from space show that clouds are abundant. Covering up to 75 percent of our planet at any given time, clouds play a prominent role in determining how much sunlight reaches Earth's surface and how much is reflected back to space. Furthermore, the amount and type of cloud cover strongly influences the amount of heat that escapes the surface in the form of longwave radiation. In short, clouds play a central role in Earth's climate system.

Recently a new tool has become available that will help researchers better understand and predict climate change. The false-color image shown in Figure 34 shows a one-month composite of cloud optical thickness measured by Moderate-resolution Imaging Spectroradiometer (MODIS). Optical thickness is a measure of how much solar radiation is able to penetrate the atmosphere. Areas shown in red and yellow indicate very cloudy skies, whereas areas that are green and light blue show moderately cloudy skies. Regions with little or no cloud cover appear dark blue. MODIS is one of five sensors aboard NASA's *Terra* satellite. In addition to determining cloud thickness, it can determine whether a cloud is composed of ice or liquid water (or both), and it can estimate the size of cloud particles. This instrument is one more tool that will help scientists better understand the complex workings of Earth's climate system.

FIGURE 34 This false-color image shows a one-month composite of cloud optical thickness measured for April 2001. Optical thickness is a measure of how much solar radiation penetrates the atmosphere. (Data from NASA)

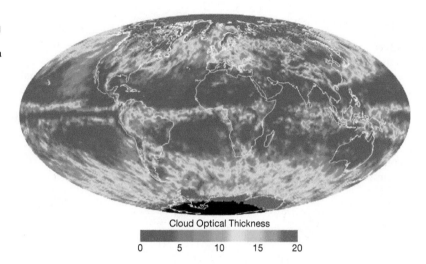

Cloud Optical Thickness

0   5   10   15   20

Chapter Summary

- *Condensation* occurs when water vapor changes to a liquid. For condensation to take place, the air must be saturated and there must be a surface on which the vapor can condense. In the air above the ground, tiny particles known as *cloud condensation nuclei* serve as the surfaces on which water vapor condenses.

- *Clouds,* visible aggregates of minute droplets of water or tiny crystals of ice, are one form of condensation. Clouds are classified on the basis of two criteria: form and height. The three basic cloud forms are *cirrus* (high, white, and thin), *cumulus* (globular, individual cloud masses), and *stratus* (sheets or layers). Cloud heights can be either *high,* with bases above 6000 meters (20,000 feet); *middle,* from 2000 to 6000 meters; or *low,* below 2000 meters (6500 feet). Based on the two criteria, 10 basic cloud types, including *cirrostratus, altocumulus,* and *stratocumulus,* are recognized.

- *Fog,* generally considered an atmospheric hazard, is a cloud with its base at or very near the ground. Fogs formed by cooling include *radiation fog* (from radiation cooling of the ground and adjacent air), *advection fog* (when warm and moist air flows over a cold surface), and *upslope fog* (created when air moves up a slope and cools adiabatically). Those formed by the addition of water vapor are *steam fog* (when water vapor evaporates from a warm water body and condenses in cool air above) and *frontal fog* (when warm air that is lifted over colder air generates precipitation that evaporates as it descends and saturates the air near the surface).

- *Dew* is the condensation of water vapor on objects that have radiated sufficient heat to lower their temperature below the dew point of the surrounding air. *White frost (hoar frost)* forms when the dew point of the air is below freezing.

- For precipitation to form, millions of cloud droplets must somehow coalesce into drops large enough to sustain themselves during their descent. The two mechanisms that have been proposed to explain this phenomenon are:

the *Bergeron process,* which produces precipitation from cold clouds primarily in the middle latitudes, and the warm-cloud process most associated with the tropics called the *collision–coalescence process.*

- The two most common and familiar forms of precipitation are *rain* (drops of water that fall from a cloud and have a diameter of at least 0.5 millimeter) and *snow* (precipitation in the form of ice crystals or, more often, aggregates of ice crystals). Other forms include *sleet* (falling small particles of ice that are clear to translucent), *glaze* (formed when supercooled raindrops turn to ice on colliding with solid objects), *hail* (hard, rounded pellets or irregular lumps of ice produced in large cumulonimbus clouds), and *rime* (a deposit of ice crystals formed by the freezing of supercooled fog or cloud droplets on objects whose surface temperature is below freezing).

- Rain, the most common form of precipitation, is probably the easiest to measure. The most common instruments used to measure rain are the *standard rain gauge,* which is read directly, and the *tipping bucket gauge* and *weighing gauge,* both of which record the amount and intensity of rain. The two most common measurements of snow are depth and water equivalent. Although the quantity of water in a given volume of snow is not constant, a general ratio of 10 units of snow to 1 unit of water is often used when exact information is not available.

- *Intentional weather modification* is deliberate human intervention to influence atmospheric processes that constitute the weather. Weather modification falls into three categories: (1) the use of energy to forcefully alter the weather, (2) modifying land and water surfaces to change their natural interaction with the lower atmosphere, and (3) triggering, intensifying, or redirecting atmospheric processes. The focus of intentional weather modification using modern weather technology is on *cloud seeding, fog and cloud dispersal, hail suppression,* and *frost prevention.*

Vocabulary Review

advection fog	cumulus	hydrophobic nuclei	snow
Bergeron process	dew	hygroscopic nuclei	standard rain gauge
cirrus	fog	intentional weather	steam fog
cloud condensation nuclei	freezing nuclei	modification	stratus
clouds	freezing rain	low clouds	supercooled
cloud seeding	frontal or precipitation fog	middle clouds	tipping-bucket gauge
clouds of vertical	frost	radiation fog	trace of precipitation
development	glaze	rain	upslope fog
collision–coalescence	hail	rime	weighing gauge
process	high clouds	sleet	white frost

Review Questions

1. Clouds are classified on the basis of two criteria. Name them.

2. Why are high clouds always thin in comparison to low and middle clouds?

3. Which cloud types are associated with the following characteristics: thunder, halos, precipitation, hail, mackerel sky, lightning, and mares' tails?

4. What do layered clouds indicate about the stability of the air? What do clouds of vertical development indicate about the stability of the air?

5. What is the importance of condensation nuclei?

6. Distinguish between clouds and fog.

7. List five types of fog and discuss how they form.

8. What actually happens when a radiation fog "lifts"?

9. Identify the fogs described in the following situations.
   a. You have stayed the night in a motel and decide to take an early morning swim. As you approach the heated swimming pool, you notice a fog over the water.
   b. You are located in the western Great Plains, and the winds are from the east and fog is extensive.
   c. You are driving through hilly terrain during the early morning hours and experience fog in the valleys but clearing on the hills.

10. Why is there a relatively high frequency of dense fog along the Pacific Coast?

11. Describe the steps in the formation of precipitation according to the Bergeron process. Be sure to include (a) the importance of supercooled cloud droplets, (b) the role of freezing nuclei, and (c) the difference in saturation vapor pressure between liquid water and ice.

12. How does the collision–coalescence process differ from the Bergeron process?

13. If snow is falling from a cloud, which process produced it? Explain.

14. Describe sleet and glaze and the circumstances under which they form. Why does glaze result on some occasions and sleet on others?

15. How does hail form? What factors govern the ultimate size of hailstones?

16. Although an open container can serve as a rain gauge, what advantages does a standard rain gauge provide?

17. How do recording rain gauges work? Do they have advantages over a standard rain gauge?

18. Describe some of the factors that could lead to an inaccurate measurement of rain or snow.

19. Why are silver iodide crystals used to seed supercooled clouds?

20. If cloud seeding is to have a chance of success, certain atmospheric conditions must exist. Name them.

21. How do frost and white frost differ?

22. Describe how smudge fires, sprinkling, and air mixing are used in frost prevention.

23. List three factors that contribute to greater precipitation in and downwind of cities.

Problems

1. Suppose that the air temperature is 20°C (68°F) and the relative humidity is 50 percent at 6:00 PM, and that during the evening the air temperature drops but its water vapor content does not change. If the air temperature drops 1°C (1.8°F) every two hours, will fog occur by sunrise (6:00 AM) the next morning? Explain your answer.

2. By using the same conditions as in Problem 1, will fog occur if the air temperature drops 1 degree every hour? If so, when will it first appear? What name is given to fog of this type that forms because of surface cooling during the night?

3. Assuming the air is still, how long would it take a large raindrop (5 mm) to reach the ground if it fell from a cloud base at 3000 meters? (See Table 3.) How long would a typical raindrop (2 mm) take if it fell from the same cloud? How about a drizzle drop (0.5 mm)?

4. Assuming the air is still, how long would it take for a typical cloud droplet (0.02 mm) to reach the ground if it fell from a cloud base at 1000 meters? (See Table 3) It is very unlikely that a cloud droplet would ever reach the ground, even if the air were perfectly still. Can you explain why?

5. What is the volume of a small raindrop that is 1000 μm diameter (1 mm diameter)? (*Hint:* See Box 2.)

6. A large raindrop 5000 μm (5 mm) in diameter is 100 times the diameter of a large cloud droplet (50 μm in diameter). How many times greater is the volume of a large raindrop than a cloud droplet? (*Hint:* See Box 2.)

7. What is the area of the "bottom" of a falling drop of 1 mm diameter?

8. How many times greater is the "bottom" area of a falling 5-mm drop?

Atmospheric Science Online

The Atmosphere 11e website uses the resources and flexibility of the Internet to aid in your study of the topics in this chapter. Written and developed by meteorology instructors, this site will help improve your understanding of meteorology. Visit **www.mygeoscience.com** in order to:

- **Review** key chapter concepts

- **Read** with links to the eBook and to chapter-specific web resources
- **Visualize** and comprehend challenging topics using learning activities in *GEODe: Atmosphere*
- **Test yourself** with online quizzes

GEODe: Atmosphere

GEODe: Atmosphere makes studying more effective by reinforcing key concepts using animation, video, narration, interactive exercises, and practice quizzes. Available at **www.mygeoscience.com**.

Cumulonimbus towers extend upward to 12 kilometers (7 miles) where their tops spread out in the shape of an anvil. These huge clouds produce heavy precipitation with accompanying lightning and thunder and occasionally hail, or even a tornado.

High in these towers the Bergeron process generates snowflakes that melt as they pass below the freezing level.

Air Pressure and Winds

From Chapter 6 of *The Atmosphere: An Introduction to Meteorology*, Eleventh Edition, Frederick K. Lutgens, Edward J. Tarbuck, Dennis Tasa. Copyright © 2010 by Pearson Education, Inc. Published by Pearson Prentice Hall. All rights reserved.

Sailboats racing in the Rolex Cup Regatta. (Photo by Neil Rabinowitz/ CORBIS)

Of the various elements of weather and climate, changes in air pressure are the least noticeable. In listening to a weather report, generally we are interested in moisture conditions (humidity and precipitation), temperature, and perhaps wind. It is the rare person, however, who wonders about air pressure. Although the hour-to-hour and day-to-day variations in air pressure are not perceptible to human beings, they are very important in producing changes in our weather. For example, it is variations in air pressure from place to place that generate winds that in turn can bring changes in temperature and humidity (Figure 1). Air pressure is one of the basic weather elements and a significant factor in weather forecasting. As we shall see, air pressure is closely tied to the other elements of weather (temperature, moisture, and wind) in a cause-and-effect relationship.

Understanding Air Pressure

Air pressure is simply the pressure exerted by the weight of air above. Average air pressure at sea level is about 1 kilogram per square centimeter, or 14.7 pounds per square inch. This is roughly the same pressure that is produced by a column of water 10 meters (33 feet) in height. With some simple arithmetic you can calculate that the air pressure exerted on the top of a small (50 centimeter by 100 centimeter) school desk exceeds 5000 kilograms (11,000 pounds), or about the weight of a 50 passenger school bus. Why doesn't the desk collapse under the weight of the ocean of air above? Simply, air pressure is exerted in all directions—down, up, and sideways. Thus, the air pressure pushing down on the desk exactly balances the air pressure pushing up on the desk.

You might be able to visualize this phenomenon better if you imagine a tall aquarium that has the same dimensions as the desktop. When this aquarium is filled to a height of 10 meters (33 feet), the water pressure at the bottom equals 1 atmosphere (14.7 pounds per square inch). Now imagine what will happen if this aquarium is placed on top of our student desk so that all the force is directed downward. Compare this to what results when the desk is placed inside the aquarium and allowed to sink to the bottom. In the latter situation the desk survives because the water pressure is exerted in all directions, not just downward, as in our earlier example. The desk, like your body, is "built" to withstand the pressure of 1 atmosphere. It is important to note that although we do not generally notice the pressure exerted by the ocean of air around us, except when ascending or descending in an elevator or airplane, it is nonetheless substantial. The pressurized suits used by astronauts on space walks are designed to duplicate the atmospheric pressure experienced at Earth's surface. Without these protective suits to keep body fluids from boiling away, astronauts would perish in minutes.

The concept of air pressure can be better understood if we examine the behavior of gases. Gas molecules, unlike those of the liquid and solid phases, are not "bound" to one another but are freely moving about, filling all space available to them. When two gas molecules collide, which happens frequently under normal atmospheric conditions, they bounce off each other like very elastic balls. If a gas is confined to a container, this motion is restricted by its sides, much like the walls of a

FIGURE 1 Gale force winds created waves that battered the coast at Blackpool, UK in February 2002. (Photo by John Giles/NewsCom)

handball court redirect the motion of the handball. The continuous bombardment of gas molecules against the sides of the container exerts an outward push that we call air pressure. Although the atmosphere is without walls, it is confined from below by Earth's surface and effectively from above because the force of gravity prevents its escape. Here we define *air pressure* as the force exerted against a surface by the continuous collision of gas molecules.

Measuring Air Pressure

Newton –
Measurement of
atmospheric
Pressure.

GEODe
THE ATMOSPHERE

Air Pressure and Winds
▸ Measuring Air Pressure

To measure atmospheric pressure, meteorologists use a unit of force from the science of physics called the **newton**.* At sea level the standard atmosphere exerts a force of 101,325 newtons per square meter. To simplify this large number, the U.S. National Weather Service adopted the **millibar** (mb), which equals 100 newtons per square meter. Thus, standard sea-level pressure is stated as 1013.25 millibars (Figure 2)**.

1 millibar = 100 Newtons

*A newton is the force needed to accelerate a 1 kilogram mass 1 meter per second squared.

**The standard unit of pressure in the SI system is the pascal, which is the name given to a newton per square meter (N/m²). In this notation a standard atmosphere has a value of 101,325 pascals, or 101.325 kilopascals. If the National Weather Service officially converts to the metric system, it will probably adopt this unit.

The millibar has been the unit of measure on all U.S. weather maps since January 1940.

Although millibars are used almost exclusively by meteorologists, you might be better acquainted with the expression "inches of mercury," which is used by the media to describe atmospheric pressure. This expression dates from 1643 when Torricelli, a student of the famous Italian scientist Galileo, invented the **mercury barometer.** Torricelli correctly described the atmosphere as a vast ocean of air that exerts pressure on us and all things about us. To measure this force, he closed one end of a glass tube and filled it with mercury. He then inverted the tube into a dish of mercury (Figure 3). Torricelli found that the mercury flowed out of the tube until the weight of the mercury column was balanced by the pressure exerted on the surface of the mercury by the air above. In other words, the weight of the mercury in the column equaled the weight of a similar diameter column of air that extended from the ground to the top of the atmosphere.

Torricelli noted that when air pressure increased, the mercury in the tube rose; conversely, when air pressure decreased, so did the height of the column of mercury. The length of the column of mercury, therefore, became the measure of the air pressure, or "inches of mercury." With some refinements the mercury barometer invented by Torricelli is still the standard pressure-measuring instrument used today. Standard atmospheric pressure at sea level equals 29.92 inches (760 millimeters) of mercury. In the United States the National Weather Service converts millibar values to inches of mercury for public and aviation use.

The need for a smaller and more portable instrument for measuring air pressure led to the development of the **aneroid barometer** (*aneroid* means without liquid). Instead of having a mercury column held up by air pressure, the aneroid barometer uses a partially evacuated metal chamber (Figure 4). The chamber, being very sensitive to variations in air pressure, changes shape, compressing as the pressure increases and expanding as the pressure decreases. A series of levers transmits the movements of the chamber to a pointer on a dial that is calibrated to read in inches of mercury and/or millibars.

As shown in Figure 4, the face of an aneroid barometer intended for home use is inscribed with words like *fair, change, rain,* and *stormy.* Notice that "fair weather" corresponds with high-pressure readings, whereas "rain" is associated with low pressures. Although barometric readings may indicate the present weather, this is not always the case. The dial may point to "fair" on a rainy day, or you may be experiencing "fair" weather when the dial indicates

FIGURE 2 A comparison of atmospheric pressure in inches of mercury and millibars.

Inches of Hg	Millibars	
32.48	1100	
32.19	1090	
31.89	1080	← Highest recorded sea level pressure: 1084 mb (32.01 in.) Agata, Siberia (December, 1968)
31.60	1070	
31.30	1060	← Highest recorded sea level pressure in United States: 1064 mb (31.42 in.) Miles City, Montana (December, 1983)
31.00	1050	
30.71	1040	← Strong high pressure system (anticyclone)
30.42	1030	
30.12	1020	
29.82	1010	← Average sea level pressure: 1013.25 mb (29.92 in.)
29.53	1000	
29.24	990	
28.94	980	← Strong low pressure system (cyclone)
28.64	970	
28.35	960	
28.05	950	
27.76	940	
27.46	930	
27.17	920	
26.87	910	
26.58	900	← Hurricane Katrina (August, 2005): 902 mb (26.71 in.)
26.28	890	Hurricane Wilma (October, 2005): 882 mb (26.12 in.)
25.99	880	← Lowest pressure recorded for an Atlantic hurricane
25.69	870	← Lowest recorded sea level pressure: 870 mb (25.70 in.) Typhoon Tip (October, 1979)
25.40	860	
25.10	850	

particular barometer readings or trends do not always correspond to specific types of weather.

One advantage of the aneroid barometer is that it can easily be connected to a recording mechanism. The resulting instrument is a **barograph,** which provides a continuous record of pressure changes with the passage of time (Figure 5). Another important adaptation of the aneroid barometer is its use to indicate altitude for aircraft, mountain climbers, and mapmakers (Box 1).

As we shall see later, meteorologists are most concerned with pressure differences that occur horizontally across the globe. Thus, they obtain pressure readings from a number of stations. To compare pressure readings from various weather stations, compensation must be made for the *elevation* of each station. This is done by converting all pressure measurements to sea-level equivalents (Figure 6). Doing so requires meteorologists to determine the pressure that would be exerted by an imaginary column of air equal in height to the elevation of the recording station and adding it to the station's pressure reading. Because temperature greatly affects the density, and hence the weight of this imaginary column, temperature also must be considered in the calculations. Thus, the corrected

FIGURE 3 Simple mercury barometer. The weight of the column of mercury is balanced by the pressure exerted on the dish of mercury by the air above. If the pressure decreases, the column of mercury falls; if the pressure increases, the column rises.

"rainy." If you want to "predict" the weather in a local area, the change in air pressure over the past few hours is more important than the current pressure reading. Falling pressure is often associated with increasing cloudiness and the possibility of precipitation, whereas rising air pressure generally indicates clearing conditions. It is useful to remember, however, that

FIGURE 4 Aneroid barometer. The aneroid barometer has a partially evacuated chamber that changes shape, compressing as atmospheric pressure increases and expanding as pressure decreases.

Students Sometimes Ask . . .

Why is mercury used in a barometer? I thought it was poisonous.

You are correct—mercury poisoning can be quite serious. However, the mercury in a barometer is held in a reservoir where the chance of spillage is minimal. A barometer could be constructed using any number of different liquids, including water. The problem with a water-filled barometer is size. Because water is 13.6 times less dense than mercury, the height of a water column at standard sea-level pressure would be 13.6 times taller than that of a mercurial barometer. Consequently, a water-filled barometer would need to be nearly 34 feet tall.

FIGURE 5 An aneroid barograph makes a continuous record of pressure changes. (Photo courtesy of Qualimetrics, Inc., Sacramento, California.)

FIGURE 6 To compare atmospheric pressures, meteorologists first convert all pressure measurements to sea-level values. This is done by adding the pressure that would be exerted by an imaginary column of air (shown in red) to the station's pressure reading.

reading would give the pressure, at that time, as if it were taken at sea level under the same conditions.

A comparison of pressure records taken over the globe reveals that horizontal variations in pressure are rather small. Extreme pressure readings are rarely greater than 30 millibars (1 inch of mercury) above average sea-level pressure or 60 millibars (2 inches) below average sea-level pressure. Occasionally, the barometric pressure measured in severe storms, such as hurricanes, is even lower (see Figure 2).

Pressure Changes with Altitude

Let us consider the decrease in pressure with altitude. The relationship between air pressure and density largely explains this observed decrease. To illustrate, imagine a cylinder fitted with a movable piston, as shown in Figure 7. If the temperature is kept constant and weights are added to the piston, the downward force exerted by gravity will squeeze (compress) the gas molecules together. The result is to increase the density of the gas and hence the number of gas molecules (per unit area) bombarding the cylinder wall as well as the bottom of the piston. Therefore, an increase in density results in an increase in pressure.

The piston will continue to compress the air molecules until the downward force is balanced by the ever increasing gas pressure. If more weight is added to the piston, the air will compress further until the pressure of the gas once again balances the new weight of the piston.

Similarly, *the pressure at any given altitude in the atmosphere is equal to the weight of the air directly above that point.* Recall that at sea level a column of air weighs 14.7 pounds per square inch and therefore exerts that amount of pressure. As we ascend through the atmosphere, we find that the air becomes less dense because of the lesser amount (weight) of air above. As would be expected, there is a corresponding *decrease in pressure with an increase in altitude.*

The fact that density decreases with altitude is why the term "thin air" is normally associated with mountainous regions. Except for the Sherpas (indigenous peoples of Nepal), most of the climbers who have reached the summit of Mount Everest (elevation 8852 meters or 29,029 feet) and survived used supplementary oxygen for the final leg of the journey. Even with the aid of supplementary oxygen, most of these climbers experienced periods of disorientation because of an inadequate supply of oxygen to their brains. The decrease in pressure with altitude also affects the boiling temperature of water, which at sea level is 100°C (212°F). For example, in Denver, Colorado—the Mile High City—water boils at 95°C (203°F). Although water comes to a boil faster in Denver than in San Diego because of its lower boiling temperature, it takes longer to cook spaghetti in Denver.

The rate at which pressure decreases with altitude is not a constant. The rate of decrease is much greater near Earth's surface, where pressure is high, than aloft, where air pressure is low. The "normal" decrease in pressure experienced with increased altitude is provided by the standard atmosphere in Table 1. The **standard atmosphere** depicts the idealized vertical distribution of atmospheric pressure (as well as temperature and density), which is taken to represent aver-

FIGURE 7 Schematic drawing showing the relationship between air pressure and density. Cylinder (a) of air fitted with movable piston. As more weight is added (b and c) to the piston, the increased number of molecules per unit volume (density) causes an increase in the pressure exerted on the walls of the cylinder and the gauge.

BOX 1 ▶ AIR PRESSURE AND AVIATION

The cockpit of nearly every aircraft contains a *pressure altimeter*, an instrument that allows a pilot to determine the altitude of a plane. A pressure altimeter is essentially an aneroid barometer and, as such, responds to changes in air pressure. Recall that air pressure decreases with an increase in altitude and that the pressure distribution with height is well established. To make an altimeter, an aneroid is simply marked in meters instead of millibars. For example, we see in Table 1 that a pressure of 795 millibars "normally" occurs at a height of 2000 meters. Therefore, if such a pressure were experienced, the altimeter would indicate an altitude of 2000 meters.

Because of temperature variations and moving pressure systems, actual conditions are usually different from those represented as standard. Consequently, the altitude of an aircraft is seldom exactly that shown by its altimeter. When the barometric pressure aloft is lower than specified by the standard atmosphere, the plane will be flying lower than the height indicated by the altimeter. This could be especially dangerous if the pilot is flying a small plane through mountainous terrain with poor visibility. To correct for these situations, pilots make altimeter corrections before takeoffs and landings, and in some cases corrections are made en route.

Above 5.5 kilometers (18,000 feet), where commercial jets fly and pressure changes are more gradual, corrections cannot be made as precisely as at lower levels. Consequently, such aircraft have their altimeters set at the standard atmosphere and fly paths of constant pressure instead of constant altitude (Figure A). Stated another way, when an aircraft flies at a constant altimeter setting, a pressure variation will result in a change in the plane's elevation. When pressure increases along a flight path, the plane will climb, and when pressure decreases, the plane will descend. There is little risk of midair collisions because all high-flying aircraft adjust their altitude in a similar manner.

Large commercial aircraft also use radio altimeters to measure heights above the terrain. The time required for a radio signal to reach the surface and return is used to accurately determine the height of the plane above the ground. This system is not without its drawbacks. Because a radio altimeter provides the elevation above the ground rather than above sea level, a knowledge of the underlying terrain is required.

FIGURE A   Aircraft above 5.5 kilometers (18,000 feet) generally fly paths of constant pressure instead of constant altitude.

Students Sometimes Ask . . .

Why do my ears sometimes feel pain when I fly?

When airplanes take off and land, some people experience pain in their ears because of a change in cabin pressure. (Although most commercial airplanes are designed to keep the cabin pressure relatively constant, small changes in pressure do occur.) Normally the air pressure in one's middle ear is the same as the pressure of the surrounding atmosphere because the Eustachian tube connects the ear to the throat. However, when an individual has a cold, his or her Eustachian tubes may become blocked, preventing the flow of air either into or out of the middle ear. The resulting pressure difference can cause mild discomfort or, less often, excruciating pain, which subsides when the ears "pop," equalizing the pressure.

age conditions in the real atmosphere. We see from Table 1 that atmospheric pressure is reduced by approximately one-half for each 5-kilometer increase in altitude. Therefore, at 5 kilometers the pressure is one-half its sea-level value; at 10 kilometers it is one-fourth; at 15 kilometers it is one-eighth; and so forth. Thus, at the altitude at which commercial jets fly (10 kilometers), the air exerts a pressure equal to only one-fourth that at sea level.

Horizontal Variations in Air Pressure

Although pressure changes with altitude are important, meteorologists are most interested in pressure differences that occur horizontally across the globe. To compare pressure readings from various weather stations, compensation must be made for the *elevation* of each station (see Figure 6). The ad-

TABLE 1	U.S. Standard Atmosphere	
Height (km)	Pressure (mb)	Temperature (°C)
50.0	0.798	−2
40.0	2.87	−22
35.0	5.75	−36
30.0	11.97	−46
25.0	25.49	−51
20.0	55.29	−56
18.0	75.65	−56
16.0	103.5	−56
14.0	141.7	−56
12.0	194.0	−56
10.0	265.0	−50
9.0	308.0	−43
8.0	356.5	−37
7.0	411.0	−30
6.0	472.2	−24
5.0	540.4	−17
4.0	616.6	−11
3.5	657.8	−8
3.0	701.2	−4
2.5	746.9	−1
2.0	795.0	2
1.5	845.6	5
1.0	898.8	9
0.5	954.6	12
0	1013.2	15

justed reading gives the pressure for each locale as if it were taken at sea level.*

A comparison of pressure records from around the globe reveals that pressure differences from place to place are relatively small. Extreme pressure readings are rarely greater than 30 millibars (1 inch of mercury) above average sea-level pressure or 60 millibars (2 inches) below average sea-level pressure. Occasionally, the barometric pressure measured in severe storms, such as hurricanes, is even lower (see Figure 2). As we shall discover shortly, these small differences in air pressure can be sufficient to generate violent winds.

Influence of Temperature and Water Vapor on Air Pressure

How do pressure differences arise? One of the easiest ways to envision this is to picture northern Canada in midwinter. Here the snow-covered surface is continually radiating heat to space, while receiving little incoming solar radiation. The frigid ground cools the air above so that daily lows of −34°C (−30°F) are common and extremes of −46°C (−50°F) can occur.

Recall that temperature is a measure of the average molecular motion (kinetic energy) of a substance. Therefore, cold

*The relationship among pressure, temperature, and density described in this section is stated in the *ideal gas law*.

Canadian air is composed of comparatively slow-moving gas molecules that are packed closely together. As the density of a column of air increases, so does the pressure it exerts on the surface (Figure 8). Thus, a mass of cold air moving into the Midwest from Canada is quite dense and will be labeled a **High**, for *high barometric pressure*, on a weather map.

In contrast, the air over the Gulf of Mexico in January is relatively warm. Because the gas molecules in warm air have abundant kinetic energy, they are more widely spaced (less dense). Warm air masses that produce *low barometric pressure* are labeled **Low** on a weather map.

It is important to remember, however, that factors other than temperature affect the amount of pressure a column of air will exert. For example, the amount of water vapor contained in a volume of air influences its density. Contrary to popular perception, water vapor *reduces* the density of air. The air may feel "heavy" on hot, humid days, but it is not. You can easily verify this fact for yourself by examining a periodic table of the elements and noting that the molecular weights of nitrogen (N_2) and oxygen (O_2) are greater than that of water vapor (H_2O). In a mass of air the molecules of these gases are intermixed, and each takes up roughly the same amount of space. As the water content of an air mass increases, lighter water vapor molecules displace heavier nitrogen and oxygen molecules. Therefore, humid air is lighter (less dense) than dry air. Nevertheless, even very humid air is only about 2 percent less dense than dry air at the same temperature.

From the preceding discussion we can conclude that a cold, dry air mass will produce higher surface pressures than a warm, humid air mass. Further, a warm, dry air mass will exhibit higher pressure than an equally warm, but humid, air

Cold (dense)   **Warm (less dense)**
Higher pressure   **Lower pressure**

FIGURE 8 A comparison of the density of a column of cold air with a column of warm air. All else being equal, cold, dense air exerts more pressure than warm, less dense air.

mass. Consequently, large air masses are responsible for some of the pressure variations observed at Earth's surface.

Airflow and Pressure

The movement of air can also cause variations in air pressure. For example, in situations where there is a net flow of air into a region, a phenomenon called **convergence,** the air piles up. Stated another way, as air converges horizontally, it must increase in height to allow for the decreased area it now occupies. This results in a "taller" and therefore heavier air column that exerts more pressure at the surface. By contrast, in regions where there is a net outflow of air, a situation referred to as **divergence,** the surface pressure drops.

As you might expect, atmospheric processes involve significantly more complex variables than have just been described. Sometimes divergence at the surface is accompanied by convergence higher in the atmosphere. In this situation, surface pressure will rise when convergence outpaces divergence, or fall when divergence exceeds convergence. We will return to this important mechanism for producing areas of high and low pressure later in this chapter.

In summary, cold, dry air masses are dense and associated with high pressure. In contrast, warm, humid air masses are less dense and tend to exhibit low pressure. Further, the pressure at the surface will increase when there is a net convergence in a region and decrease when there is a net divergence.

The importance of atmospheric pressure to Earth's weather cannot be overemphasized. Differences in air pressure create global winds that become organized into the systems that "bring us our weather."

Factors Affecting Wind

Air Pressure and Winds
▶ Factors Affecting Wind

We discussed the upward movement of air and its importance in cloud formation. As important as vertical motion is, far more air is involved in horizontal movement, the phenomenon we call **wind.** Although we know that air will move vertically if it is warmer and thus more buoyant than surrounding air, what causes air to move horizontally?

Simply stated, _wind is the result of horizontal differences in air pressure._ Air flows from areas of higher pressure to areas of lower pressure. You may have experienced this condition when opening a vacuum-packed can of coffee. The noise you hear is caused by air rushing from the area of higher pressure outside the can to the lower pressure inside. Wind is nature's attempt to balance inequalities in air pressure. Because unequal heating of Earth's surface continually generates these pressure differences, solar radiation is the ultimate energy source for most wind.

If Earth did not rotate and if there were no friction, air would flow directly from areas of higher pressure to areas of lower pressure. Because both factors exist, however, wind is controlled by a combination of forces, including:

1. the pressure-gradient force
2. the Coriolis force
3. friction

Pressure-Gradient Force

To get anything to accelerate (change its velocity) requires an unbalanced force in one direction. The force that generates winds results from horizontal pressure differences. When air is subjected to greater pressure on one side than on another, the imbalance produces a force that is directed from the region of higher pressure toward the area of lower pressure. Thus, pressure differences cause the wind to blow, and the greater these differences, the greater the wind speed.

Variations in air pressure over Earth's surface are determined from barometric readings taken at hundreds of weather stations. These pressure data are shown on surface weather maps by means of isobars. **Isobars** are lines connecting places of equal air pressure (_iso_ = equal, _bar_ = pressure), as shown in Figure 9. The _spacing_ of the isobars indicates the amount of pressure change occurring over a given distance and is expressed as the **pressure gradient.** The mathematical expression of the pressure-gradient force is provided in Box 2.

You might find it easier to visualize the concept of a pressure gradient if you think of it as being analogous to the slope of a hill. A steep pressure gradient, like a steep hill, causes greater acceleration of a parcel of air than does a weak pressure gradient (a gentle hill). Thus, the relationship between wind speed and the pressure gradient is straightforward. Closely spaced isobars indicate a steep pressure gradient and strong winds; widely spaced isobars indicate a weak pressure gradient and light winds. Figure 10 illustrates the relationship between the spacing of isobars and wind speed. Note also that the pressure-gradient force is always directed at _right angles_ to the isobars.

Pressure differences observed on the daily weather map result from complex factors. However, the underlying cause of these differences is simply _unequal heating of Earth's land–sea surface._

Horizontal Pressure Gradients and Wind   To illustrate how temperature differences can generate a horizontal pressure gradient and thereby create winds, let us look at a common example, the _sea breeze._ Figure 11a shows a vertical cross-section of a coastal location just before sunrise. At this time we are assuming that temperatures and pressures do not vary horizontally at any level. This assumption is shown in Figure 11a by the horizontal pressure surfaces that indicate the equal pressure at equal heights. Because there is no horizontal variation in pressure (zero horizontal pressure gradient), there is no wind.

After sunrise, however, the unequal rates at which land and water heat will initiate pressure differences and, therefore, airflow (Figure 11b). Surface temperatures over the ocean change only slightly on a daily basis. On the other

ff	Miles per hour
◎	Calm
—	1–2
⌐	3–8
⌐	9–14
⌐	15–20
⌐	21–25
⌐	26–31
⌐	32–37
⌐	38–43
⌐	44–49
⌐	50–54
⌐	55–60
⌐	61–66
⌐	67–71
⌐	72–77
⌐	78–83
⌐	84–89
⌐	119–123

FIGURE 9 Isobars are lines connecting places of equal sea-level pressure. They are used to show the distribution of pressure on daily weather maps. Isobars are seldom straight, but usually form broad curves. Concentric rings of isobars indicate cells of high and low pressure. The "wind flags" indicate the expected airflow surrounding pressure cells and are plotted as "flying" with the wind (that is, the wind blows toward the station circle). Notice on this map that the isobars are more closely spaced and the wind speed is faster around the low-pressure center than around the high.

FIGURE 10 Pressure-gradient force. Closely spaced isobars indicate a strong pressure gradient and high wind speeds, whereas widely spaced isobars indicate a weak pressure gradient and low wind speeds.

ff	Miles per hour
◎	Calm
—	1–2
⌐	3–8
⌐	9–14
⌐	15–20
⌐	21–25
⌐	26–31
⌐	32–37
⌐	38–43
⌐	44–49
⌐	50–54
⌐	55–60
⌐	61–66
⌐	67–71
⌐	72–77
⌐	78–83
⌐	84–89
⌐	119–123

(a) **Before sunrise**

(b) **Shortly after sunrise**

(c) **Sea breeze established**

FIGURE 11 Cross-sectional view illustrating the formation of a sea breeze. (a) Just before sunrise; (b) after sunrise; (c) sea breeze established.

An important relationship exists between pressure and temperature, as you saw in the preceding discussion. Temperature variations create pressure differences and hence wind. The greater these temperature differences, the stronger the horizontal pressure gradient and resultant wind. Daily temperature differences and the pressure gradients so generated are generally confined to a zone that is only a few kilometers thick. On a global scale, however, variations in the amount of solar radiation received due to variations in Sun angle with latitude generate the much larger pressure systems that in turn produce the planetary atmospheric circulation.

If the pressure-gradient force was the only force acting on the wind, air would flow directly from areas of higher pressures to areas of lower pressure and the lows would be quickly filled. Thus, the well-developed high and low pressure systems that dominate our daily weather maps could never sustain themselves. Instead, Earth's atmosphere would, at best, develop only very weak and short-lived pressure systems. Therefore, most locations would experience long periods of very still air that would occasionally be disrupted by gentle breezes.

Fortunately, for those of us who like more varied weather, this is not the case. Once the pressure-gradient force starts the air in motion, the Coriolis force, friction, and other forces come into play. Although these forces cannot generate wind (with the exception of gravity), they do *greatly modify airflow*. By doing so, these forces help sustain and even enhance the development of the Earth's pressure systems. We will consider some of these important *modifying* forces shortly.

Vertical Pressure Gradient As you learned earlier, airflow is from areas of higher pressure to areas of lower pressure. Further, you are aware that air pressure is highest near Earth's surface and gets progressively lower as you move upward through the atmosphere. Combining these two ideas, you might wonder why air does not rapidly accelerate upward and escape into space. In fact, it would do just that if it were not for the force of gravity, which acts in the opposite direction to the upward directed, *vertical pressure gradient*. The important balance that is usually maintained between these two opposing forces is called **hydrostatic equilibrium.**

In general, the atmosphere is in or near hydrostatic balance. On those occasions when the gravitational force slightly

hand, land surfaces and the air above can be substantially warmed during a single daylight period. As air over the land warms, it expands, causing a reduction in density. This in turn results in pressure surfaces that are bent upward, as shown in Figure 11b. Although this warming does not by itself produce a surface pressure change, a given pressure surface aloft does become elevated over the land compared to over the ocean. The resultant pressure gradient aloft causes the air aloft to move from the land toward the ocean.

The mass transfer of air seaward creates a surface high-pressure area over the ocean, where the air is collecting, and a surface low over the land. The surface circulation that develops from this redistribution of air aloft is from the sea toward the land (sea breeze), as shown in Figure 11c. Thus, a simple thermal circulation develops, with a seaward flow aloft and a landward flow at the surface. Note that *vertical* movement also is required to make the circulation complete. (We will consider the vertical pressure gradient next.)

BOX 2 ▶ PRESSURE-GRADIENT FORCE

Gregory J. Carbone*

The magnitude of the pressure-gradient force is a function of the pressure difference between two points and air density. It can be expressed as

$$F_{PG} = \frac{1}{d} \times \frac{\Delta_p}{\Delta_n}; \text{ where}$$

F_{PG} = pressure-gradient force per unit mass

d = density of air

p = pressure difference between two points

n = distance between two points

Let us consider an example where the pressure 5 kilometers above Little Rock, Arkansas, is 540 millibars, and at 5 kilometers above St. Louis, Missouri, it is 530 millibars. The distance between the two cities is 450 kilometers, and the air density at 5 kilometers is 0.75 kilogram per cubic meter. In order to use the pressure-gradient equation, we must use compatible units. We must first convert pressure from millibars to pascals, another measure of pressure that has units of (kilograms $\times$ meters^{-1} $\times$ second^2).

In our example, the pressure difference above the two cities is 10 millibars, or 1000 pascals (1000 kg/m·s^2) Thus, we have

$$F_{PG} = \frac{1}{0.75} \times \frac{1000}{450,000} = 0.0029 \frac{m}{s^2}$$

Newton's second law states that force equals mass times acceleration ($F = m \times a$). In our example, we have considered pressure-gradient force *per unit mass;* therefore, our result is an acceleration ($F/m = a$). Because of the small units shown, pressure-gradient *acceleration* is often expressed as centimeters per second squared. In this example, we have 0.296 cm/s^2.

*Professor Carbone is a faculty member in the Department of Geography at the University of South Carolina.

exceeds the vertical pressure-gradient force, slow downward airflow results. This occurs, for example, within a dense Arctic air mass, where cold air is subsiding and spreading out at the surface. Most large-scale downward (and upward) motions are slow, averaging a few centimeters per second (less than 1 mile per day). However, some smaller-scale vertical motions are much more rapid. For example, strong updrafts and downdrafts associated with severe thunderstorms can reach 100 kilometers (62 miles) per hour or more. Fortunately, these phenomena are sporadic and localized. Overall, the state of the atmosphere is in hydrostatic equilibrium, where the upward pressure-gradient force is balanced by the downward force of gravity.

In summary, the horizontal pressure gradient is the driving force of wind. It has both magnitude and direction. Its magnitude is determined from the spacing of isobars, and the direction of force is always from areas of higher pressure to areas of lower pressure and at right angles to the isobars. By contrast, the vertical pressure gradient is usually in, or near, balance with gravity. Thus, upward and downward flow in the atmosphere is comparatively slow (with the exception of localized updrafts and downdrafts).

Coriolis Force

The weather map in Figure 9 shows the typical air movements associated with surface high- and low-pressure systems. As expected, the air moves out of the regions of higher pressure and into the regions of lower pressure. However, the wind does not cross the isobars at right angles, as the pressure-gradient force directs. This deviation is the result of Earth's rotation and has been named the **Coriolis force** after the French scientist Gaspard Gustave Coriolis, who first expressed its magnitude quantitatively.

All free-moving objects, including wind, are deflected to the *right* of their path of motion in the Northern Hemisphere

and the *left* in the Southern Hemisphere. The reason for this deflection can be illustrated by imagining the path of a rocket launched from the North Pole toward a target on the equator (Figure 12). If the rocket took an hour to reach its target, Earth would have rotated 15° to the east during its flight. To someone standing on Earth, it would look as if the rocket veered off its path and hit Earth 15° west of its target. The true path of the rocket was straight and would appear so to someone out in space looking down at Earth. It was Earth turning under the rocket that gave it its apparent deflection. Note that the rocket was deflected to the right of its path of motion because of the counterclockwise rotation of the Northern Hemisphere. Clockwise rotation produces a similar deflection in the Southern Hemisphere, but to the left of the path of motion.

Although it is usually easy for people to visualize the Coriolis deflection when the motion is from north to south, as in our rocket example, it is not so easy to see how a west-to-east flow would be deflected. Figure 13 illustrates this situation using winds blowing eastward at four different latitudes (0°, 20°, 40°, and 60°). Notice that after a few hours the winds along the 20th, 40th, and 60th parallels appear to be veering off course. However, when viewed from space, it is apparent that these winds have maintained their original direction. It is the North American continent changing its orientation as Earth turns on its axis that produces the deflection we observe.

We can also see in Figure 13 that the amount of deflection is greater at 60° latitude than at 40° latitude, which is greater than at 20°. Furthermore, there is no deflection observed for the airflow along the equator. We conclude, therefore, that the magnitude of the deflecting force (Coriolis force) is dependent on latitude; it is strongest at the poles, and it weakens equatorward, where it eventually becomes nonexistent. We can also see that the amount of Coriolis deflection increases with wind speed. This results because faster winds

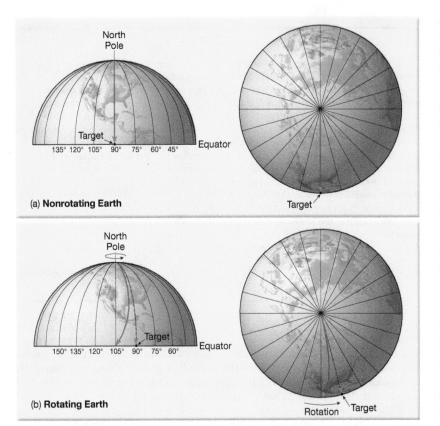

FIGURE 12 The Coriolis force illustrated using the one-hour flight of a rocket traveling from the North Pole to a location on the equator. (a) On a nonrotating Earth, the rocket would travel straight to its target. (b) However, Earth rotates 15° each hour. Thus, although the rocket travels in a straight line, when we plot the path of the rocket on Earth's surface, it follows a curved path that veers to the right of the target.

FIGURE 13 Coriolis deflection of winds blowing eastward at different latitudes. After a few hours the winds along the 20th, 40th, and 60th parallels appear to veer off course. This deflection (which does not occur at the equator) is caused by Earth's rotation, which changes the orientation of the surface over which the winds are moving.

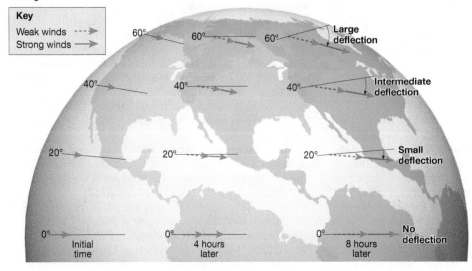

cover a greater distance than do slower winds in the same time period. A mathematical treatment of the Coriolis force is provided in Box 3.

It is of interest to point out that any "free-moving" object will experience a similar deflection. This fact was dramatically discovered by our navy in World War II. During target practice long-range guns on battleships continually missed their targets by as much as several hundred yards until ballistic corrections were made for the changing position of a seemingly stationary target. Over a short distance, however, the Coriolis force is relatively small. Nevertheless, in the middle latitudes this deflecting force is great enough to potentially affect the outcome of a baseball game. A ball hit a horizontal distance of 100 meters (330 feet) in 4 seconds down the right field line will be deflected 1.5 centimeters (more than 1/2 inch) to the right by the Coriolis force. This could be just enough to turn a potential home run into a foul ball!

In summary, on a rotating Earth the Coriolis force acts to change the direction of a moving body to the right in the Northern Hemisphere and to the left in the Southern Hemisphere. This deflecting force (1) is always directed at right angles to the direction of airflow; (2) affects only wind direction, not wind speed; (3) is affected by wind speed (the stronger the wind, the greater the deflecting force); and (4) is strongest at the poles and weakens equatorward, becoming nonexistent at the equator.

Friction

Earlier we stated that the pressure-gradient force is the primary driving force of the wind. As an unbalanced force, it causes air to accelerate from regions of higher pressure to regions of lower pressure. Thus, wind speeds should continually increase (accelerate) for as long as this imbalance exists. But we know from personal experience that winds do not become faster indefinitely. Some other force, or forces, must oppose the pressure-gradient force to moderate airflow.

BOX 3 ▶ CORIOLIS FORCE AS A FUNCTION OF WIND SPEED AND LATITUDE

Gregory J. Carbone*

Figure 13 shows how wind speed and latitude conspire to affect the Coriolis force. Consider a west wind at four different latitudes (0°, 20°, 40°, and 60°). After several hours Earth's rotation has changed the orientation of latitude and longitude of all locations except the equator such that the wind appears to be deflected to the right. The degree of deflection for a given wind speed increases with latitude because the orientation of latitude and longitude lines changes more at higher latitudes. The degree of deflection of a given latitude increases with wind speed because greater distances are covered in the period of time considered.

We can show mathematically the importance of latitude and wind speed on Coriolis force:

$$F_{CO} = 2v\,\Omega\,\sin\phi$$

where F_{CO} = Coriolis force *per unit mass of air*

v = wind speed

Ω = Earth's rate of rotation or angular velocity (which is 7.29×10^{-5} radians per second)

ϕ = latitude

[Note that $\sin\phi$ is a trigonometric function equal to zero for an angle of 0° (equator) and 1 when $\phi = 90°$ (poles).]

As an example, the Coriolis force per unit mass that must be considered for a 10-meter-per-second (m/s) wind at 40° is calculated as:

$$F_{CO} = 2\Omega\,\sin\phi v$$
$$F_{CO} = 2\Omega\,\sin 40 \times 10 \text{ m/s}$$
$$F_{CO} = 2(7.29 \times 10^{-5}\text{ s}^{-1})$$
$$0.64(10/\text{ms})$$
$$F_{CO} = 0.00094 \text{ meter per second squared}$$
$$= 0.094 \text{ cm s}^{-2}$$

The result (0.094 cm s^{-2}) is expressed as an acceleration because we are considering

force per unit mass and force = mass × acceleration.

Using this equation, one could calculate the Coriolis force for any latitude or wind speed. Consider Table A, which shows the Coriolis force per unit mass for three specific wind speeds at various latitudes. All values are expressed in centimeters per second squared (cm s^{-2}). Because pressure gradient and Coriolis force approximately balance under geostrophic conditions, we can see from our table that the pressure-gradient force (per unit mass) of 0.296 cm s^{-2} illustrated in Box 2 would produce relatively high winds.

———

*Professor Carbone is a faculty member in the Department of Geography at the University of South Carolina.

TABLE A	Coriolis Force for Three Wind Speeds at Various Latitudes				
Wind speed		**Latitude (ϕ)**			
		0°	20°	40°	60°
(m/s)	(kph)	Coriolis force (cm/s²)			
5	18	0	0.025	0.047	0.063
10	36	0	0.050	0.094	0.126
25	90	0	0.125	0.235	0.316

From our everyday experience we know that friction acts to slow a moving object. Although friction significantly influences airflow near Earth's surface, its effect is negligible above a height of a few kilometers (Figure 14). For this reason, we

will divide our discussion. First, we will examine the flow aloft, where the effect of friction is small. Then we will analyze surface winds, where friction significantly influences airflow.

Winds Aloft and Geostrophic Flow

This section will deal only with airflow above a few kilometers, where the effects of friction are small enough to disregard.

Aloft, the Coriolis force is responsible for balancing the pressure-gradient force and thereby directing airflow. Figure 15 shows how a balance is reached between these opposing forces. For illustration only, we assume a nonmoving parcel of air at the starting point in Figure 15. (Remember that air is rarely stationary in the atmosphere.) Because our parcel of air has no motion, the Coriolis force exerts no influence; only the pressure-gradient force can act at the starting point. Under the influence of the pressure-gradient force, which is always directed perpendicularly to the isobars, the parcel begins to accelerate directly toward the area of low pressure. As soon as the flow begins, the Coriolis force comes into play and causes a deflection to the right for winds in the Northern Hemisphere. As the parcel continues to accelerate, the Coriolis force intensifies (recall that the magnitude of the Coriolis force is

Students Sometimes Ask . . .

I've been told that water goes down a sink in one direction in the Northern Hemisphere and in the opposite direction in the Southern Hemisphere. Is that true?

No! The origin of this myth comes from applying a scientific principle to a situation where it does not fit. Recall that the Coriolis deflection causes cyclonic systems to rotate counterclockwise in the Northern Hemisphere and clockwise in the Southern Hemisphere. It was inevitable that someone would suggest (without checking) that a sink should drain in a similar manner. However, a cyclone is more than 1000 kilometers in diameter and may exist for several days. By contrast, a typical sink is less than a meter in diameter and drains in a matter of seconds. On this scale, the Coriolis force is minuscule. Therefore, the shape of the sink and how level it is has more to do with the direction of water flow than the Coriolis force.

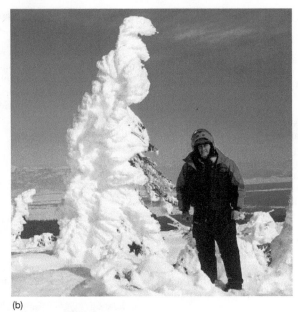

FIGURE 14 (a) Wind increases in strength with an increase in altitude because it is less affected by friction from objects near Earth's surface. (b) This snow-covered tree shows the effects of strong winds in a high mountain setting. (Photo by E. J. Tarbuck)

proportional to wind speed). Thus, the increased speed results in further deflection.

Eventually the wind turns so that it is flowing parallel to the isobars. When this occurs, the pressure-gradient force is balanced by the opposing Coriolis force, as shown in Figure 15. As long as these forces remain balanced, the resulting wind will continue to flow parallel to the isobars at a constant speed. Stated another way, the wind can be considered to be coasting (not accelerating or decelerating) along a pathway defined by the isobars.

FIGURE 15 The geostrophic wind. The only force acting on a stationary parcel of air is the pressure-gradient force. Once the air begins to accelerate, the Coriolis force deflects it to the right in the Northern Hemisphere. Greater wind speeds result in a stronger Coriolis force (deflection) until the flow is parallel to the isobars. At this point the pressure-gradient force and Coriolis force are in balance and the flow is called a *geostrophic wind*. It is important to note that in the "real" atmosphere, airflow is continually adjusting for variations in the pressure field. As a result, the adjustment to geostrophic equilibrium is much more irregular than shown.

Under these idealized conditions, when the Coriolis force is exactly equal and opposite to the pressure-gradient force, the airflow is said to be in *geostrophic balance*. The winds generated by this balance are called **geostrophic winds** (geostrophic means "turned by Earth"). Geostrophic winds flow in a straight path, parallel to the isobars, with velocities proportional to the pressure-gradient force. A steep pressure gradient creates strong winds, and a weak pressure gradient produces light winds.

It is important to note that the geostrophic wind is an idealized model that only approximates the actual behavior of airflow aloft. In the real atmosphere, winds are never purely geostrophic. Nonetheless, the geostrophic model offers a useful approximation of the actual winds aloft. By measuring the pressure field (orientation and spacing of isobars) that exists aloft, meteorologists can determine both wind direction and speed (Figure 16).

The idealized geostrophic flow predicts winds parallel to the isobars with speeds that depend on isobaric spacing. That is, the closer the isobars, the higher the wind speed. Of equal importance to meteorologists is that the same method can be used in reverse. In other words, the distribution of pressure aloft can be determined from airflow measurements. The interrelationship between pressure and wind greatly enhances the reliability of upper-air weather charts by providing checks and balances. In addition, it minimizes the number of direct observations required to describe adequately the conditions aloft, where accurate data are most expensive and difficult to obtain.

As we have seen, wind direction is directly linked to the prevailing pressure pattern. Therefore, if we know the wind direction, we can, in a crude sort of way, also establish the pressure distribution. This rather straightforward relationship between wind direction and pressure distribution was first formulated by the Dutch meteorologist Buys Ballot in 1857. Essentially, **Buys Ballot's law** states: In the Northern Hemisphere *if you stand with your back to the wind, low pressure will be found to your left and high pressure to your right*. In the Southern Hemisphere, the situation is reversed.

Although Buys Ballot's law holds for airflow aloft, it must be used with caution when applied to surface winds. At the surface, friction and topography interfere with the idealized circulation. At the surface, if you stand with your back to the wind, then turn clockwise about 30°, low pressure will be to your left and high pressure to your right.

In summary, winds above a few kilometers can be considered geostrophic—that is, they flow in a straight path parallel to the isobars at speeds that can be calculated from the

Upper-level weather chart

Representation of upper-level chart

ff	Miles per hour
◎	Calm
—	1–2
⌐	3–8
⌐	9–14
⌐	15–20
⌐	21–25
⌐	26–31
⌐	32–37
⌐	38–43
⌐	44–49
⌐	50–54
▬	55–60
▬	61–66
▬	67–71
▬	72–77
▬	78–83
▬	84–89
▬	119–123

FIGURE 16 Upper-air weather chart. This simplified weather chart shows the direction and speed of the upper-air winds. Note from the flags that the airflow is almost parallel to the contours. Like most upper-air charts, this one shows variations in the height (in meters) at which a selected pressure (500 millibars) is found, instead of showing variations in pressure at a fixed height like surface maps. Do not let this confuse you, because there is a simple relationship between height contours and pressure. Places experiencing 500-millibar pressure at higher altitudes (toward the south) are experiencing higher pressures than places where the height contours indicate lower altitudes. Thus, *higher-elevation* contours indicate *higher* pressures, and *lower-elevation* contours indicate *lower* pressures.

pressure gradient. The major discrepancy from true geostrophic winds involves the flow along highly curved paths, a topic considered next.

Curved Flow and the Gradient Wind

Even a casual glance at a weather map shows that the isobars are not generally straight; instead, they make broad, sweeping curves (see Figure 9). Occasionally the isobars connect to form roughly circular cells of either high or low pressure. Thus, unlike geostrophic winds that flow in a straight path, winds around cells of high or low pressure follow curved paths in order to parallel the isobars. Winds of this nature, which blow at a constant speed parallel to curved isobars, are called **gradient winds.**

Let us examine how the pressure-gradient force and Coriolis force combine to produce gradient winds. The left portion of Figure 17 shows the gradient flow around a center of low pressure. As soon as the flow begins, the Coriolis force causes the air to be deflected. In the Northern Hemisphere, where the Coriolis force deflects the flow to the right, the resulting wind blows counterclockwise about a low. Conversely, around a high-pressure cell, the outward-directed pressure-gradient force is opposed by the inward-directed Coriolis force, and a clockwise flow results. The right portion of Figure 17 illustrates this idea.

Because the Coriolis force deflects the winds to the left in the Southern Hemisphere, the flow is reversed there—clockwise around low-pressure centers and counterclockwise around high-pressure centers.

It is common practice to call all centers of low pressure **cyclones** and the flow around them cyclonic. **Cyclonic flow** has the same direction of rotation as Earth: counterclockwise in the Northern Hemisphere and clockwise in the Southern Hemisphere. Centers of high prsssure are frequently called **anticyclones** and exhibit **anticyclonic flow** (opposite that of Earth's rotation). Whenever isobars curve to form elongated regions of low and high pressure, these areas are called **troughs** and **ridges,** respectively (Figure 16). The flow about a trough is cyclonic; the flow around a ridge is anticyclonic.

Now let us consider the forces that produce the gradient flow associated with cyclonic and anticyclonic circulations. Wherever the flow is curved, a force has deflected the air (changed its direction), even when no change in speed results. This is a consequence of Newton's first law of motion, which states that a moving object will continue to move in a straight line unless acted upon by an unbalanced force. You have undoubtedly experienced the effect of Newton's law when the automobile in which you were riding made a sharp turn and your body tried to continue moving straight ahead.

Referring back to the left portion of Figure 17, we see that in a low-pressure center, the inward-directed pressure-gradient force is opposed by the outward-directed Coriolis force. But to keep the path curved (parallel to the isobars), the inward pull of the pressure-gradient force must be strong enough to balance the Coriolis force as well as to turn (accelerate) the air inward. The inward turning of the air is called *centripetal acceleration.* Stated another way, the pressure-gradient force must exceed the Coriolis force to overcome the air's tendency to continue moving in a straight line.*

The opposite situation exists in anticyclonic flows, where the inward-directed Coriolis force must balance the

---

*The tendency of a particle to move in a straight line when rotated creates an imaginary outward force called *centrifugal force.*

FIGURE 17   Idealized illustration showing expected airflow aloft around low- and high-pressure centers. It is important to note that in the "real" atmosphere, airflow is continually adjusting for variations in the pressure field by slightly changing speed and direction.

Cyclonic flow (Northern Hemisphere)

Anticyclonic flow (Northern Hemisphere)

BOX 4 ▶ DO BASEBALLS REALLY FLY FARTHER AT DENVER'S COORS FIELD?

Since Denver's Coors Field was built, in 1995, it has become known as the "home-run hitter's ballpark" (Figure B). This notoriety is warranted since Coors Field led all major-league ballparks in both the total home runs and home runs per at-bat during seven of its first eight seasons.

In theory, a well-struck baseball should travel roughly 10 percent farther in Denver (elevation 5280 feet) than it would in a ballpark at sea level. This so-called elevation enhancement results from low air density at mile-high Coors Field. According to Robert Adair, Sterling Professor Emeritus of Physics at Yale University, a 400-foot blast in Atlanta could carry perhaps 425 feet in Denver, although Adair admits that calculating the actual difference is tricky for reasons having to do with subtleties of fluid dynamics.

Recently a group of researchers at the University of Colorado at Denver tested the assumption that batted balls travel farther in the "thin air" at Coors Field than in ballparks near sea level. They concluded that the assumed elevation enhancement of fly-ball distance has been greatly overestimated. Instead, they suggest that the hitter-friendly conditions should be attributed to the prevailing weather conditions of the nearby Front Range of the Rocky Mountains and the effects of low air density on the act of pitching a baseball.

For example, wind can make or break a home run. According to Professor Adair, if there's a 10-mile-an-hour breeze behind a batter, it will add an extra 30 feet to a 400-foot home run. Conversely, if the wind is blowing in toward home plate at 10 miles per hour, the flight of the ball will be reduced by about 30 feet. During the summer months winds most frequently blow from the south and southwest in the Denver area. Because of the orientation of Coors Field, these winds are blowing toward the outfield, thus aiding the hitters rather than the pitchers. Speaking of pitchers, the act of pitching a baseball is also greatly affected by air density. In particular, part of what determines how much a curveball will curve is air density. At higher elevations, thinner air causes a ball to break less, which makes it easier for a batter to hit a pitch.

In summary, it appears that several factors have contributed to Coors Field being known as a hitter's paradise.

FIGURE B   Denver's Coors Field, home of the Colorado Rockies, is nearly one mile above sea-level. It is known as a "hitter's ballpark." (Photo by Ronald Martinez/Getty Images)

pressure-gradient force as well as provide the inward acceleration needed to turn the air. Notice in Figure 17 that the pressure-gradient and Coriolis force are not balanced (the arrow lengths are different), as they are in geostrophic flow. This imbalance provides the change in direction (centripetal acceleration) that generates curved flow.

Despite the importance of centripetal acceleration in establishing curved flow aloft, near the surface, friction comes into play and greatly overshadows this much weaker force. Consequently, except for rapidly rotating storms such as tornadoes and hurricanes, the effect of centripetal acceleration is negligible and therefore is not considered in the discussion of surface circulation.

Surface Winds

Friction as a factor affecting wind is important only within the first few kilometers of Earth's surface. We know that friction acts to slow the movement of air (Figure 18). By slowing air movement, friction also reduces the Coriolis force, which is proportional to wind speed. Because the pressure-gradient

FIGURE 18 A snow fence slows the wind, thereby decreasing the wind's ability to transport snow. As a result, snow accumulates on the downwind side of the fence. (Photo by Stephen Trimble)

force is not affected by wind speed, it wins the tug of war against the Coriolis force and wind direction changes (Figure 19). The result is the movement of air at an angle across the isobars, toward the area of lower pressure.

The roughness of the terrain determines the angle at which the air will flow across the isobars as well as influences the speed at which it will move. Over the relatively smooth ocean surface, where friction is low, air moves at an angle of 10° to 20° to the isobars and at speeds roughly two-thirds of geostrophic flow. Over rugged terrain, where friction is high, the angle can be as great as 45° from the isobars, with wind speeds reduced by as much as 50 percent.

Near the surface, friction plays a major role in redistributing air within the atmosphere by changing the direction of

airflow. This is especially noticeable when considering the motion around surface cyclones and anticyclones, two of the most common features on surface weather maps.

We have learned that above the friction layer in the Northern Hemisphere, winds blow counterclockwise around a cyclone and clockwise around an anticyclone, with winds nearly parallel to the isobars. When we add the effect of friction, we notice that the airflow crosses the isobars at varying angles, depending on the roughness of the terrain, but always from higher to lower pressure. In a cyclone, in which pressure decreases inward, friction causes a net flow *toward* its center (Figure 20). In an anticyclone just the opposite is true: The pressure decreases outward, and friction causes a net flow *away* from the center. Therefore, the resultant winds blow into and counterclockwise about a surface cyclone (Figure 21), and outward and clockwise about a surface anticyclone. Of course, in the Southern Hemisphere the Coriolis force deflects the winds to the left and reverses the direction of flow.

In whatever hemisphere, however, friction causes a net inflow (*convergence*) around a cyclone and a net outflow (*divergence*) around an anticyclone. This very important relationship between cyclonic flow and convergence and anticyclonic flow and divergence will be considered again.

How Winds Generate Vertical Air Motion

GE⊕De Air Pressure and Winds
THE ATMOSPHERE ▸ Highs and Lows

So far we have discussed wind without regard to how airflow in one region might affect airflow elsewhere. As one researcher put it, a butterfly flapping its wings in South America can generate a tornado in the United States. Although this is an exaggeration, it does illustrate how airflow in one region might cause a change in weather at some later time and at a different location.

Of particular importance is the question of how horizontal airflow (winds) relates to vertical flow. Although vertical transport is small compared to horizontal motion, it is very important as a weather maker. Rising air is associated with cloudy conditions and precipitation, whereas subsidence produces adiabatic heating and clearing conditions. In this section we will discern how the movement of air (dynamic effect) can itself create pressure change and hence generate winds. In doing so, we will examine the interrelationship between horizontal and vertical flow and its effect on the weather.

FIGURE 19 Comparison between upper-level winds and surface winds showing the effects of friction on airflow. Friction slows surface wind speed, which weakens the Coriolis force, causing the winds to cross the isobars.

Upper-level wind (no friction)

Surface wind (effect of friction)

FIGURE 20 Cyclonic and anticyclonic winds in the Northern Hemisphere. Arrows show the winds blowing inward and counterclockwise around a low, and outward and clockwise around a high.

Vertical Airflow Associated with Cyclones and Anticyclones

Let us first consider the situation around a surface low-pressure system (cyclone) in which the air is spiraling inward (see Figure 20). Here the net inward transport of air causes a shrinking of the area occupied by the air mass, a process called *horizontal convergence* (Figure 22). Whenever air converges horizontally, it must pile up—that is, it must increase in height to allow for the decreased area it now occupies. This process generates a "taller" and therefore heavier air column, yet a surface low can exist only as long as the column of air above

FIGURE 21 Cyclonic circulation in the Northern and Southern hemispheres. The cloud patterns in these images allow us to "see" the circulation pattern in the lower atmosphere. (a) This satellite image shows a large low-pressure center in the Gulf of Alaska on August 17, 2004. The cloud pattern clearly shows an inward and *counterclockwise* spiral. (b) This image from March 26, 2004, shows a strong cyclonic storm in the South Atlantic near the coast of Brazil. The cloud pattern reveals an inward and *clockwise* circulation. (NASA Images)

(a)

(b)

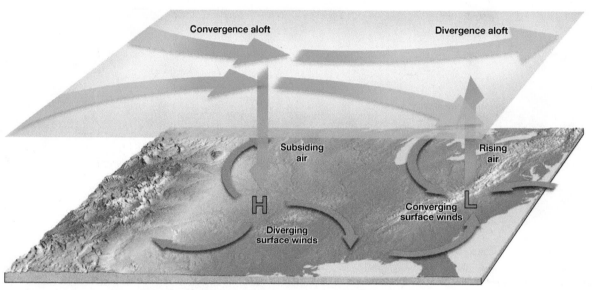

FIGURE 22 Airflow associated with surface cyclones (**L**) and anticyclones (**H**). A low, or cyclone, has converging surface winds and rising air causing cloudy conditions. A high, or anticyclone, has diverging surface winds and descending air, which leads to clear skies and fair weather.

remains light. We seem to have encountered a paradox—low-pressure centers cause a net accumulation of air, which increases their pressure. Consequently, a surface cyclone should quickly eradicate itself in a manner not unlike what happens to the vacuum in a coffee can when it is opened.

You can see that for a surface low to exist for very long, compensation must occur aloft. For example, surface convergence could be maintained if *divergence* (spreading out) aloft occurred at a rate equal to the inflow below. Figure 22 diagrammatically shows the relationship between surface convergence (inflow) and the divergence aloft (outflow) that is needed to maintain a low-pressure center.

Divergence aloft may even exceed surface convergence, thereby resulting in intensified surface inflow and accelerated vertical motion. Thus, divergence aloft can intensify storm centers as well as maintain them. On the other hand, inadequate divergence aloft permits surface flow to "fill" and weaken the accompanying cyclone.

Note that surface convergence about a cyclone causes a *net upward movement.* The rate of this vertical movement is slow, generally less than 1 kilometer per day. (Recall that updrafts in thunderstorms sometimes exceed 100 kilometers per hour.) Nevertheless, because rising air often results in cloud formation and precipitation, the passage of a low-pressure center generally is related to unstable conditions and stormy weather.

As often as not, it is divergence aloft that creates a surface low. Spreading out aloft initiates upflow in the atmosphere directly below, eventually working its way to the surface, where inflow is encouraged.

Like their cyclonic counterparts, anticyclones must also be maintained from above. Outflow near the surface is accompanied by convergence aloft and general subsidence of the air column (Figure 22). Because descending air is compressed and warmed, cloud formation and precipitation are unlikely in an anticyclone. Thus, fair weather can usually be expected with the approach of a high-pressure system.

For reasons that should now be obvious, it has been common practice to write the word "stormy" at the low end of household barometers and "fair" at the high end (Figure 23). By noting the pressure trend—rising, falling, or steady—we have a good indication of forthcoming weather. Such a determination, called the **pressure tendency** or **barometric tendency,** is useful in short-range weather prediction. The generalizations relating cyclones and anticyclones to weather conditions are stated nicely in this verse ("glass" refers to the barometer):

When the glass falls low,

Prepare for a blow;

When it rises high,

Let all your kites fly.

In conclusion, you should now be better able to understand why local television weather broadcasters emphasize the positions and projected paths of cyclones and anticyclones. The "villain" on these weather programs is always the cyclone, which produces "bad" weather in any season. Lows move in roughly a west-to-east direction across the United States and require from a few days to more than a week for the journey. Because their paths can be erratic, accurate prediction of their migration is difficult and yet essential for short-range forecasting. Meteorologists must also determine if the flow aloft will intensify an embryo storm or act to suppress its development.

(a)

(b)

FIGURE 23 These two photographs illustrate the basic weather generalizations associated with pressure centers. (a) A rainy day in New York City. Centers of low pressure are frequently associated with cloudy conditions and precipitation. (Photo by David Grossman/Alamy Images) (b) By contrast, clear skies and "fair" weather may be expected when an area is under the influence of high pressure. This scene is in New York City's Central Park. (Photo by Joseph A. Rosen/Ambient Images)

Factors That Promote Vertical Airflow

Because of the close tie between vertical motion in the atmosphere and our daily weather, we will consider some other factors that contribute to surface convergence (uplifting) and surface divergence (subsidence).

Friction can cause convergence and divergence in several ways. When air moves from the relatively smooth ocean surface onto land, for instance, the increased friction causes an abrupt drop in wind speed. This reduction of wind speed downstream results in a pile-up of air upstream. Thus, converging winds and ascending air accompany flow off the ocean. This effect contributes to the cloudy conditions over land often associated with a sea breeze in a humid region like Florida. Conversely, when air moves from land onto the ocean, general divergence and subsidence accompany the seaward flow of air because of lower friction and increasing wind speed over the water. (It should be noted that if cool air moves over a comparatively warm water body, heating from below tends to destabilize the air.)

Mountains also hinder the flow of air and cause divergence and convergence. As air passes over a mountain range, it is compressed vertically, which produces horizontal spreading (divergence) aloft. On reaching the lee side of the mountain, the air experiences vertical expansion, which causes horizontal convergence. This effect greatly influences the weather in the United States east of the Rocky Mountains, as we shall examine later. When air flows equatorward, where the Coriolis force is weakened, divergence and subsidence prevail; during poleward migration, convergence and slow uplift are favored.

As a result of the close tie between surface conditions and those aloft, great emphasis has been placed on understanding total atmospheric circulation, especially in the midlatitudes.

FIGURE 24 Wind vane (right) and cup anemometer (left). The wind vane shows wind direction, and the anemometer measures wind speed. (Photo by Belfort Instrument Company)

Wind Measurement

Two basic wind measurements—direction and speed—are important to the weather observer. Winds are always labeled by the direction *from* which they blow. A north wind blows from the north toward the south; an east wind blows from the east toward the west. One instrument that is commonly used to determine wind direction is the **wind vane** (Figure 24). This instrument, which is a common sight on many buildings, always points into the wind. Sometimes the wind direction is shown on a dial that is connected to the wind vane. The dial indicates the direction of the wind either by points of the compass—that is, N, NE, E, SE, and so on—or by a scale of 0 to 360°. On the latter scale 0° (or 360°) is north, 90° is east, 180° is south, and 270° is west.

When the wind consistently blows more often from one direction than from any other, it is called a **prevailing wind.** You may be familiar with the prevailing westerlies that dominate the circulation in the mid-latitudes. In the United States, for example, these winds consistently move the "weather" from west to east across the continent. Embedded within this general eastward flow are cells of high and low pressure with their characteristic clockwise and counterclockwise flow. As a result, the winds associated with the westerlies, as measured at the surface, often vary considerably from day to day and from place to place. By contrast, the direction of airflow associated with

the belt of trade winds is much more consistent, as can be seen in Figure 25.

A *wind rose* provides a method of representing prevailing winds by indicating the percentage of time the wind blows from various directions (Figure 25). The length of the lines on the wind rose indicates the percentage of time the wind blew from that direction. Knowledge of the wind patterns for a particular area can be useful. For example, during the construction of an airport, the runways are aligned with the prevailing wind to assist in takeoffs and landings. Furthermore, prevailing winds greatly affect the weather and climate of a region. North–south trending mountain ranges, such as the Cascade Range of the Pacific Northwest, for example, causes the ascent of the prevailing westerlies. Thus, the windward (west) slopes of these ranges are rainy, whereas the leeward (east) sides are dry.

Wind speed is often measured with a **cup anemometer** (Figure 24). The wind speed is read from a dial much like the speedometer of an automobile. Sometimes an **aerovane** is used instead of a wind vane and cup anemometer. As can be seen in Figure 26, this instrument resembles a wind vane with a propeller at one end. The fin keeps the propeller facing into the wind, allowing the blades to rotate at a rate that is proportional to the wind speed. This instrument is commonly attached to a recorder to keep a continuous record of wind speed and direction. Places where winds are steady and speeds are relatively high are potential sites for tapping wind energy (Box 5).

At small airstrips *wind socks* are frequently used. They consist of a cone-shaped bag that is open at both ends and free to change position with shifts in wind direction. The degree to which the sock is inflated is an indication of the strength of the wind.

Recall that 70 percent of Earth's surface is covered by water where conventional methods of measuring wind speed are not possible. Although weather buoys and ships at sea do

FIGURE 25 Wind roses showing the percentage of time airflow is from various directions. (a) Wind frequency for the winter in the eastern United States. (b) Wind frequency for the winter in northern Australia. Note the reliability of the southeast trades in Australia as compared to the westerlies in the eastern United States. (Data from G. T. Trewartha)

(a) **Westerlies (winter)**

(b) **Southeast Trades (winter)**

FIGURE 26 An aerovane. (Photo by Warren Faidley/ Weatherstock)

provide some coverage, weather forecasts have improved dramatically since the 1990s due to the availability of satellite-derived wind data. One way wind speed and direction can be established is by using satellite images to track cloud movements. This is currently being accomplished by comparing a sequence of GOES images separated by intervals of 5 to 30 minutes (Figure 27). This innovation has been especially useful in predicting the timing and location of where a hurricane will make landfall.

FIGURE 27 Upper-level winds obtained from the GOES meteorological satellite.

BOX 5 ▶ WIND ENERGY: AN ALTERNATIVE WITH POTENTIAL

Nearly one hundred years ago electricity became available to much of rural America. This development led to the gradual decline of the "farm windmill" which provided power for pumping water, grinding grain, and sawing logs. Today, with the high cost of fossil fuels that are used to produce electricity, modern wind turbines are being installed at break-neck speeds (Figure C). In fact, worldwide, in 2007 there was 32 percent more wind energy harnessed than in the previous year. Much of this growth was led by the United States, China, and Spain.

Although Germany was the number one producer of wind energy in 2007, generating 22,247 megawatts*, the United States is expected to overtake it as the leader in wind energy production by the end of 2009. However, within the next decade China is expected to produce the most wind generated electricity.

Wind speed is a crucial element in determining whether a place is a suitable site for installing a wind-energy facility. Generally a minimum average wind speed of 21 kilometers (13 miles) per hour is necessary for a large-scale wind-power plant to be profitable.

A small difference in wind speed results in a large difference in energy production, and therefore a large difference in the cost of the electricity generated. For example, a turbine operating on a site with an average wind speed of 12-mph would generate about 33 percent more electricity than one operating at 11-mph conditions. Also, there is little energy to be harvested a low wind speeds—6-mph winds contain less than one-eighth the energy of 12-mph winds.

The United States has tremendous wind energy resources. Currently 34 states have

FIGURE C   These wind turbines are operating near Palm Springs, California. Although, California is the place where wind-power development began in the United States, it has recently been replaced by Texas as the leading producer of wind-generated electricity. As of January 2007, Texas had a total of 4,356 megawatts of installed capacity. That's enough electricity to supply more than one million average American households. (Photo by John Mead/Science Photo Library/Photo Researchers, Inc.)

Chapter Summary

- *Air pressure* is the pressure exerted by the weight of air above. Average air pressure at sea level is about 1 kilogram per square centimeter, or 14.7 pounds per square inch. Another way to define air pressure is that it is the force exerted against a surface by the continuous collision of gas molecules.

- The *newton* is the unit of force used by meteorologists to measure atmospheric pressure. A *millibar* (mb) equals 100 newtons per square meter. Standard sea-level pressure is 1013.25 millibars. Two instruments used to measure atmospheric pressure are the *mercury barometer*, where the height of a mercury column provides a measure of air pressure (standard atmospheric pressure at sea level equals 29.92 inches or 760 millimeters), and the *aneroid barometer*, which uses a partially evacuated metal chamber that changes shape as air pressure changes.

- The pressure at any given altitude is equal to the weight of the air above that point. Furthermore, the rate at which commercial facilities that produce electricity from wind power. In 2008 the leading states in installed capacity were Texas, number one, followed by California and Minnesota. Despite the fact that California gave birth to the modern U.S. wind industry, 16 states have greater wind potential. As shown in Table B, the top five states for wind energy potential include North Dakota, Texas, Kansas, South Dakota, and Montana. Although only a little more than one percent of U.S. electrical generation currently comes from wind energy, it has been estimated that wind energy potential equals more than twice the total electricity currently consumed (Figure D).

Recent technological improvements have made the cost of wind-generated electricity more competitive. As a result, the growth of installed capacity has grown dramatically. Worldwide, the total amount of installed wind power grew from 7636 megawatts in 1997 to 94,123 megawatts in 2007. This is enough electricity to supply more than 20 million average American households, or as much as could be generated by more than 30 large nuclear power plants.

The U.S. Department of Energy has announced a goal of obtaining 5 percent of U.S. electricity from wind by the year 2020—a goal that seems consistent with the current growth rate of wind energy nationwide. Thus, wind-generated electricity appears to be shifting from being an "alternative" to a "mainstream" energy source.

———

*One megawatt is enough electricity to supply 250–300 average American households.

TABLE B   The Leading States for Wind Energy Potential

Rank	State	Potential*
1	North Dakota	1,210
2	Texas	1,190
3	Kansas	1,070
4	South Dakota	1,030
5	Montana	1,020
6	Nebraska	868
7	Wyoming	747
8	Oklahoma	725
9	Minnesota	657
10	Iowa	551
11	Colorado	481
12	New Mexico	435
13	Idaho	73
14	Michigan	65
15	New York	62
16	Illinois	61
17	California	59
18	Wisconsin	58
19	Maine	56
20	Missouri	52

*The total amount of electricity that could potentially be generated each year, measured in *billions* of kilowatt hours. A typical American home would use several hundred kilowatt hours per month.

FIGURE D   The wind energy potential for the United States. Large wind systems require average wind speeds of about 6 meters per second (13 miles per hour). In the key "moderate" refers to regions that experience wind speeds of 6.4–6.9 meters per second (m/s), "good" means 7–7.4 m/s, and "excellent" means 7.5 m/s and higher.

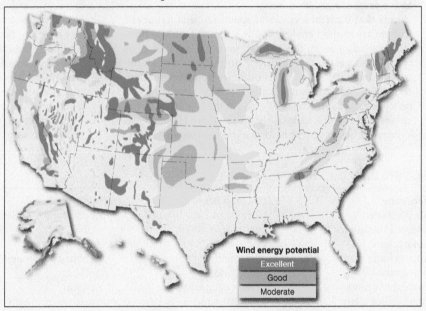

Wind energy potential
Excellent
Good
Moderate

pressure decreases with an increase in altitude is much greater near Earth's surface. The "normal" decrease in pressure experienced with increased altitude is provided by the *standard atmosphere*, which depicts the idealized vertical distribution of atmospheric pressure.

- In calm air, the two factors that largely determine the amount of air pressure exerted by an air mass are temperature and humidity. A cold, dry air mass will produce higher surface pressures than a warm, humid air mass.
- *Wind* is the result of horizontal differences in air pressure. If Earth did not rotate and there were no friction, air would flow directly from areas of higher pressure to areas of lower pressure. However, because both factors exist, wind is controlled by a combination of (1) the *pressure-gradient force*, (2) the *Coriolis force*, and (3) *friction*. The pressure-gradient force is the primary driving force of wind that results from pressure differences that occur over a given distance, as depicted by the spacing of *isobars*, lines drawn on maps that connect places of equal air pressure. The spacing of isobars indicates the amount of pressure change occurring over a given distance, expressed as the *pressure gradient*. Closely spaced isobars indicate a steep

pressure gradient and strong winds; widely spaced isobars indicate a weak pressure gradient and light winds. There is also an upward-directed vertical pressure-gradient, which is usually balanced by gravity in what is referred to as *hydrostatic equilibrium.* On those occasions when the gravitational force slightly exceeds the vertical pressure-gradient force, slow downward airflow results. The Coriolis force produces a deviation in the path of wind due to Earth's rotation (to the right in the Northern Hemisphere and to the left in the Southern Hemisphere). The amount of deflection is greatest at the poles and decreases to zero at the equator. The amount of Coriolis deflection also increases with wind speed. Friction, which significantly influences airflow near Earth's surface, is negligible above a height of a few kilometers.

- Above a height of a few kilometers, the effect of friction on airflow is small enough to disregard. Here, as the wind speed increases, the deflection caused by the Coriolis force also increases. Winds in which the Coriolis force is equal to and opposite the pressure-gradient force are called *geostrophic winds.* Geostrophic winds flow in a straight path, parallel to the isobars, with velocities proportional to the pressure-gradient force.

- Winds that blow at a constant speed parallel to curved isobars are termed *gradient winds.* In centers of low pressure, called *cyclones,* the circulation of air, referred to as *cyclonic flow,* is counterclockwise in the Northern Hemisphere and clockwise in the Southern Hemisphere. Centers of high pressure, called *anticyclones,* exhibit *anticyclonic flow,* which is clockwise in the Northern Hemisphere and counterclockwise in the Southern Hemisphere. Whenever isobars curve to form elongated regions of low

and high pressure, these areas are called *troughs* and *ridges,* respectively.

- Near the surface, friction plays a major role in redistributing air within the atmosphere by changing the direction of airflow. The result is a movement of air at an angle across the isobars, toward the area of lower pressure. Therefore, the resultant winds blow into and counterclockwise about a Northern Hemisphere surface cyclone. In a Northern Hemisphere surface anticyclone, winds blow outward and clockwise. Regardless of the hemisphere, friction causes a net inflow (*convergence*) around a cyclone and a net outflow (*divergence*) around an anticyclone.

- A surface low-pressure system with its associated horizontal convergence is maintained or intensified by divergence (spreading out) aloft. Inadequate divergence aloft will weaken the accompanying cyclone. Because surface convergence about a cyclone accompanied by divergence aloft causes a net upward movement of air, the passage of a low pressure center is often associated with stormy weather. By contrast, fair weather can usually be expected with the approach of a high-pressure system. As a result of the general weather patterns usually associated with cyclones and anticyclones, the *pressure tendency* or *barometric tendency* (the nature of the change of the barometer over the past several hours) is useful in short-range weather prediction.

- Two basic wind measurements—direction and speed—are important to the weather observer. Wind direction is commonly determined using a *wind vane.* When the wind consistently blows more often from one direction than from any other, it is called a *prevailing wind.* Wind speed is often measured with a *cup anemometer.*

Vocabulary Review

aerovane	convergence	high	pressure tendency
air pressure	Coriolis force	hydrostatic equilibrium	prevailing wind
aneroid barometer	cup anemometer	isobar	ridge
anticyclone	cyclone	low	standard atmosphere
anticyclonic flow	cyclonic flow	mercury barometer)	trough
barograph	divergence	millibar	wind
barometric tendency	geostrophic wind	newton	wind vane
Buys Ballot's law	gradient wind	pressure gradient	

Review Questions

1. What is standard sea-level pressure in millibars? In inches of mercury? In pounds per square inch?

2. Describe the operating principles of the mercury barometer and the aneroid barometer. List two advantages of the aneroid barometer.

3. Explain why air pressure decreases with an increase in altitude.

4. Explain why a cold, dry air mass produces a higher surface pressure than a warm, humid air mass.

5. Compare convergence with divergence.

6. What force is responsible for *generating* wind?

7. Write a generalization relating the spacing of isobars to the speed of wind.

8. Temperature variations create pressure differences, which in turn produce winds. On a small scale, the sea breeze illustrates this principle nicely. Describe how a sea breeze forms.

9. Although vertical pressure differences may be great, such variations do not generate strong vertical currents. Explain.

10. Briefly describe how the Coriolis force modifies the movement of air.

11. Which two factors influence the magnitude of the Coriolis force?

12. Explain the formation of a geostrophic wind.

13. Unlike winds aloft, which blow nearly parallel to the isobars, surface winds generally cross the isobars. Explain what causes this difference.

14. Prepare a diagram (isobars and wind arrows) showing the winds associated with surface cyclones and anticyclones in both the Northern and Southern Hemispheres.

15. For surface low pressure to exist for an extended period, what condition must exist aloft?

16. What are the general weather conditions to be expected when the pressure tendency is rising? When the pressure tendency is falling?

17. Converging winds and ascending air are often associated with the flow of air from the oceans onto land. Conversely, divergence and subsidence often accompany the flow of air from land to sea. What causes this convergence over land and divergence over the ocean?

18. A southwest wind blows from the _____ (direction) toward the _____ (direction).

19. The wind direction is 315°. From what compass direction is the wind blowing?

Problems

1. Calculate the magnitude of the pressure-gradient force (per unit mass) between two cities 500 kilometers apart if pressure at the respective cities is 1010 mb and 1017 mb?

2. Calculate the magnitude of Coriolis force acting on air moving at:
   a. 36 kilometers per hour (10 meters per second) at 35° latitude.
   b. 36 kilometers per hour (10 meters per second) at 65° latitude.
   c. 54 kilometers per hour (15 meters per second) at 35° latitude.

Atmospheric Science Online

The Atmosphere 11e website uses the resources and flexibility of the Internet to aid in your study of the topics in this chapter. Written and developed by meteorology instructors, this site will help improve your understanding of meteorology. Visit **www.mygeoscience.com** in order to:

- **Review** key chapter concepts

- **Read** with links to the eBook and to chapter-specific web resources

- **Visualize** and comprehend challenging topics using learning activities in *GEODe: Atmosphere*

- **Test yourself** with online quizzes

GEODe: Atmosphere

GEODe: Atmosphere makes studying more effective by reinforcing key concepts using animation, video, narration, interactive exercises, and practice quizzes. Available at **www.mygeoscience.com**.

Circulation of the Atmosphere

From Chapter 7 of *The Atmosphere: An Introduction to Meteorology*, Eleventh Edition, Frederick K. Lutgens, Edward J. Tarbuck, Dennis Tasa. Copyright © 2010 by Pearson Education, Inc. Published by Pearson Prentice Hall. All rights reserved.

Gale force winds from a storm in the North Atlantic created these large waves along the coast of Scotland. (Photo by John Giles/PA Photo)

The main goal of this chapter is to gain an understanding of Earth's highly integrated wind system. Global atmospheric circulation can be thought of as a series of deep rivers of air that encircle the planet. Embedded in the main currents are vortices of various sizes including hurricanes, tornadoes, and mid-latitude cyclones (Figure 1). Like eddies in a stream, these rotating wind systems develop and die out with somewhat predictable regularity. In general, the smallest eddies, such as dust devils, last only a few minutes, whereas larger and more complex systems, such as hurricanes, may survive for several days.

Winds are generated by pressure differences that arise because of unequal heating of Earth's surface. Global winds are generated because the tropics receive more solar radiation than Earth's polar regions. Thus, Earth's winds blow in an unending attempt to balance inequalities in surface temperatures. Because the zone of maximum solar heating migrates with the seasons—moving northward during the Northern Hemisphere summer and southward as winter approaches—the wind patterns that make up the general circulation also migrate latitudinally.

Although we will focus on the global circulation, local wind systems will also be considered. The chapter concludes with a discussion of global precipitation patterns. As you will see, the global distribution of precipitation is closely linked to the patterns of atmospheric pressure and thus the global wind system.

Scales of Atmospheric Motion

Those who live in the United States are familiar with the term "westerlies" to describe the winds that predominantly blow from west to east. But all of us have experienced winds from the south and north and even directly from the east. You may

FIGURE 1 In this satellite image, low clouds reveal a swirling wind pattern on the lee of Guadalupe Island. The airflow develops substantial rotation when it is too stable to flow over the top of a barrier such as this isolated island. (Photo courtesy of NASA/Visuals Unlimited, Inc.)

even recall being in a storm when shifts in wind direction and speed came in such rapid succession that it was impossible to determine the wind's direction. With such variations, how can we describe our winds as westerly? The answer lies in our attempt to simplify descriptions of the atmospheric circulation by sorting out events according to *size*. On the scale of a weather map, for instance, where observing stations are spaced about 150 kilometers apart, small whirlwinds that carry dust skyward are far too small to show up. Instead, weather maps reveal larger-scale wind patterns, such as those associated with traveling cyclones and anticyclones.

Not only do we separate winds according to the size of the system, but equal consideration is also given to the time frame in which they occur. In general, large weather patterns have longer life spans than do their smaller counterparts. For example, dust devils usually last a few minutes and rarely occur for more than an hour. By contrast, mid-latitude cyclones typically take a few days to cross the United States and occasionally dominate the weather for a week or longer. The time and size scales we will use for atmospheric motions are provided in Table 1.

Large- and Small-Scale Circulation

The wind systems shown in Figure 2 illustrate the three major categories of atmospheric circulation: macroscale, mesoscale, and microscale. *Macroscale* circulation includes large planetary-scale flow, such as the trade winds that blow consistently for weeks or longer as well as smaller features like hurricanes (Figure 2a). *Mesoscale* circulation is associated with tornadoes, thunderstorms, and numerous *local winds* that generally last from minutes to hours. Finally, *microscale* events have life spans of from a few seconds to minutes and include dust devils, gusts, and general atmospheric turbulence.

Macroscale Winds The largest wind patterns, called **macroscale winds,** are exemplified by the westerlies and trade winds that carried sailing vessels back and forth across the Atlantic during the opening of the New World. These *planetary-scale* flow patterns extend around the entire globe and can remain essentially unchanged for weeks at a time.

A somewhat smaller macroscale circulation is called *synoptic scale,* or *weather-map scale.* Two well-known synoptic scale systems are the individual traveling cyclones and anticyclones that appear on weather maps as areas of low and high pressure, respectively. These weather producers are found in the middle latitudes where they move from west to east as part of the larger westerly flow. Furthermore, these rotating systems usually persist for days or occasionally weeks and have a horizontal dimension of hundreds to thousands of kilometers. Recall that the direction of surface flow around a cyclone is toward the center with a general upward component. Anticyclones, in contrast, are areas of subsidence associated with outward flow near the surface. The average rate of vertical motion within these systems is slow, typically less than 1 kilometer per day.

Somewhat smaller macroscale systems are the tropical cyclones and hurricanes that develop in late summer and early fall over the warm tropical oceans. Airflow in these systems is inward and upward as in the larger mid-latitude cyclones. However, the rate of horizontal flow associated with hurricanes is usually more rapid than that of their more poleward cousins.

Mesoscale Winds **Mesoscale winds** generally last for several minutes and may exist for hours. These middle-size phenomena are usually less than 100 kilometers (62 miles) across. Further, some mesoscale winds—for example, thunderstorms and tornadoes—also have a strong vertical component (Figure 2b). It is important to remember that thunderstorms and tornadoes are always embedded within and thus move as part of the larger macroscale circulation. Further, much of the vertical air movement within a mid-latitude cyclone, or hurricane, is provided by thunderstorms, where updrafts in excess of 100 kilometers (62 miles) per hour have been measured. Land and sea breezes, as well as mountain and valley winds, also fall into this category and will be discussed in the next section along with other mesoscale winds.

Microscale Winds The smallest scale of air motion is referred to as **microscale circulation.** These small, often chaotic winds normally last for seconds or at most minutes. Examples include simple gusts, which hurl debris into the air (Figure 2c) and small, well-developed vortices such as dust devils (see Box 1).

Structure of Wind Patterns

Although it is common practice to divide atmospheric motions according to scale, remember that global winds are a composite of all scales of motion—much like a meandering river that contains large eddies composed of smaller eddies containing still smaller eddies. For example, let us examine the flow

TABLE 1 Time and Space Scales for Atmospheric Motions			
Scale	Time scale	Distance scale	Examples
Macroscale			
Planetary	Weeks or longer	1000–40,000 km	Westerlies and trade winds
Synoptic	Days to weeks	100–5000 km	Mid-latitude cyclones, anticyclones, and hurricanes
Mesoscale	Minutes to hours	1–100 km	Thunderstorms, tornadoes, and land–sea breeze
Microscale	Seconds to minutes	<1 km	Turbulence, dust devils, and gusts

FIGURE 2 Three scales of atmospheric motion. (a) Satellite image of Hurricane Nora, an example of macroscale circulation. (b) Tornadoes exemplfy mesoscale wind systems. (c) Gusts illustrate microscale winds. (Photos by (a) NASA/Science Photo Library/Photo Researchers, Inc., (b) A. and J. Verkaik/CORBIS/The Stock Market, (c) E. J. Tarbuck)

(a)   (b)   (c)

associated with hurricanes that form over the North Atlantic. When we view one of these tropical cyclones on a satellite image, the storm appears as a large whirling cloud migrating slowly across the ocean (Figure 2a). From this perspective, which is at the weather-map (synoptic) scale, the general counterclockwise rotation of the storm can be easily seen.

When we average the winds of hurricanes, we find that they often have a net motion from east to west, thereby indicating that these larger eddies are embedded in a still larger flow (planetary scale) that is moving westward across the tropical portion of the North Atlantic.

If we examine a hurricane more closely by flying an airplane through it, some of the small-scale aspects of the storm become noticeable. As the plane approaches the outer edge of the system, it becomes evident that the large rotating cloud that we saw in the satellite images is made of many individual cumulonimbus towers (thunderstorms). Each of these mesoscale phenomena lasts for only a few hours and must

be continually replaced by new ones if the hurricane is to persist. As we fly into these storms, we quickly realize that the individual clouds are made up of even smaller-scale turbulences. The small thermals of rising air that occur in these clouds make for a rather rough trip.

Thus, a typical hurricane exhibits several scales of motion, including many mesoscale thunderstorms, which, in turn, consist of numerous microscale turbulences. Furthermore, the counterclockwise circulation of the hurricane (weathermap scale) is embedded in the global winds (planetary scale) that flow from east to west in the tropical North Atlantic.

Local Winds

Before examining the large macroscale circulation for Earth, let us turn to some mesoscale winds (time frame of minutes to hours and size of 1 to 100 kilometers—see Table 1).

1 ▶ DUST DEVILS

A common phenomenon in arid regions of the world is the whirling vortex called the *dust devil* (Figure A). Although they resemble tornadoes, dust devils are generally much smaller and less intense than their destructive cousins. Most dust devils are only a few meters in diameter and reach heights no greater than about 100 meters (300 feet). Further, these whirlwinds are usually short-lived microscale phenomena. Most form and die out within minutes. In rare instances dust devils have lasted for hours.

Unlike tornadoes, which are associated with convective clouds, dust devils form on days when clear skies dominate. Further, these whirlwinds form from the ground upward, exactly opposite of tornadoes.

Because surface heating is critical to their formation, dust devils occur most frequently in the afternoon when surface temperatures are highest.

Recall that when the air near the surface is considerably warmer than the air a few dozen meters overhead, the layer of air near Earth's surface becomes unstable. In this situation warm surface air begins to rise, causing air near the ground to be drawn into the developing whirlwind. The rotating winds that are associated with dust devils are produced by the same phenomenon that causes ice skaters to spin faster as they pull their arms closer to their body. As the inwardly spiraling air rises, it carries sand, dust, and other loose debris dozens of meters into the

air. It is this material that makes a dust devil visible. Occasionally, dust devils form above vegetated surfaces. Under these conditions, the vortices may go undetected unless they interact with objects at the surface.

Most dust devils are small and short-lived; consequently, they are not generally destructive. Occasionally, however, these whirlwinds grow to be 100 meters or more in diameter and over a kilometer high. With wind speeds that may reach 100 kilometers (60 miles) per hour, large dust devils can do considerable damage. Fortunately, such occurrences are few and far between.

FIGURE A Dust devil. Although these whirling vortices resemble tornadoes, they have different origins and are much smaller and less intense. (Courtesy of St. Meyers/Okapia/Photo Researchers, Inc.)

Students Sometimes Ask . . .

What is the highest wind speed ever recorded?

The highest wind speed recorded at a surface station is 372 kilometers (231 miles) per hour, measured April 12, 1934, at Mount Washington, New Hampshire. Located at an elevation of 1879 meters (6,262 feet), the observatory atop Mount Washington has an average wind speed of 56 kilometers (35 miles) per hour. Faster wind speeds have undoubtedly occurred on mountain peaks, but no instruments were in place to record them.

Remember that all winds have the same cause: pressure differences that arise because of temperature differences caused by unequal heating of Earth's surface. Local winds are medium-scale winds produced by a locally generated pressure gradient.

Although many winds are given local names, some are actually part of the global wind system. The "norther" of Texas, for instance, is a cold southward flow produced by the circulation around anticyclones that invade the United States from Canada in the winter. Because these winds are not locally generated, they cannot be considered true local winds. Others, like those about to be described, are truly mesoscale and are caused either by topographic effects or variations in local surface composition.

(a) **Sea breeze**

(b) **Land breeze**

FIGURE 3 Illustration of a sea breeze and a land breeze. (a) During the daylight hours the air above the land heats and expands, creating an area of lower pressure. Cooler and denser air over the water moves onto the land, generating a sea breeze. (b) At night the land cools more rapidly than the sea, generating an offshore flow called a *land breeze*.

Recall that winds are named for the direction *from which they blow*. This holds true for local winds. Thus, a sea breeze originates over water and blows toward the land, whereas a valley breeze blows upslope away from its source.

Land and Sea Breezes

Land is heated more intensely during daylight hours than is an adjacent body of water. As a result, the air above the land surface heats and expands, creating an area of low pressure. A **sea breeze** then develops, as cooler air over the water moves onto the land (Figure 3a). At night, the reverse may take place; the land cools more rapidly than the sea and a **land breeze** develops (Figure 3b).

The sea breeze has a significant moderating influence on coastal temperatures. Shortly after the breeze begins, air temperatures over the land may drop by as much as 5° to 10°C. However, the cooling effect of these breezes generally reaches a maximum of only about 100 kilometers (60 miles) inland in the tropics and often less than half that distance in the middle latitudes. These cool sea breezes generally begin shortly before noon and reach their greatest intensity, about 10 to 20 kilometers per hour, in the midafternoon.

Smaller-scale sea breezes can also develop along the shores of large lakes. People who live in a city near the Great Lakes, such as Chicago, recognize the "lake effect," especially in the summer. Residents are reminded daily by reports of the cooler temperatures near the lake compared to warmer outlying areas. In many places sea breezes also affect the amount of cloud cover and rainfall. The peninsula of Florida, for example, experiences a summer precipitation maximum caused partly by the convergence of sea breezes from both the Atlantic and Gulf coasts.

The intensity and extent of land and sea breezes depend on the location and the time of year. Tropical areas where intense solar heating is continuous throughout the year experience more frequent and stronger sea breezes than do mid-latitude locations. The most intense sea breezes develop along tropical coastlines adjacent to cool ocean currents. In the middle latitudes, sea breezes are most common during the warmest months, but the counterpart, the land breeze, is often missing, for the land does not always cool below the ocean temperature. In the higher middle latitudes the frequent migration of high- and low-pressure systems dominates the circulation, so land and sea breezes are less noticeable.

Mountain and Valley Breezes

A daily wind similar to land and sea breezes occurs in many mountainous regions. During the day, air along mountain slopes is heated more intensely than air at the same elevation over the valley floor (Figure 4a). This warmer air glides up along the mountain slope and generates a **valley breeze.** The occurrence of these daytime upslope breezes can often be identified by the isolated cumulus clouds that develop over adjacent mountain peaks (Figure 5). This also causes the late afternoon thundershowers so common on warm summer days in the mountains. After sunset the pattern is reversed. Rapid radiation heat loss along the mountain slopes cools the air, which drains into the valley below and causes a **mountain breeze** (Figure 4b). Similar cool air drainage can occur in regions that have little slope. The result is that the coldest pockets of air are usually found in the lowest spots, a phenomenon you likely have experienced while walking in hilly terrain. Consequently, low areas are the first to experience radiation fog and are the most likely spots for frost damage to crops.

Like many other winds, mountain and valley breezes have seasonal preferences. Although valley breezes are most

(a) **Valley breeze**   (b) **Mountain breeze**

FIGURE 4 Valley and mountain breezes. (a) Heating during the daylight hours warms the air along the mountain slopes. This warm air rises, generating a valley breeze. (b) After sunset, cooling of the air near the mountain can result in cool air drainage into the valley, producing the mountain breeze.

common during the warm season when solar heating is most intense, mountain breezes tend to be more frequent during the cold season.

Chinook (Foehn) Winds

Warm, dry winds sometimes move down the east slopes of the Rockies, where they are called **chinooks,** and the Alps, where they are called **foehns.** Such winds are often created when a strong pressure gradient develops in a mountainous region. As the air descends the leeward slopes of the mountains, it is heated adiabatically (by compression). Because condensation may have occurred as the air ascended the windward side, releasing latent heat, the air descending the leeward side will be warmer and drier than at a similar elevation on the windward side. Although the temperature of these winds is generally less than 10°C (50°F), which is not particularly warm, they usually occur in the winter and spring when the affected area may be experiencing subfreezing temperatures. Thus, by comparison, these dry, warm winds often bring drastic change. Within minutes of the arrival of a chinook, the temperature may climb 20°C (36°F). When the ground has a snow cover, these winds melt it in short order. The Native American word *chinook* means "snow-eater."

The chinook is viewed by some as beneficial to ranchers east of the Rockies, for it keeps their grasslands clear of snow

during much of the winter, but this benefit is offset by the loss of moisture that the snow would bequeath to the land if it remained until the spring melt.

Another chinooklike wind that occurs in the United States is the **Santa Ana.** Found in southern California, these hot, desiccating winds greatly increase the threat of fire in this already dry area (see Box 2).

Katabatic (Fall) Winds

In the winter, areas adjacent to highlands may experience a local wind called a **katabatic or fall wind.** These winds originate when cold air, situated over a highland area such as the

FIGURE 5 The occurrence of a daytime upslope (valley) breeze is identified by cloud development on mountain peaks, sometimes progressing to a midafternoon thunderstorm. (Photo by James E. Patterson/James Patterson Collection)

2 ▶ ATMOSPHERIC HAZARD

Santa Ana Winds and Wildfires

FIGURE B   Ten large wildfires rage across Southern California in this image taken on October 27, 2003, by NASA's *Aqua* satellite. (Photo courtesy of NASA)

ice sheets of Greenland or Antarctica, is set in motion. Under the influence of gravity, the cold air cascades over the rim of a highland like a waterfall. Although the air is heated adiabatically, as are chinooks, the initial temperatures are so low that the wind arrives in the lowlands still colder and more dense than the air it displaces. In fact, this air *must* be colder than the air it invades, for it is the air's greater density that causes it to descend. As this frigid air descends, it occasionally is channeled into narrow valleys, where it acquires velocities capable of great destruction.

A few of the better-known katabatic winds have local names. Most famous is the **mistral,** which blows from the French Alps toward the Mediterranean Sea. Another is the **bora,** which originates in the mountains of Yugoslavia and blows to the Adriatic Sea.

Country Breezes

One mesoscale wind, called a **country breeze,** is associated with large urban areas. As the name implies, this circulation pattern is characterized by a light wind blowing into the city from the surrounding countryside. The country breeze is best developed on relatively clear, calm nights. Under these conditions cities, because they contain massive buildings composed of rocklike materials, tend to retain the heat accumulated during the day more than the less built up outlying areas. The result is that the warm, less dense air over the city rises, which in turn initiates the country-to-city flow.

One investigation in Toronto showed that heat accumulated within this city created a rural/city pressure difference

People living in southern California are well aware of chinook-type winds called the *Santa Anas*. These hot, dry, dust-bearing winds invade California most often in autumn when they bring temperatures that often approach 32°C (90°F) and may occasionally exceed 38°C (100°F). When a strong anticyclone is centered over the Great Basin, the clockwise flow directs desert air from Arizona and Nevada westward toward the Pacific. The wind gains speed as it is funneled through the canyons of the Coast Ranges, in particular the Santa Ana Canyon, from which the winds derive their name. Compressional heating of this already warm, dry air as it descends mountain slopes further accentuates the already parched conditions. Vegetation, seared by the summer heat, is dried even further by these desiccating winds.

In late October 2003, Santa Anas began blowing toward the coast of southern California, with speeds that sometimes exceeded 100 kilometers (60 miles) per hour. Much of this area is covered by brush known as chaparral and related shrubs. It didn't take much—a careless camper or motorist, a lightning strike, or an arsonist—to ignite a fire. Soon a number of outbreaks occurred in portions of Los Angeles, San Bernardino, Riverside, and San Diego counties (Figure B). Several developed quickly into wildfires that moved almost as fast as

FIGURE C Flames from a wildfire fanned by Santa Ana winds move toward a home south of Valley Center, California, on October 27, 2003. (Photo by Denis Poroy/Associated Press)

the ferocious Santa Ana winds sweeping through the canyons.

Within a few days more than 13,000 firefighters were on firelines that extended from north of Los Angeles to the Mexican border. Nearly two months later, when all the fires were officially extinguished, more than 742,000 acres had been scorched, over 3000 homes destroyed, and 26 people killed (Figure C). The Federal Emergency Management Agency put the dollar losses at over $2.5 billion. The 2003 southern California wildfires became the worst fire disaster in the state's history.

Strong Santa Ana winds, coupled with dry summers, have produced wildfires in southern California for a millennia. These fires are nature's way of burning out chaparral thickets and sage scrub to prepare the land for new growth. The problem began when people started to crowd into the fire-prone area between Santa Barbara and San Diego. Residents have compounded the danger by landscaping their yards with highly flammable eucalyptus and pine trees. Furthermore, successful fire prevention has allowed the buildup of even more flammable material. Clearly, wildfires will remain a major threat in these areas into the foreseeable future.

that was sufficient to cause an inward and counterclockwise circulation centered on the downtown area. One of the unfortunate consequences of the country breeze is that pollutants emitted near the urban perimeter tend to drift in and concentrate near the city's center.

Global Circulation

Our knowledge of global winds comes from two sources: the patterns of pressure and winds observed worldwide, and theoretical studies of fluid motion. We first consider the classical model of global circulation that was developed largely from average worldwide pressure distribution. We then add to this idealized circulation more recently discovered aspects of the atmosphere's complex motions.

Students Sometimes Ask . . .

What is a haboob?

A haboob is a type of local wind that occurs in arid regions. The name was originally applied to strong dust storms in the African Sudan, where one city experiences an average of 24 per year. (The name comes from the Arabic word *habb,* meaning "wind.") Haboobs generally occur when downdrafts from large thunderstorms swiftly move across the desert. Tons of silt, sand, and dust are lifted, forming a whirling wall of debris hundreds of meters high. These dense, dark "clouds" can completely engulf desert towns and deposit enormous quantities of sediment. The deserts of the southwestern United States occasionally experience dust storms produced in this manner.

FIGURE 6 Global circulation on a nonrotating Earth. A simple convection system is produced by unequal heating of the atmosphere on a nonrotating Earth.

Single-Cell Circulation Model

One of the first contributions to the classical model of global circulation came from George Hadley in 1735. Hadley was well aware that solar energy drives the winds. He proposed that the large temperature contrast between the poles and the equator creates one large *convection cell* in each hemisphere (Northern and Southern), as shown in Figure 6.

In Hadley's model, intensely heated equatorial air rises until it reaches the tropopause, where it begins to spread toward the poles. Eventually, this upper-level flow would reach the poles, where cooling would cause it to sink and spread out at the surface as equatorward-moving winds. As this cold polar air approached the equator, it would be reheated and rise again. Thus, the circulation proposed by Hadley has upper-level air flowing poleward and surface air moving equatorward.

Although correct in principle, Hadley's model does not take into account the fact that Earth rotates on its axis. (Hadley's model would better approximate the circulation of a *nonrotating* planet.) As Earth's pressure and wind patterns became better known, it was clear that the single-cell model (in each hemisphere) could not create the global circulation that was actually observed. Consequently, the Hadley model was replaced by a model that better fit observations.

Three-Cell Circulation Model

In the 1920s a three-cell circulation model (for each hemisphere) was proposed. Although this model has been modified to fit upper-air observations, it remains a useful way to examine global circulation. Figure 7 illustrates the idealized three-cell model and the surface winds that result.

In the zones between the equator and roughly 30° latitude north and south, the circulation closely resembles the model used by Hadley for the whole Earth. Consequently, the name **Hadley cell** is generally applied. Near the equator, the warm rising air that releases latent heat during the formation of cumulus towers is believed to provide the energy to drive the Hadley cells. The clouds also provide the rainfall that maintains the lush vegetation of the rain forests of southeast Asia, equatorial Africa, and South America's Amazon Basin.

As the flow aloft in Hadley cells moves poleward, it begins to subside in a zone between 20° and 35° latitude. Two factors contribute to this general subsidence: (1) As upper-level flow moves away from the stormy equatorial region, where the release of latent heat of condensation keeps the air warm and buoyant, radiation cooling increases the density of the air. Satellites that monitor radiation emitted in the upper troposphere record considerable outward-emitted radiation over the tropics. (2) Because the Coriolis force becomes stronger with increasing distance from the equator, the poleward-moving upper air is deflected into a nearly west-to-east flow by the time it reaches 25° latitude. Thus, a restricted poleward flow of air ensues. Stated another way, the Coriolis force causes a general pileup of air (convergence) aloft. As a result, general subsidence occurs in the zones located between 20° and 35° latitude.

This subsiding air is relatively dry, because it has released its moisture near the equator. In addition, the effect of adiabatic heating during descent further reduces the relative

FIGURE 7 Idealized global circulation proposed for the three-cell circulation model of a rotating Earth.

humidity of the air. Consequently, this zone of subsidence is the site of the world's subtropical deserts. The Sahara Desert of North Africa and the Great Australian Desert are located in these regions of sinking air.

Because winds are generally weak and variable near the center of this zone of descending air, this region is popularly called the **horse latitudes.** The name is believed to have been coined by Spanish sailors, who, while crossing the Atlantic, were sometimes becalmed in these waters and reportedly were forced to throw horses overboard when they could no longer water or feed them.

From the center of the horse latitudes, the surface flow splits into a poleward branch and an equatorward branch. The equatorward flow is deflected by the Coriolis force to form the reliable **trade winds,** so called because they enabled early sailing ships to trade between continents. In the Northern Hemisphere, the trades blow from the northeast, where they provided the sail power for exploration of the New World in the sixteenth and seventeenth centuries. In the Southern Hemisphere, the trades are from the southeast. The trade winds from both hemispheres meet near the equator in a region that has a weak pressure gradient. This region is called the **doldrums.** Here light winds and humid conditions provide the monotonous weather that is the basis for the expression "down in the doldrums."

In the three-cell model the circulation between 30° and 60° latitude (north and south) is more complicated than that within the Hadley cells (see Figure 7). The net surface flow is poleward, and because of the Coriolis force, the winds have a strong westerly component. These **prevailing westerlies** were known to Benjamin Franklin, perhaps the first American weather forecaster, who noted that storms migrated from west to east across the colonies. Franklin also observed that the westerlies were much more sporadic and, therefore, less reliable than the trade winds for sail power. We now know that it is the migration of cyclones and anticyclones across the midlatitudes that disrupts the general westerly flow at the surface. Because of the importance of the midlatitude circulation in producing our daily weather, we will consider the westerlies in more detail in a later section.

Relatively little is known about the circulation in high (polar) latitudes. It is generally understood that subsidence near the poles produces a surface flow that moves equatorward and is deflected into the **polar easterlies** of both hemispheres. As these cold polar winds move equatorward, they eventually encounter the warmer westerly flow of the midlatitudes. The region where the flow of warm air clashes with cold air has been named the **polar front.** The significance of this region will be considered later.

Observed Distribution of Pressure and Winds

As you might expect, Earth's global wind patterns are associated with a distinct distribution of surface air pressure. To simplify this discussion, we will first examine the idealized pressure distribution that would be expected if Earth's surface were uniform, that is, composed of all sea or all smooth land.

Idealized Zonal Pressure Belts

If Earth had a uniform surface, two latitudinally oriented belts of high and two of low pressure would exist (Figure 8a). Near the equator, the warm rising branch of the Hadley cells

FIGURE 8 (a) An imaginary uniform Earth with idealized zonal (continuous) pressure belts. (b) The real Earth with disruptions of the zonal pattern caused by large landmasses. These disruptions break up pressure zones into semipermanent high- and low-pressure cells.

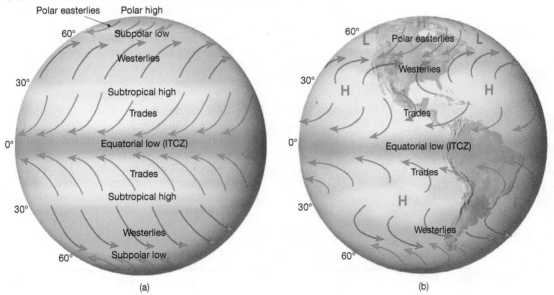

(a)

(b)

is associated with the pressure zone known as the **equatorial low.** This region of ascending moist, hot air is marked by abundant precipitation. Because it is the region where the trade winds converge, it is also referred to as the **intertropical convergence zone (ITCZ)**. In Figure 9, the ITCZ is visible as a band of heavy precipitation north of the equator.

In the belts about 20° to 35° on either side of the equator, where the westerlies and trade winds originate and go their separate ways, are the pressure zones known as the **subtropical highs.** These zones of high pressure are caused mainly by the Coriolis deflection, which restricts the poleward movement of the upper-level branch of the Hadley cells. As a result, a high-level pileup of air occurs around 20° to 35° latitude. Here a subsiding air column and diverging winds at the surface result in warm and clear weather. Recall that many large deserts lie near 30° latitude, within this zone of sinking air. Generally, the rate at which air accumulates in the upper troposphere exceeds the rate at which the air descends and spreads out at the surface. Thus, the subtropical highs exist throughout most of the year and are regarded as *semipermanent* features of the general circulation.

Another low-pressure region is situated at about 50° to 60° latitude, in a position corresponding to the polar front. Here the polar easterlies and westerlies clash to form a convergent zone known as the **subpolar low.** As you will see later, this zone is responsible for much of the stormy weather in the middle latitudes, particularly in the winter.

Finally, near Earth's poles are the **polar highs,** from which the polar easterlies originate (see Figure 8a). The high-pressure centers that develop over the cold polar areas are generated by entirely different processes than those that create the subtropical highs. Recall that the high-pressure zones in the subtropics result because the rate at which air piles up aloft exceeds the rate at which it spreads out at the surface. Stated another way, more air accumulates near 30° latitude than leaves these air columns. By contrast, the polar highs exhibit high surface pressure mainly because of surface cooling. Because air near the poles is cold and dense, it exerts a higher than average pressure.

Semipermanent Pressure Systems: The Real World

Up to this point, we have considered the global pressure systems as if they were continuous belts around Earth. However, because Earth's surface is not uniform, the only true zonal distribution of pressure exists along the subpolar low in the Southern Hemisphere, where the ocean is continuous. To a lesser extent, the equatorial low is also continuous. At other latitudes, particularly in the Northern Hemisphere, where there is a higher proportion of land compared to ocean, the zonal pattern is replaced by semipermanent cells of high and low pressure.

The idealized pattern of pressure and winds for the "real" Earth is illustrated in Figure 8b. Although representative, the pattern shown is always in a state of flux because of seasonal temperature changes, which serve to either strengthen or weaken these pressure cells. In addition, the latitudinal position of these pressure systems moves either poleward or equatorward along with the seasonal migration of the zone of maximum solar heating. This is particularly true of the low-pressure belt associated with the intertropical convergence zone. The position of this thermally produced belt of low pressure is highly dependent on solar heating. As a consequence of these factors, Earth's pressure patterns vary in strength or location during the course of the year. A view of the average global pressure patterns and resulting winds for the months of January and July are shown in Figure 10. Notice on these pressure maps that, for the most part, the observed pressure regimes are cellular (or elongated) instead of zonal. The most prominent features on both maps are the subtropical highs. These systems are centered between 20° and 35° latitude over all the larger subtropical oceans.

When we compare Figures 10a (January) and 10b (July), we see that some pressure cells are more or less year-round features, like the subtropical highs. Others, however, are seasonal, such as the low over the southwestern United States in the summer, which appears on only the July map. Relatively little pressure variation occurs from midsummer to midwinter in the Southern Hemisphere, a fact we attribute to the dominance of water in that hemisphere. Numerous departures from the idealized zonal pattern are evident in the Northern Hemisphere. The main cause of these variations is the seasonal temperature fluctuations experienced over the landmasses, especially those in the middle and higher latitudes.

January Pressure and Wind Patterns On the January pressure map shown in Figure 10a, note that a very strong high-pressure center, called the **Siberian high,** is posi-

FIGURE 9 The intertropical convergence zone (ITCZ) is seen as the band of heavy rainfall shown in reds and yellows, which extends east–west just north of the equator. (Courtesy of NOAA)

FIGURE 10 Average surface pressure and associated global circulation for (a) January and (b) July.

tioned over the frozen landscape of northern Asia. A weaker polar high is located over the chilled North American continent. These cold anticyclones consist of very dense air that accounts for the weight of these air columns. In fact, the highest sea-level pressure ever measured, 1084 millibars (32.01 inches of mercury) was recorded in December 1968 at Agata, Siberia.

The polar highs are prominent features of the winter circulation over the northern continents. Subsidence within these air columns results in clear skies and divergent surface flow. The resulting winds are called *polar easterlies*.

As the Arctic highs strengthen over the continents, a weakening is observed in the subtropical anticyclones situated over the oceans. Further, the average position of the subtropical highs tends to be closer to the eastern margin of the oceans in January than in July. Notice in Figure 10a that the center of the subtropical high located in the North Atlantic (sometimes called the **Azores high**) is positioned close to the northwest coast of Africa.

Also shown on the January map but absent in July are two intense semipermanent low-pressure centers. Named the **Aleutian low** and the **Icelandic low,** these cyclonic cells are situated over the North Pacific and North Atlantic, respectively. They are not stationary cells, but rather the composite of numerous cyclonic storms that traverse these regions. In other words, so many cyclones are present that these regions of the globe are almost always experiencing low pressure, hence the term *semipermanent.* Remember that cyclones are traveling low-pressure centers with low-level convergence and an upward flow. As a result, the areas affected by the Aleutian and Icelandic lows experience cloudy conditions and abundant winter precipitation.

The cyclones that form the Aleutian low are produced as frigid air, directed by the Siberian high, flows off the continent of Asia and overruns comparatively warm air over the Pacific. The strong temperature contrast creates a steep pressure gradient that becomes organized into a counterclockwise rotating storm cell. Nevertheless, with the large number of cyclonic storms that form over the North Pacific and travel eastward, it should be no surprise that the coastal areas of southern Alaska receive abundant precipitation. This fact is exemplified by the climate data for Sitka, Alaska, a coastal town that receives 215 centimeters (85 inches) of precipitation each year, over five times that received in Churchill, Manitoba, Canada. Although both towns are situated at roughly the same latitude, Churchill is located in the continental interior far removed from the influence of the Aleutian low.

July Pressure and Wind Patterns   The pressure pattern over the Northern Hemisphere changes dramatically with the onset of summer as increased amounts of radiation strike the northern landmasses (see Figure 10b). High surface temperatures over the continents generate lows that replace the winter highs. These thermal lows consist of warm ascending air that induces inward directed surface flow. The strongest of these low-pressure centers develops over southern Asia. A weaker thermal low is also found in the southwestern United States.

Notice in Figure 10 that during the summer months, the subtropical highs in the Northern Hemisphere migrate westward and become more intense than during the winter months. These strong high-pressure centers dominate the summer circulation over the oceans and pump warm moist air onto the continents that lie to the west of these highs. This results in an increase in precipitation over parts of eastern North America and Southeast Asia.

During the peak of the summer season, the subtropical high found in the North Atlantic is positioned near the island of Bermuda, hence the name **Bermuda high.** (Bermuda is located about 1500 kilometers, or 900 miles, east of the South Carolina coast.) Recall that in the Northern Hemisphere win-

ter the Bermuda high is located near Africa and goes by the alias *Azores high* (see Figure 10).

Monsoons

The greatest *seasonal* change in Earth's global circulation is the monsoon. Contrary to popular belief, **monsoon** does not mean "rainy season"; rather, it refers to a wind system that exhibits a pronounced seasonal reversal in direction. In general, winter is associated with winds that blow predominantly off the continents and that produce a dry winter monsoon. By contrast, in summer, warm moisture-laden air blows from the sea toward the land. Thus, the summer monsoon, which is usually associated with abundant precipitation, is the source of the misconception.

The Asian Monsoon

The best-known and most pronounced monsoon circulation is found in southern and southeastern Asia. Like all winds, the Asian monsoon is driven by pressure differences that are generated by unequal heating of Earth's surface. As summer approaches, the temperatures in India and surrounding Southeast Asia soar. For example, summertime temperatures at New Delhi, India, often exceed 40°C (104°F). This intense solar heating generates a low-pressure area over southern Asia. Recall that thermal lows form because intense surface heating causes expansion of the overlying air column. This in turn generates outflow aloft that encourages inward flow at the surface. With the development of the low-pressure center over India, moisture-laden air from the Indian Ocean flows landward, thereby generating a pattern of precipitation typical of the summer monsoon.

One of the world's rainiest regions is found on the slopes of the Himalayas where orographic lifting of moist air from the Indian Ocean produces copious precipitation. Cherrapunji, India, once recorded an annual rainfall of 25 meters (82.5 feet), most of which fell during the four months of the summer monsoon (Figure 11b).

As winter approaches, long nights and low sun angles result in the accumulation of frigid air over the vast landscape of northern Russia. This generates a cold anticyclone called the *Siberian high,* which begins to dominate the winter circulation over Asia. The subsiding dry air of the Siberian high produces surface flow that moves across southern Asia producing predominantly offshore winds (Figure 11a). By the time this flow reaches India, it has warmed considerably but remains extremely dry. For example, Bombay, India, receives less than 1 percent of its annual precipitation in the winter. The remainder comes in the summer, with the vast majority falling from June through September.

The Asian monsoon is complex and is strongly influenced by the seasonal change in the amount of solar heating received by the vast Asian continent. However, another factor, related to the annual migration of the Sun, also contributes to the pronounced monsoon circulation of southeastern Asia.

(a) **Winter monsoon**

(b) **Summer monsoon**

FIGURE 11   Asia's monsoon circulation occurs in conjunction with the seasonal shift of the intertropical convergence zone (ITCZ). (a) In January a strong high pressure develops over Asia and cool, dry, continental air generates the dry winter monsoon. (b) With the onset of summer, the ITCZ migrates northward and draws warm, moist air onto the continent.

As shown in Figure 11, the Asian monsoon is associated with a larger than average seasonal migration of the intertropical convergence zone (ITCZ). With the onset of summer the ITCZ moves northward over the continent and is accompanied by peak rainfall. The opposite occurs in the Asian winter as the ITCZ moves south of the equator. (Recall the ITCZ is a belt of low pressure and rising air that drives the Hadley cells.)

The migration of the ITCZ is accompanied by a dramatic change in pressure. The strong high-pressure system and subsidence that dominates the winter flow is replaced by low pressure and convergence during the summer months. This significant shift in pressure is thought to aid the northward movement of the ITCZ.

Of major importance are the Himalaya Mountains and the huge Tibetan Plateau, which have an *average* elevation that is higher than the highest peaks in the Colorado Rockies. During the winter months these topographic barriers contribute to the extreme temperature difference that exists between the cold continental interior and the milder coastal areas. This temperature contrast produces a strong jet stream that becomes anchored over these highlands. The role that this jet stream plays in the dry winter monsoon is not known with certainty. Nevertheless, in the summer, as the temperature differential over the continent diminishes, the jet stream breaks down. Clearly, these topographic barriers and the resulting upper airflow play a major role in the migration of the ITCZ.

Nearly half the world's population inhabits regions affected by monsoonal circulation. Further, many of these people depend on subsistence agriculture for their livelihood. Therefore, the timely arrival of the monsoon rains often means the difference between adequate nutrition and widespread malnutrition.

The North American Monsoon

Many regions of the globe experience seasonal wind shifts like those associated with the Asian monsoon. Although none are as dramatic as the Asian monsoon, these smaller features are important elements of the global circulation and affect most of Earth's landmasses.

For example, a relatively small seasonal wind shift influences a portion of North America. Sometimes called the *North American monsoon*, this circulation pattern produces a dry spring followed by a comparatively rainy summer that impacts large areas of the southwestern United States and northwestern Mexico.* This is illustrated by Tucson, Arizona, which typically receives almost sixty times more precipitation in July than in May. As shown in Figure 12, these summer rains typically last into September when drier conditions reestablish themselves.

Summer daytime temperatures in the American Southwest, particularly in the low deserts, can be extremely hot. This intense surface heating generates a low-pressure center over Arizona. The resulting circulation pattern brings warm, moist air from the Gulf of California (Figure 13). The Gulf of Mexico is also thought to be a source of some of the moisture responsible for the summer precipitation. The supply of atmospheric moisture from nearby marine sources, coupled with the convergence and upward flow of the thermal low, is conducive to generating the precipitation this region experiences during the hottest months. Although often associated with the state of Arizona, this monsoon is actually strongest in northwestern Mexico and is quite pronounced in New Mexico.

---

*This event is also called the *Arizona monsoon* and the *Southwest monsoon* because it has been extensively studied in this part of the United States.

FIGURE 12 Climate diagram for Tucson, Arizona, showing a summer precipitation maximum produced by a monsoon circulation that draws moist air in from the Gulf of California and to a lesser extent from the Gulf of Mexico.

The Westerlies

Prior to World War II, upper-air observations were scarce. Since then, aircraft and radiosondes have provided a great deal of data about the upper troposphere. Among the most important discoveries was that airflow aloft in the middle latitudes has a strong west-to-east component, thus the name *westerlies*.

Why Westerlies?

Let us consider the reason for the predominance of westerly flow aloft. Recall that winds are created and maintained by pressure differences that are a result of temperature differences.

Students Sometimes Ask . . .

Does monsoon mean "rainy season"?

No. Regions that experience monsoons typically have both a wet and a dry season. Monsoon refers to a wind system that exhibits a pronounced seasonal reversal in direction. In general, winter is associated with winds that blow predominantly off the continents and produce a dry winter monsoon. By contrast, in summer, warm moisture-laden air blows from the sea toward the land. Thus, the summer monsoon, which is usually associated with abundant precipitation, is the source of the misconception.

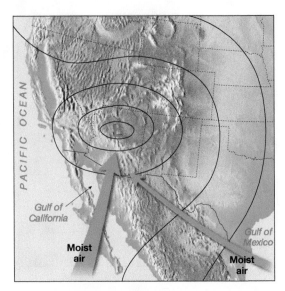

FIGURE 13 High summer temperatures over the southwestern United States create a thermal low that draws moist air from the Gulf of California and the Gulf of Mexico. This summer monsoon produces an increase in precipitation, which often comes in the form of thunderstorms, over the southwestern United States and northwestern Mexico.

In the case of the westerlies, it is the temperature contrast between the poles and equator that drives these winds. Figure 14 illustrates the pressure distribution with height over the cold polar region as compared to the much warmer tropics. Because cold air is more dense (compact) than warm air, air pressure decreases more rapidly in a column of cold air than in a column of warm air. The pressure surfaces (planes) in Figure 14 represent a grossly simplified view of the pressure distribution we would expect to observe from pole to equator.

Over the equator, where temperatures are higher, air pressure decreases more gradually than over the cold polar regions. Consequently, at the same altitude above Earth's surface, higher pressure exists over the tropics and lower pressure is the norm above the poles. Thus, the resulting pressure gradient is directed from the equator (area of higher pressure) toward the poles (area of lower pressure).

Once the air from the tropics begins to advance poleward in response to this pressure-gradient force (red arrow in Figure 14), the Coriolis force comes into play to change the direction of airflow. Recall that in the Northern Hemisphere the Coriolis force causes winds to be deflected to the right. Eventually, a balance is reached between the poleward-directed pressure-gradient force and the Coriolis force to generate a wind with a strong west-to-east component (Figure 14). Recall that such winds are called *geostrophic winds*. Because the equator-to-pole temperature gradient shown in Figure 14 is typical over the globe, a westerly flow aloft should be expected, and on most occasions it is observed.

It can also be shown that the pressure gradient increases with altitude; as a result, so should wind speeds. This increase in wind speed continues only to the tropopause, where it starts to decrease upward into the stratosphere.

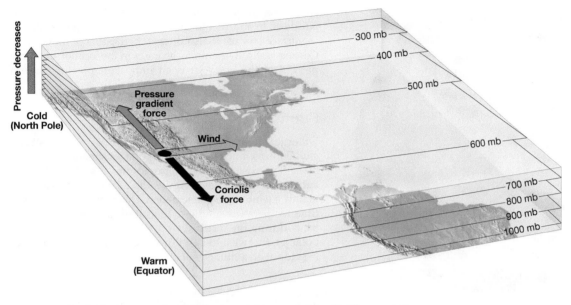

FIGURE 14 Idealized pressure gradient that develops aloft because of density differences between cold polar air and warm tropical air. Notice that the poleward-directed pressure-gradient force is balanced by an equatorward-directed Coriolis force. The result is a prevailing flow from west to east, which is called the *westerlies*.

Jet Streams

Embedded within the westerly flow aloft are narrow ribbons of high-speed winds that meander for thousands of kilometers (Figure 15a). These fast streams of air once were considered analogous to jets of water and thus were named **jet streams.** These high-speed air currents have widths that vary from less than 100 kilometers (60 miles) to over 500 kilometers (300 miles) and are generally a few kilometers thick. Wind speeds are frequently in excess of 200 kilometers (120 miles) per hour but rarely exceed 400 kilometers (240 miles) per hour.

Although jet streams had been predicted earlier, their existence was first dramatically illustrated during World War II. American bombers heading westward toward Japanese-occupied islands occasionally made little headway. On abandoning their missions, the planes on their return flight experienced westerly tail winds that sometimes exceeded 300 kilometers per hour. Even today commercial aircraft use these strong tail winds to increase their speed when making eastward flights around the globe. On westward flights, of course, these fast currents of air are avoided when possible.

Origin of the Polar Jet Stream

What is the origin of these distinctive, energetic winds that exist within the slower, general westerly flow? The key is that large temperature contrasts at the surface produce steep pressure gradients aloft and hence faster upper air winds. In winter it is not unusual to have a warm balmy day in southern Florida and near-freezing temperatures in Georgia, only a few hundred kilometers to the north. Such large wintertime temperature contrasts lead us to expect faster westerly flow

at that time of year. Observations substantiate these expectations. In general, the fastest upper air winds are located above regions of the globe having large temperature contrasts across very narrow zones. Stated another way, jet streams are located in regions of the atmosphere where large horizontal temperature differences occur over short distances.

These large temperature contrasts occur along linear zones called *fronts*. The best-known jet stream occurs along a major frontal zone called the *polar front* and is appropriately named the **polar jet stream,** or simply the *polar jet* (Figure 15b). Because this jet stream occurs mainly in the middle latitudes it is also known as the *mid-latitude jet stream*. Recall that the polar front is situated between the cool winds of the polar easterlies and the relatively warm westerlies. Instead of flowing nearly straight west-to-east, the polar jet stream usually has a meandering path. Occasionally, it flows almost due north–south. Sometimes it splits into two jets that may, or may not, rejoin. Like the polar front, this jet is not continuous around the globe.

Occasionally, the polar jet exceeds 500 kilometers (300 miles) per hour. On the average, however, it travels at 125 kilometers (75 miles) per hour in the winter and roughly half that speed in the summer (Figure 16). This seasonal difference is due to the much stronger temperature gradient that exists in the middle latitudes during the winter.

Because the location of the polar jet roughly coincides with that of the polar front, its latitudinal position migrates with the seasons. Thus, like the zone of maximum solar heating, the jet moves northward during summer and southward in winter. During the cold winter months, the polar jet stream may extend as far south as 30° north latitude (Figure 16). With the coming of spring, the zone of maximum solar heating, and

(a)

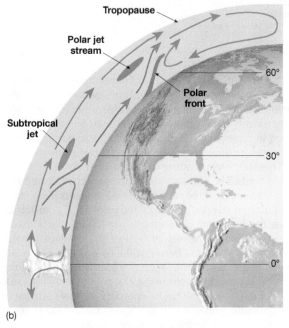

(b)

FIGURE 15 Jet streams. (a) Approximate positions of the polar and subtropical jet streams. Note that these fast-moving currents are generally not continuous around the entire globe. (b) A cross-sectional view of the polar and subtropical jets.

therefore the jet, begins a gradual northward migration. By midsummer, its average position is about 50° north latitude, but it may penetrate much farther poleward.

As the polar jet shifts northward, there is a corresponding change in the region where outbreaks of severe thunderstorms and tornadoes occur. For example, in February most tornadoes occur in the states bordering the Gulf of Mexico. By midsummer the center of this activity shifts to the northern plains and Great Lakes states. As you can see, the polar jet

stream plays a very important role in the weather of the midlatitudes. In addition to supplying energy to the circulation of surface storms, it also directs their paths of movement. Consequently, determining changes in the location and flow pattern of the polar jet is an important part of modern weather forecasting.

Subtropical Jet Stream

Other jet streams are known to exist, but none have been studied in as much detail as the polar jet stream. A semipermanent jet exists over the subtropics and as such is called the **subtropical jet stream** (Figure 15b). The subtropical jet is mainly a wintertime phenomenon. Due to the weak summertime temperature gradient, the subtropical jet is relatively weak during the warm season. Somewhat slower than the polar jet, this west-to-east flowing current is centered at 25° latitude at an altitude of about 13 kilometers (8 miles).

Waves in the Westerlies

It is important to remember that the mid-latitude jet stream is an integral part of the westerlies. It is not a dramatic anomaly like a hurricane. In fact, the jet stream can be more accurately described as the fast core of the overall westerly flow, like the fastest moving portion of a river (Figure 17). Studies of upper-level wind charts reveal that the westerlies follow wavy paths that have rather long wavelengths. Much of our knowledge of these large-scale motions is attributed to C. G. Rossby, who first explained the nature of these waves. The longest wave patterns (called *Rossby waves*) have wavelengths of 4000 to 6000 kilometers, so that three to six waves will fit around the globe (Figure 17). Although the air flows eastward along this wavy path, these long waves tend to remain stationary or move slowly.

FIGURE 16 The position and speed of the polar jet stream changes with the seasons, migrating freely between about 30° and 70° latitude. Shown are flow patterns that are common for summer and winter.

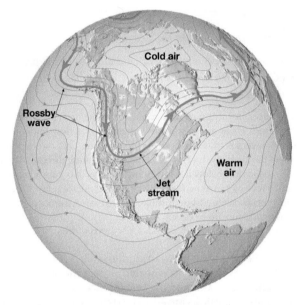

FIGURE 17 Idealized airflow of the westerlies at the 500-millibar level. The five long-wavelength undulations, called *Rossby waves*, compose this flow. The jet stream is the fast core of this wavy flow.

Although much remains to be learned about the wavy flow of the westerlies, its basic features are understood with some certainty. Among the most obvious characteristics of the flow aloft are its seasonal changes. The higher wind speeds in the cool season are depicted on upper-air charts by more closely spaced contour lines, as shown in Figure 18. The summer-to-winter change in wind speed is a consequence of the seasonal contrasts of the temperature gradients. The steep temperature gradient across the middle latitudes in winter corresponds to a stronger flow aloft.

In addition to seasonal changes in the strength of its flow, the position of the polar jet stream also shifts from summer to winter. With the approach of winter, the jet migrates equatorward. As summer nears, it moves back toward the poles (Figure 16). By midwinter the jet core may penetrate as far south as central Florida. Because the paths of cyclonic systems are guided by the flow aloft, we can expect the southern tier of states to encounter most of their severe weather in the winter. During hot summer months, the storm track is across the northern states, and some cyclones never leave Canada. In addition to seasonal changes in storm tracks, the number of cyclones generated also varies seasonally. The largest number form in the cooler months when temperature contrasts are most pronounced.

As you might expect, a close relationship exists between the location of the polar jet stream and conditions near the surface, particularly temperatures. When the mid-latitude jet is situated equatorward of your location, the weather will usually be colder and stormier than normal. Conversely, when the polar jet moves poleward of your location, warmer and drier conditions are likely to prevail. Further, when the

In addition to Rossby waves, shorter waves occur in the middle and upper troposphere. These shorter waves are often associated with cyclones at the surface and, like these storms, they travel from west to east around the globe at rates of up to 15° of longitude per day.

FIGURE 18 Simplified 500-millibar height-contour chart for January. The position of the jet-stream core is shown in dark red.

ff	Miles per hour
⊚	Calm
—	1–2
⌐	3–8
⌐	9–14
⌐	15–20
⌐	21–25
⌐	26–31
⌐	32–37
⌐	38–43
⌐	44–49
⌐	50–54
⌐	55–60
⌐	61–66
⌐	67–71
⌐	72–77
⌐	78–83
⌐	84–89
⌐	119–123

position of the jet stream remains fixed for extended periods, weather extremes can result. Thus, depending on the position of the jet stream, the weather could be hotter, colder, drier, or wetter than normal. We shall return later to this important relationship between the jet stream and middle latitude weather.

Westerlies and Earth's Heat Budget

Now let us return to the wind's function of maintaining Earth's heat budget by transporting heat from the equator toward the poles. The equator receives more solar radiation than it radiates back into space, whereas the poles experience the reverse situation. Thus, the equator has excess heat, whereas the poles experience a deficit. Although the flow near the equator is somewhat *meridional* (north to south), at most other latitudes the flow is *zonal* (west to east). The reason for the zonal flow, as we have seen, is the Coriolis force. The question we now consider is: *How can wind with a west-to-east flow transfer heat from south to north?*

In addition to its seasonal migrations, the polar jet can change positions on shorter time scales as well. There may be periods of a week or more when the flow is nearly west to east, as shown in Figure 19a. When this condition prevails, relatively mild temperatures occur and few disturbances are experienced in the region south of the jet stream. Then without warning, the flow aloft begins to meander and produces large-amplitude waves and a general north-to-south flow (Figure 19b and c). Such a change allows cold air to advance southward. Because this influx intensifies the temperature gradient, the flow aloft is also strengthened. Recall that strong temperature contrasts create steep pressure gradients that organize into rotating cyclonic systems. The jet stream supports these lows by providing divergence aloft that enhances the inward flow at the surface.

During these periods, cyclonic activity dominates the weather. For a week or more, cyclonic storms redistribute large quantities of heat across the middle latitudes by moving cold air equatorward and warm air poleward. This redistribution eventually results in a weakened temperature gradient and a return to a flatter flow aloft and less intense weather at the surface (Figure 19d). Cycles such as these, which consist of alternating periods of calm and stormy weather, can last from one to six weeks.

Laboratory experiments using rotating fluids to simulate Earth's circulation support the existence of waves and eddies that carry on the task of heat transfer in

the middle latitudes. In these studies, called *dishpan experiments*, a large circular pan is heated around the outer edge to represent the equator and the center is cooled to duplicate a pole. Colored particles are added so that the flow can be easily observed and photographed. When the pan is heated, but not rotated, a simple convection cell forms to redistribute the

FIGURE 19 Cyclic changes that occur in the upper-level airflow of the westerlies. The flow, which has the jet stream as its axis, starts out nearly straight and then develops meanders and cyclonic activity that dominate the weather.

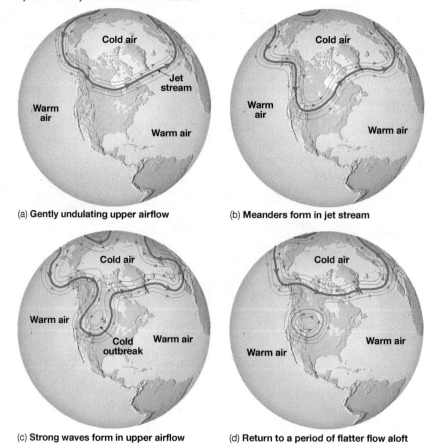

(a) **Gently undulating upper airflow**

(b) **Meanders form in jet stream**

(c) **Strong waves form in upper airflow**

(d) **Return to a period of flatter flow aloft**

FIGURE 20 Photograph obtained from a *dishpan experiment*. The pan is heated around the edge to represent the equator, and the center is cooled to duplicate the poles. When the pan is rotated, a wavy flow develops with eddies embedded between meanders, as shown. This flow pattern closely parallels that produced in the "real" atmosphere, where the meanders represent the wavy flow of the westerlies and the eddies are cyclonic and anticyclonic systems embedded within this larger circulation. (Courtesy of D. H. Fultz, University of Chicago Hydrodynamics Laboratory)

heat. This cell is similar to the Hadley cell considered earlier. When the pan is rotated, however, the simple circulation breaks down and the flow develops a wavy pattern with eddies embedded between meanders, as seen in Figure 20.

These experiments indicate that changing the rate of rotation and varying the temperature gradient largely determine the flow pattern produced. Such studies have added greatly to our understanding of global circulation.

In summary, we now understand that the wavy flow aloft is largely responsible for producing surface weather patterns. During periods when the flow aloft is relatively flat (small-amplitude waves), little cyclonic activity is generated at the surface. Conversely, when the flow exhibits large-amplitude waves having short wavelengths, vigorous cyclonic storms are created.

Global Winds and Ocean Currents

Where the atmosphere and ocean are in contact, energy is passed from moving air to the water through friction. As a consequence, the drag exerted by winds blowing steadily across the ocean causes the surface layer of water to move (see Box 3). Thus, because winds are the primary driving force of **ocean currents,** a relationship exists between the oceanic circulation and the general atmospheric circulation. A comparison of Figures 21 and 10 illustrates this. A further clue to the influence of winds on ocean circulation is provided by the currents in the northern Indian Ocean, where there are seasonal wind shifts known as the *summer* and *winter monsoons.* When the winds change directions, the surface currents also reverse direction. North and south of the equator are two westward-moving currents, the North and South Equatorial currents, which derive their energy principally from the trade winds that blow from the northeast and southeast, respectively,

FIGURE 21 Major ocean currents. Poleward-moving currents are warm, and equatorward-moving currents are cold.

FIGURE 22 Enhanced satellite image of the complex flow of the Gulf Stream. Reds and yellows indicate warmer waters. Note that the Gulf Stream flows northward along the Florida coast (lower left) and then diagonally toward the upper right of the image. (Courtesy of O. Brown, R. Evans, and M. Carle/Rosenstiel School of Marine and Atmospheric Science)

toward the equator. These equatorial currents can be thought of as the backbone of the system of ocean currents. Because of the Coriolis force, these currents are deflected poleward to form clockwise spirals in the Northern Hemisphere and counterclockwise spirals in the Southern Hemisphere. These nearly circular ocean currents are found in each of the major ocean basins centered around the subtropical high-pressure systems (see Figure 21).

In the North Atlantic, the equatorial current is deflected northward through the Caribbean, where it becomes the *Gulf Stream.* As the Gulf Stream moves along the eastern coast of the United States, it is strengthened by the prevailing westerly winds and is deflected to the east (to the right) between 35° north and 45° north latitude (Figure 22). As it continues northeastward beyond the Grand Banks, it gradually widens and decreases speed until it becomes a vast, slowly moving current known as the North Atlantic Drift. As the North Atlantic Drift approaches Western Europe, it splits, with part moving northward past Great Britain and Norway. The other part is deflected southward as the cool Canaries current. As the Canaries current moves south, it eventually merges into the North Equatorial current.

The Importance of Ocean Currents

In addition to being significant considerations in ocean navigation, currents have an important effect on climate. The moderating effect of poleward-moving warm ocean currents is well known. The North Atlantic Drift, an extension of the warm

Gulf Stream, keeps Great Britain and much of northwestern Europe warmer than one would expect for their latitudes.

In addition to influencing temperatures of adjacent land areas, cold currents have other climatic influences. For example, where tropical deserts exist along the west coasts of continents, cold ocean currents have a dramatic impact. The principal west-coast deserts are the Atacama in Peru and Chile, and the Namib in southern Africa. The aridity along these coasts is intensified because the lower air is chilled by cold offshore waters. When this occurs, the air becomes very stable and resists the upward movements necessary to create precipitation-producing clouds. In addition, the presence of cold currents causes temperatures to approach and often reach the dew point. As a result, these areas are characterized by high relative humidities and much fog. Thus, not all tropical deserts are hot with low humidities and clear skies. Rather, the presence of cold currents transforms some tropical deserts into relatively cool, damp places that are often shrouded in fog.

Ocean currents also play a major role in maintaining Earth's heat balance. They accomplish this task by transferring heat from the tropics, where there is an excess of heat, to the polar regions, where a deficit exists. Ocean water movements account for about a quarter of this total heat transport and winds the remaining three-quarters.

Ocean Currents and Upwelling

In addition to producing surface currents, winds can also cause vertical water movements. **Upwelling,** the rising of cold water from deeper layers to replace warmer surface water, is a common wind-induced vertical movement. It is most characteristic along the eastern shores of the oceans, most notably along the coasts of California, Peru, and West Africa.

Upwelling occurs in these areas when winds blow toward the equator parallel to the coast. Because of the Coriolis force, the surface-water movement is directed away from the shore. As the surface layer moves away from the coast, it is replaced by water that "upwells" from below the surface. This slow upward flow from depths of 50 to 300 meters (165 to 1000 feet) brings water that is cooler than the original surface water and creates a characteristic zone of lower temperatures near the shore.

For swimmers who are accustomed to the waters along the mid-Atlantic shore of the United States, a dip in the Pacific off the coast of central California can be a chilling surprise. In August, when temperatures in the Atlantic are 21°C (70°F) or higher, central California's surf is only about 15°C (60°F). Coastal upwelling also brings to the ocean surface greater concentrations of dissolved nutrients, such as nitrates and phosphates. These nutrient-enriched waters from below promote the growth of plankton, which in turn supports extensive populations of fish.

El Niño and La Niña

As shown in Figure 23a, during normal years the atmospheric circulation in the tropical Pacific is dominated by strong trade winds. These wind systems, in turn, generate a strong equa-

(a) **Normal conditions**

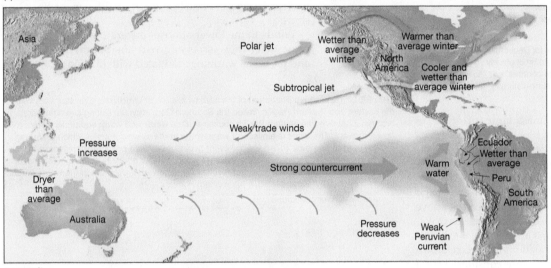

(b) **El Niño**

FIGURE 23 The relationship between the Southern Oscillation and El Niño is illustrated on these simplified maps. (a) Normally, the trade winds and strong equatorial currents flow toward the west. At the same time, the strong Peruvian current causes upwelling of cold water along the west coast of South America. (b) When the Southern Oscillation occurs, the pressure over the eastern and western Pacific flip-flops. This causes the trade winds to diminish, leading to an eastward movement of warm water along the equator. As a result, the surface waters of the central and eastern Pacific warm, with far-reaching consequences to weather patterns.

torial current that flows westward from South America toward Australia and the Philippines. In addition, a cold oceanic current flows equatorward along the coast of Ecuador and Peru. The latter flow, called the Peruvian current, encourages upwelling of cold, nutrient-filled waters that serve as the primary food source for millions of small fish, particularly anchovies. Near the end of each year, however, a warm countercurrent, which flows eastward along the equator, develops. As a result, warm water begins to accumulate along the coasts of Ecuador and Peru.

During the nineteenth century the local residents named this warm countercurrent El Niño ("the child") after the

Christ child because it usually appeared during the Christmas season. Normally, these warm countercurrents last for, at most, a few weeks when they again give way to the cold Peruvian flow. However, at irregular intervals of three to seven years, these countercurrents become unusually strong and replace normally cold offshore waters with warm equatorial waters (Figure 23b). Today scientists use the term **El Niño** for these episodes of ocean warming that affect the tropical Pacific (Figure 24a).

The onset of El Niño is marked by abnormal weather patterns that drastically affect the economies of Ecuador and Peru. As shown in Figure 23b, these unusually strong

225

Sea surface temperature anomalies (°C)

−5.0   0.0   5.0

(a) **El Niño (December 1997)**

(b) **La Niña (December 2000)**

FIGURE 24   El Niño verses La Niña. These maps show sea-surface temperature anomalies for December 1997 and December 2000. (a) El Niño events are characterized by unusually warm ocean temperatures in the equatorial Pacific. (b) In contrast, La Niña events are characterized by unusually cool ocean temperatures in the equatorial Pacific.

causing unprecedented beach erosion, landslides, and floods. In the southern United States, heavy rains also brought floods to Texas and the Gulf states. The same energized jet stream that produced heavy rains in the South disrupted the development of hurricanes that were forming over the Atlantic. It was one of the quietest Atlantic hurricane seasons on record.

Major El Niño events, such as the one in 1997 and 1998, are intimately related to the large-scale atmospheric circulation. Each time an El Niño occurs, the barometric pressure drops over large portions of the southeastern Pacific, whereas in the western Pacific, near Indonesia and northern Australia, the pressure rises (Figure 25). Then, as a major El Niño event comes to an end, the pressure difference between these two regions swings back in the opposite direction. This seesaw pattern of atmospheric pressure between the eastern and western Pacific is called the **Southern Oscillation**. It is an inseparable part of the El Niño warmings that occur in the Pacific every three to seven years. Therefore, this phenomenon is often termed El Niño/Southern Oscillation, or ENSO for short.

Winds in the lower atmosphere are the link between the pressure change associated with the Southern Oscillation and the ocean warming associated with El Niño (Box 4). Dur-

countercurrents amass large quantities of warm water that block the upwelling of colder, nutrient-filled water. As a result, the anchovies, which support the population of game fish, starve which devastates the fishing industry. At the same time, some inland areas that are normally arid receive above average rainfall. In these areas, yields of cotton and other crops are far above average. These climatic fluctuations have been known for years, but they were considered local phenomena. Today, we know that El Niño is part of the global atmospheric circulation pattern and affects the weather at great distances from Peru and Ecuador.

Two of the strongest El Niño events on record occurred between 1982–83 and 1997–98, and were responsible for weather extremes of a variety of types in many parts of the world. During the 1982–83 El Niño event, heavy rains and flooding plagued normally dry portions of Ecuador and Peru. Some locations that usually receive only 10 to 13 centimeters of rain each year had as much as 350 centimeters of precipitation. At the same time, severe drought beset Australia, Indonesia, and the Philippines. Huge crop losses, property damage, and much human suffering were recorded.

The 1997–98 El Niño brought ferocious storms that struck the California coast,

FIGURE 25   Simplified illustration of the seesaw pattern of atmospheric pressure between the eastern and western Pacific, called the *Southern Oscillation*. (a) During average years, high pressure over the eastern Pacific causes surface winds and warm equatorial waters to flow westward. The result is a pileup of warm water in the western Pacific, which promotes the lowering of pressure. (b) An El Niño event begins as surface pressure increases in the western Pacific and decreases in the eastern Pacific. This air pressure reversal weakens, or may even reverse the trade winds, and results in an eastward movement of the warm waters that had previously accumulated in the western Pacific.

(a) **Normal years**

(b) **El Niño years**

ing a typical year the trade winds converge near the equator and flow westward toward Indonesia (Figure 25a). This steady westward flow creates a warm surface current that moves from east to west along the equator. The result is a "piling up" of a thick layer of warm surface water that produces higher sea levels (by 30 centimeters) in the western Pacific. Meanwhile, the eastern Pacific is characterized by a strong Peruvian current and upwelling of cold water.

Then when the Southern Oscillation occurs, the normal situation just described changes dramatically. Barometric pressure rises in the Indonesian region, causing the pressure gradient along the equator to weaken or even to reverse. As a consequence, the once-steady trade winds diminish and may even change direction. This reversal creates a major change in the equatorial current system, with warm water flowing eastward (Figure 25b). With time, water temperatures in the central and eastern Pacific increase and sea level in the region rises. This eastward shift of the warmest surface water marks the onset of El Niño and sets up changes in atmospheric circulation that affect areas far outside the tropical Pacific.

When an El Niño began in the summer of 1997, forecasters predicted that the pool of warm water over the Pacific would displace the paths of both the subtropical and polar jet streams, which steer weather systems across North America (see Figure 23). As predicted, the subtropical jet brought rain to the Gulf Coast, where Tampa, Florida, received more than three times its normal winter precipitation. Furthermore, the mid-latitude jet pumped warm air far north into the continent. As a result, winter temperatures east of the Rockies were significantly above normal.

The effects of El Niño are somewhat variable depending in part on the temperatures and size of the warm pools. Nevertheless, some locales appear to be affected more consistently. In particular, during most El Niños, warmer-than-normal winters occur in the northern United States and Canada, and cooler-than-normal winters are experienced in the Southwest and Southeast. In addition, the eastern United States experiences wetter-than-normal conditions. By contrast, drought conditions are generally observed in Indonesia, Australia, and the Philippines. One major benefit of the circulation associated with El Niño is a suppression of the number of Atlantic hurricanes.

The opposite of El Niño is an atmospheric phenomenon known as **La Niña** (Figure 24b and Figure 26). Once thought to be the normal conditions that occur between two El Niño events, meteorologists now consider La Niña an important atmospheric phenomenon in its own right. Researchers have come to recognize that when surface temperatures in the Pacific are *colder than average*, a La Niña event is triggered that has a distinctive set of weather patterns. Typical La Niña weather patterns include cool conditions over the Pacific Northwest and especially cold winter temperatures in the Great Plains. In addition, unusually dry conditions occur in the Southwest and Southeast. However, increased precipitation is expected in the Northwest. During the La Niña winter of 1998–99, a world record snowfall for one season occurred in Washington State. Another La Niña impact is

FIGURE 26 This graph illustrates the cyclical nature of El Niño/Southern Oscillation (ENSO). Negative values (blue) represent the cold La Niña phase, while positive values (red) represent the warm El Niño phase. The graph was created by analyzing six variables, including sea-surface temperatures and sea-level pressures. (After Wolter and Timlin/NOAA)

greater hurricane activity in the Atlantic. A recent study concluded that the cost of hurricane damages in the United States is 20 times greater in La Niña years as compared to El Niño years.

Global Distribution of Precipitation

A casual glance at Figure 27a reveals a complex pattern for the distribution of precipitation. Although the map appears to be complicated, the general features of the pattern can be explained using our knowledge of global winds and pressure systems. In general, regions influenced by high pressure, with its associated subsidence and divergent winds, experience dry conditions. Conversely, regions under the influence of low pressure and its converging winds and ascending air receive ample precipitation. However, if the wind-pressure regimes were the only control of precipitation, the pattern shown in Figure 27a would be much simpler.

The inherent nature of the air is also important in determining precipitation potential. Because cold air has a low capacity for moisture compared with warm air, we would expect a latitudinal variation in precipitation, with low latitudes receiving the greatest amounts of precipitation and high latitudes receiving the least. Figure 27a indeed reveals heavy precipitation in equatorial regions and meager moisture near the landmasses poleward of 60° latitude. A noticeably arid region, however, is also found in the subtropics. This situation can be explained by examining the global wind-pressure regimes.

In addition to latitudinal variations in precipitation, the distribution of land and water complicates the precipitation pattern. Large landmasses in the middle latitudes commonly experience decreased precipitation toward their interiors. For example, central North America and central Eurasia receive considerably less precipitation than do coastal regions at the same latitude. Furthermore, the effects of mountain barriers

3 ▶ MONITORING WINDS FROM SPACE

The global ocean makes up 71 percent of Earth's surface. Winds moving over the sea surface effectively move heat and moisture from place to place, while driving ocean currents and ultimately Earth's weather and climate. Surface-based methods of monitoring winds using ships and data buoys provide only a glimpse of the wind patterns over the ocean. Today, using data collected by NASA's *QuickSTAT* spacecraft, researchers are creating maps that display how frequently strong winds blow over the open ocean at various times of the year.

From this data researchers found that Earth's windiest ocean location is Cape Farewell, Greenland, where gale force winds (winds greater than 45 mph) are common, particularly in the winter (Figure D). Many of the windiest spots occur where elevated coastlines or mountains meet the sea, and strong winds form when mid-latitude storms pass over the Gulf Stream where it flows northward into the cold Atlantic. The data also provides insight into many other phenomena, such as how high winds play a role in Earth's climate.

QuickSTAT carries the *SeaWinds* scatterometer, a specialized type of radar that operates by transmitting microwave pulses to the ocean surface and measuring the amount of energy that is bounced back (or echoed) to the satellite. Smooth ocean surfaces return weaker signals because less energy is reflected, while rough water returns a stronger signal. From such data, scientists can compute wind speed and direction. By measuring global sea-surface winds, *Sea Winds* helps researchers more accurately predict marine phenomena that have the potential to affect human endeavors. For example, navigators can use these maps to chart shipping routes. Energy companies can use the data to determine where to place offshore wind farms and to track oil spills. The U.S. Coast Guard can use the information to give advance warning of high waves to vessels at sea and to conduct search and rescue efforts.

In addition, these snapshots of ocean winds help researchers better understand and predict the development of large storm systems, such as mid-latitude cyclones and hurricanes, as well as aid in our understanding of global weather events such as El Niño. (Figure E)

FIGURE D Map produced from *SeaWind* data showing the frequency of gale force winds in the North Atlantic during winter. Notice that off the coast of Cape Farewell, Greenland, gale force winds (winds greater than 45 mph) occur more than 18 percent of the time.

FIGURE E This image shows Hurricane Ivan as it roared through the Caribbean as a deadly category 5 storm early on September 9, 2004. Data from the *SeaWinds* scatterometer aboard NASA's *QuickSCAT* spacecraft augments traditional satellite images of clouds by providing direct measurements of surface winds to compare with observed cloud patterns in an effort to better determine a storm's structure and strength.

(a) **Annual**

(b) **July**

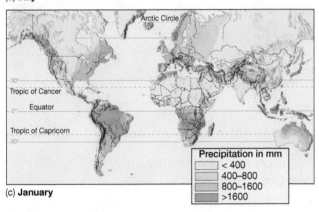

Precipitation in mm
< 400
400–800
800–1600
>1600

(c) **January**

FIGURE 27 Global distribution of precipitation: (a) annual, (b) July, and (c) January.

alter the idealized precipitation regimes we would expect solely from the global wind systems. Windward mountain slopes receive abundant precipitation, whereas leeward slopes and adjacent lowlands are usually deficient in moisture.

Zonal Distribution of Precipitation

Let us first examine the zonal distribution of precipitation that we would expect on a uniform Earth, and then add the variations caused by land and water influences. Recall from our earlier discussion that on a uniform Earth, four major pressure zones emerge in each hemisphere (see Figure 8a).

These zones include the equatorial low (ITCZ), the subtropical high, the subpolar low, and the polar high. Also, remember that these pressure belts show a marked seasonal shift toward the summer hemisphere.

The idealized precipitation regimes expected from these pressure systems are shown in Figure 28, in which we can see that the equatorial regime is centered over the equatorial low throughout most of the year. In this region, where the trade winds converge (ITCZ), heavy precipitation is experienced in all seasons. Poleward of the equatorial low in each hemisphere lie the belts of subtropical high pressure. In these regions, subsidence contributes to the dry conditions found there throughout the year. Between the wet equatorial regime and the dry subtropical regime lies a zone that is influenced by both pressure systems. Because the pressure systems migrate seasonally with the Sun, these transitional regions receive most of their precipitation in the summer when they are under the influence of the ITCZ. They experience a dry season in the winter when the subtropical high moves equatorward.

The midlatitudes receive most of their precipitation from traveling cyclonic storms (Figure 29). This region is the site of the polar front, the convergent zone between cold polar air and the warmer westerlies. It is along the polar front that cy-

FIGURE 28 Zonal precipitation patterns.

FIGURE 29 Satellite image of a well-developed mid-latitude cyclone over the British Isles. These traveling storms produce most of the precipitation in the middle latitudes. (Courtesy of European Space Agency/Science Photo Library/ Photo Researchers, Inc.)

clones are frequently generated. Because the position of the polar front migrates freely between approximately 30° and 70° latitude, most midlatitude areas receive ample precipitation. But the mean position of this zone also moves north and south with the Sun, so that a narrow belt between 30° and 40° latitude experiences a marked seasonal fluctuation in precipitation.

In winter, this zone receives precipitation from numerous cyclones as the position of the polar front moves equatorward. During the summer, however, this region is dominated by subsidence associated with the dry subtropical high. Compare the July and January precipitation data for the west coast of North America by referring to Figure 27b and c.

The polar regions are dominated by cold air that holds little moisture. Throughout the year, these regions experience only meager precipitation. Even in the summer, when temperatures rise, these areas of ice and snow are dominated by high pressure that blocks the movement of the few cyclones that do travel poleward.

Distribution of Precipitation over the Continents

The zonal pattern outlined in the previous section roughly approximates general global precipitation. Abundant precipitation occurs in the equatorial and mid-latitude regions, whereas substantial portions of the subtropical and polar realms are relatively dry. Yet numerous exceptions to this idealized zonal pattern are obvious in Figure 27a.

For example, several arid areas are found in the midlatitudes. The desert region of southern South America, known as Patagonia, is one example. Mid-latitude deserts such as Patagonia exist mostly on the leeward (rain shadow) side of a mountain barrier or in the interior of a continent, cut off from a source of moisture. Most other departures from the idealized zonal scheme result from the distribution of continents and oceans.

The most notable anomaly in the zonal distribution of precipitation occurs in the subtropics. Here we find not only many of the world's great deserts but also regions of abundant rainfall (Figure 27a). This pattern results because the subtropical high-pressure centers that dominate the circulation in these latitudes have different characteristics on their eastern and western flanks (Figure 30). Subsidence is most pronounced on the eastern side of these oceanic highs, and a strong temperature inversion is encountered very near the surface and results in stable atmospheric conditions. The upwelling of cold water along the west coasts of the adjacent continents cools the air from below and adds to the stability on the eastern sides of these highs.

Because these anticyclones tend to crowd the eastern side of an ocean, particularly in the winter, we find that the western sides of the continents adjacent to these subtropical highs are arid (Figure 30). Centered at approximately 25° north or south latitude on the western side of their respective continents, we find the Sahara Desert of North Africa, the Namib of southwest Africa, the Atacama of South America, the deserts of the Baja Peninsula of North America, and the Great Desert of Australia.

On the western side of these highs, however, subsidence is less pronounced, and convergence with associated rising air appears to be more prevalent. In addition, as this air travels over a large expanse of warm water, it acquires moisture through evaporation that acts to enhance its instability. Consequently, the eastern regions of subtropical continents generally receive ample precipitation throughout the year. Southern Florida is a good example.

Precipitation Regimes on a Hypothetical Continent

When we consider the influence of land and water on the distribution of precipitation, the pattern illustrated in Figure 31 emerges. This figure is a highly idealized precipitation scheme for a hypothetical continent located in the Northern Hemisphere. The "continent" is shaped as it is to approximate the percentage of land found at various latitudes.

FIGURE 30 Characteristics of subtropical high-pressure systems. Subsidence on the east side of these systems produces stable conditions and aridity. Convergence and uplifting on the western flank promote uplifting and instability.

Notice that this hypothetical landmass has been divided into seven zones. Each zone represents a different precipitation regime. Stated another way, all locations within the same zone (precipitation regime) experience roughly the same precipitation pattern. As we shall see, the odd shape and size of these zones reflect the way precipitation is normally distributed across landmasses located in the Northern Hemisphere. The cities shown are representatives of the precipitation pattern of each location. With this in mind, we will now examine each precipitation regime (numbered 1 through 7) to see the influences of land and water on the distribution of precipitation.

First, compare the precipitation patterns for the nine cities. Notice that the precipitation regimes for west coast locations correspond to the zonal pressure and precipitation pattern shown in Figure 28: Zone 6 equates to the equatorial low (wet all year); Zone 4 matches the subtropical high (dry all year), and so on.

For illustration, Aklavik, Canada, which is strongly influenced by the polar high, has scant moisture, whereas Singapore, near the equator, has plentiful rain every month. Also note that precipitation varies seasonally with both latitude and each city's location with respect to the ocean.

For example, precipitation graphs for San Francisco and Mazatlan, Mexico, illustrate the marked seasonal variations found in zones 3 and 5. Recall that it is the seasonal migration of the pressure systems that causes these fluctuations. Notice that Zone 2 shows a precipitation maximum in the fall and early winter, as illustrated by data for Juneau, Alaska. This pattern occurs because cyclonic storms over the North Pacific are more prevalent in the coolest half of the year. Further, the average path of these storms moves equatorward during the winter, impacting locations as far south as southern California.

The eastern half of the continent shows a marked contrast to the zonal precipitation pattern on the western side. Only the dry polar regime (Zone 1) is similar in size and position on both the Eastern and Western seaboards. The most noticeable departure from the zonal pattern is the absence of the arid subtropical region from the east coast. As noted earlier, this difference is caused by the behavior of subtropical anticyclones located over the oceans. Recall that southern Florida, which is located on the east coast of the continent, receives ample precipitation year-round, whereas the Baja Peninsula on the west coast is arid. Moving inland from the east coast, observe how precipitation decreases (compare total precipitation westward for New York, Chicago, and Omaha). This decrease, however, does not hold true for mountainous regions; even relatively small ranges, like the Appalachians, are able to extract a greater share of precipitation.

Another variation is seen with latitude. As we move poleward along the eastern half of our hypothetical continent, note the decrease in precipitation (compare Singapore, New York, and Aklavik). This is the decrease we would expect with cooler air temperatures and corresponding lower moisture capacities. We do not, however, find a similar decrease in precipitation in the higher middle latitudes along the west coast.

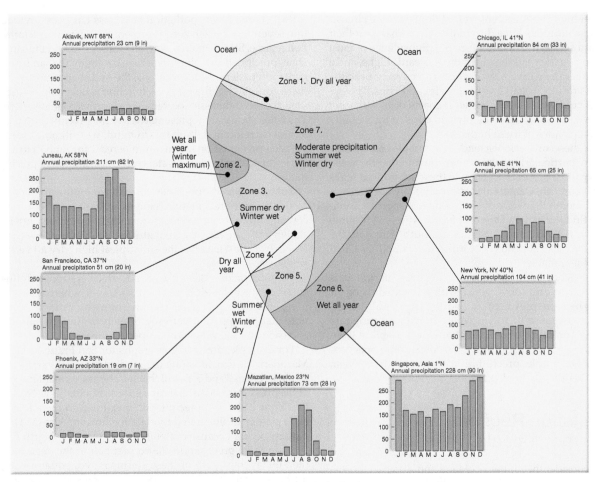

FIGURE 31 Idealized precipitation regimes for a hypothetical landmass in the Northern Hemisphere.

Because this region lies in the westerly wind belt, the west coasts of mid-latitude regions, such as Alaska, Canada, and Norway, receive abundant moisture from storms that originate over the adjacent oceans. In fact, some of the rainiest regions on Earth are found in such settings. In contrast, the east coasts of mid-latitude locations experience temperature and moisture regimes more typical of continental locations, particularly in the winter when the airflow is off the land.

Consider next the continental interior, which shows a somewhat different precipitation pattern, especially in the middle latitudes. Because cyclones are more common in the winter, we would expect mid-latitude locations also to experience maximum precipitation in the winter. The precipitation regimes of the interior, however, are affected to a degree by a type of monsoon circulation. Cold winter temperatures and dominance of flow off the land in the winter make it the drier season (Omaha and Chicago). Although cyclonic storms frequent the continental interior in the winter, they do not become precipitation producers until they have drawn in abundant moist air from the Gulf of Mexico. Thus, most of the winter precipitation falls in the eastern one-third of the United States. The lack of abundant winter precipitation in the Plains states, compared with the East, can be seen in the data for Omaha and New York City.

In the summer, the inflow of warm, moist air from the ocean is aided by the thermal low that develops over the land and causes a general increase in precipitation over the mid-continent. The dominance of summer monsoon-type precipitation is evident when we compare the patterns for India in summer and winter by using Figure 27b and c. In the United States, places in the Southeast begin their rainy season in early spring, whereas more northerly and westerly locations do not experience their peak precipitation until summer or early fall.

4 ▶ TRACKING EL NIÑO FROM SPACE

The images in Figure F show the progression of the 1997–98 El Niño as derived from the TOPEX/Poseidon satellite.* This satellite uses radar altimeters to bounce radar signals off the ocean surface to obtain precise measurements of the distance between the satellite and the sea surface. This information is combined with high-precision orbital data from the Global Positioning System (GPS) of satellites to produce maps of sea-surface height. Such maps show the topography of the sea surface. Elevated topography ("hills") indicates warmer-than-average water, whereas areas of low topography ("valleys") indicate cooler-than-

normal water. With this detailed information, scientists can determine the speed and direction of surface ocean currents.

The colors represented in these images show sea-level height relative to average. Remember, "hills" are warm and "valleys" are cool. The white and red areas indicate places of higher-than-normal sea-surface heights ("hills"). In the white areas the sea surface is between 14 and 32 centimeters above normal; in the red areas sea level is elevated by about 10 centimeters. Green areas indicate average conditions, whereas purple shows zones that are at least 18 centimeters below average sea level.

The images depict the progression of the large warm water mass from west to east across the equatorial Pacific. At its peak in November 1997, the surface area covered by the warm water mass was about one and a half times the size of the contiguous 48 states. The added amount of warm water in the eastern Pacific with a temperature between 21° and 30°C was about 30 times the combined volume of the water in all of the U.S. Great Lakes.

_____

*This box is based on material published by NASA's Goddard Space Flight Center.

FIGURE F The image for April 25, 1997, shows the Pacific on the eve of the 1997–98 El Niño event. By examining the images for July 25 and November 10, you can see the dramatic buildup of warm water (white and red areas) in the eastern Pacific and the enlarging region of cool water (purple) in the western Pacific. By the time of the March 14, 1998, image, the area of warm water in the eastern Pacific was *much* smaller. (Courtesy of NASA Goddard Space Flight Center)

Chapter Summary

- The largest planetary-scale wind patterns, called *macroscale winds*, include the westerlies and trade winds. A somewhat smaller macroscale circulation is called *synoptic scale*, or *weather-map scale*. *Mesoscale winds*, such as thunderstorms, tornadoes, and land and sea breezes, influence smaller areas and often exhibit intense vertical flow. The smallest scale of air motion is the *microscale*. Examples of these very local, often chaotic winds include gusts and dust devils.

- All winds have the same cause: pressure differences that arise because of temperature differences that are caused by unequal heating of Earth's surface. In addition to *land* and *sea breezes* brought about by the daily temperature contrast between land and water, other mesoscale winds include *mountain* and *valley breezes*, *chinook (foehn)* winds, *katabatic (fall)* winds, and *country breezes*. Mountain and valley breezes develop as air along mountain slopes is heated more intensely than air at the same elevation over the valley floor. Chinooks are warm, dry winds that sometimes move down the east slopes of the Rockies. In the Alps, winds similar to chinooks are called foehns. Katabatic (fall) winds originate when cold air, situated over a highland area such as the ice sheets of Greenland and Antarctica, is set in motion under the influence of gravity. Country breezes are associated with large urban areas where the circulation pattern is characterized by a light wind blowing into the city from the surrounding countryside.

- A simplified view of global circulation is a three-cell circulation model for each hemisphere. Because the circulation patterns between the equator and roughly 30° latitude north and south closely resemble a single-cell model developed by George Hadley in 1735, the name *Hadley cell* is generally applied. According to the three-cell circulation model, in each hemisphere, atmospheric circulation cells are located between the equator and 30° latitude, 30° and 60° latitude, and 60° latitude and the pole. The areas of general subsidence in the zone between 20° and 35° are called the *horse latitudes*. In each hemisphere, the equatorward flow from the horse latitudes forms the reliable *trade winds*. Convergence of the trade winds from both hemispheres near the equator produces a region of light winds called the *doldrums*. The circulation between 30° and 60° latitude (north and south) results in the *prevailing westerlies*. Air that moves equatorward from the poles produces the *polar easterlies* of both hemispheres. The area where the cold polar easterlies clash with the warm westerly flow of the midlatitudes is referred to as the *polar front*, an important meteorological region.

- If Earth's surface were uniform, two latitudinally oriented belts of high and two of low pressure would exist. Beginning at the equator, the four belts would be the (1) *equatorial low*, also referred to as the *intertropical convergence zone (ITCZ)*, because it is the region where the trade winds converge, (2) *subtropical high*, at about 20° to 35° on either side of the equator, (3) *subpolar low*, situated at about 50° to 60° latitude, and (4) *polar high*, near Earth's poles.

- In reality, the only true zonal pattern of pressure exists along the subpolar low in the Southern Hemisphere. At other latitudes, particularly in the Northern Hemisphere, where there is a higher proportion of land compared to ocean, the zonal pattern is replaced by semipermanent cells of high and low pressure. January pressure and wind patterns show a very strong high-pressure center, called the *Siberian High*, positioned over the frozen landscape of northern Asia. Also evident in January, but absent in July, are two intense semipermanent low-pressure centers, the *Aleutian* and *Icelandic lows*, situated over the North Pacific and North Atlantic, respectively. With the onset of summer the pressure pattern over the Northern Hemisphere changes dramatically and high temperatures over the continents generate lows that replace the winter highs. During the peak summer season, the subtropical high found in the North Atlantic (called the *Azores high* in winter) is positioned near the island of Bermuda and is called the *Bermuda high*.

- The greatest seasonal change in Earth's global circulation is the development of *monsoons*, wind systems that exhibit a pronounced seasonal reversal in direction. The best-known and most pronounced monsoonal circulation, the *Asian monsoon* found in southern and southeastern Asia, is a complex seasonal change that is strongly influenced by the amount of solar heating received by the vast Asian continent. The *North American monsoon* (also called the *Arizona monsoon* and *Southwest monsoon*), a relatively small seasonal wind shift, produces a dry spring followed by a comparatively rainy summer that impacts large areas of southwestern United States and northwestern Mexico.

- The temperature contrast between the poles and the equator drives the westerly winds (*westerlies*) located in the middle latitudes. Embedded within the westerly flow aloft are narrow ribbons of high-speed winds, called *jet streams*, that meander for thousands of kilometers. The key to the origin of polar jet streams is found in great temperature contrasts at the surface. In the region between 30° and 70°, the *polar jet stream* occurs in association with the *polar front*.

- Studies of upper-level wind charts reveal that the westerlies follow wavy paths that have rather long wavelengths. The longest wave patterns are called *Rossby waves*. During periods when the flow aloft is relatively flat, little cyclonic activity is generated at the surface. Conversely, when the flow exhibits large-amplitude waves having short wavelengths, vigorous cyclonic storms are created. In addition to seasonal changes in the strength of its flow, the position of the polar jet also shifts from summer to winter.

- Because winds are the primary driving force of ocean currents, a relationship exists between the oceanic circulation and the general atmospheric circulation. In general, in response to the circulation associated with the subtropical highs, ocean currents form clockwise spirals in the Northern Hemisphere and counterclockwise spirals in the Southern Hemisphere. In addition to influencing temperatures of adjacent land areas, cold ocean currents also transform some subtropical deserts into relatively cool, damp places that are often shrouded in fog. Furthermore, ocean currents play a major role in maintaining Earth's heat balance. In addition to producing surface currents, winds may also cause vertical water movements, such as the *upwelling* of cold water from deeper layers to replace warmer surface water.

- *El Niño* refers to episodes of ocean warming caused by a warm countercurrent flowing toward the coasts of Ecuador and Peru that replaces the cold Peruvian current. The events are part of the global circulation and related to a seesaw pattern of atmospheric pressure between the eastern and western Pacific called the *Southern Oscillation*. El Niño events influence weather at great distances from Peru and Ecuador. Two of the strongest El Niño events (1982–83 and 1997–98) were responsible for a variety of weather extremes in many parts of the world. When surface temperatures in the eastern Pacific are colder than average, a *La Niña* event is triggered. A typical La Niña winter blows colder than normal air over the Pacific Northwest and the northern Great Plains while warming much of the rest of the United States.

- The general features of the global distribution of precipitation can be explained by global winds and pressure systems. In general, regions influenced by high pressure, with its associated subsidence and divergent winds, experience dry conditions. On the other hand, regions under the influence of low pressure and its converging winds and ascending air receive ample precipitation.

- On a uniform Earth throughout most of the year, heavy precipitation would occur in the equatorial region, the midlatitudes would receive most of their precipitation from traveling cyclonic storms, and polar regions would be dominated by cold air that holds little moisture. The most notable anomaly to this zonal distribution of precipitation occurs in the subtropics, where many of the world's great deserts are located. In these regions, pronounced subsidence on the eastern side of subtropical high-pressure centers results in stable atmospheric conditions. Upwelling of cold water along the west coasts of the adjacent continents further adds to the stable and dry conditions. On the other hand, the east coast of the adjacent continent receives abundant precipitation year-round due to the convergence and rising air associated with the western side of the oceanic high.

Vocabulary Review

Aleutian low	Icelandic low	mountain breeze)	subtropical high
Azores high	intertropical convergence	ocean currents	subtropical jet stream
bora	zone (ITCZ)	polar easterlies	trade winds
Bermuda high	jet stream	polar front	upwelling
chinook	katabatic or fall wind	polar high	valley breeze
country breeze	land breeze	polar jet stream	
doldrums	La Niña	prevailing westerlies	
El Niño	macroscale winds	Santa Ana	
equatorial low	mesoscale winds	sea breeze	
foehn	microscale circulation	Siberian high	
Hadley cell	mistral	Southern Oscillation	
horse latitudes	monsoon	subpolar low	

Review Questions

1. Distinguish among macroscale, mesoscale, and microscale winds. Give an example of each.

2. If you were to view a weather map of the entire world for any single day of the year, would the global pattern of winds likely be visible? Explain your answer.

3. Why is the well-known Texas "norther" not a true local (mesoscale) wind?

4. The most intense sea breezes develop along tropical coasts adjacent to cool ocean currents. Explain.

5. What are katabatic (fall) winds? Name two examples.

6. Explain how cities create their own local winds.

7. Briefly describe the idealized global circulation proposed by George Hadley. What are the shortcomings of the Hadley model?

8. Which factors cause air to subside between 20° and 35° latitude?

9. If Earth rotated more rapidly, the Coriolis force would be stronger. How would a faster rate of rotation affect the location (latitude) of Earth's belts of subtropical high pressure?

10. Referring to the idealized three-cell model of atmospheric circulation, most of the United States is situated in which belt of prevailing winds?

11. Briefly explain each of the following statements that relate to the global distribution of surface pressure:

    a. The only true zonal distribution of pressure exists in the region of the subpolar low in the Southern Hemisphere.
    b. The subtropical highs are stronger in the North Atlantic in July than in January.
    c. The subpolar low in the Northern Hemisphere is represented by individual cyclonic storms that are more common in the winter.
    d. A strong high-pressure cell develops in the winter over northern Asia.

12. Explain the cause of the Asian monsoon. In which season (summer or winter) does it rain?

13. What area of North America experiences a pronounced monsoon circulation?

14. Why is the flow aloft predominantly westerly?

15. At what time of year should we expect the fastest westerly flow? Explain.

16. Describe the situation in which jet streams were first encountered.

17. Describe the manner in which pressure distribution is shown on upper-air charts. How are high- and low-pressure areas depicted on these charts?

18. What were the *dishpan experiments* and what have we learned from them?

19. Describe how a major El Niño event in the tropical Pacific might affect the weather in other parts of the globe.

20. How is La Niña different from El Niño?

21. What factors, other than global wind and pressure systems, exert an influence on the world distribution of precipitation?

Atmospheric Science Online

The Atmosphere 11e website uses the resources and flexibility of the Internet to aid in your study of the topics in this chapter. Written and developed by meteorology instructors, this site will help improve your understanding of meteorology. Visit **www.mygeoscience.com** in order to:

- **Review** key chapter concepts

- **Read** with links to the eBook and to chapter-specific web resources
- **Visualize** and comprehend challenging topics using learning activities in *GEODe: Atmosphere*
- **Test yourself** with online quizzes

Air Masses

From Chapter 8 of *The Atmosphere: An Introduction to Meteorology*, Eleventh Edition, Frederick K. Lutgens, Edward J. Tarbuck, Dennis Tasa. Copyright © 2010 by Pearson Education, Inc. Published by Pearson Prentice Hall. All rights reserved.

Cumulonimbus clouds building over the Sonoran Desert in southern Arizona. The source of moisture for these summer storms is maritime tropical air from the eastern North Pacific. (Photo by H. H. Huey/ CORBIS)

M ost people living in the middle latitudes have experienced hot, "sticky" summer heat waves and frigid winter cold waves. In the first case, after several days of sultry weather, the spell may come to an abrupt end that is marked by thundershowers and followed by a few days of relatively cool relief. In the second case, thick stratus clouds and snow may replace the clear skies that had prevailed, and temperatures may climb to values that seem mild compared with what preceded them. In both examples, what was experienced was a period of generally uniform weather conditions followed by a relatively short period of change and the subsequent reestablishment of a new set of weather conditions that remained for perhaps several days before changing again.

What Is an Air Mass?

 Basic Weather Patterns
THE ATMOSPHERE ▸ Air Masses

The weather patterns just described are the result of the movements of large bodies of air, called air masses. An **air mass**, as the term implies, is an immense body of air, usually 1600 kilometers (1000 miles) or more across and perhaps several kilometers thick, which is characterized by homogeneous physical properties (in particular, temperature and moisture content) at any given altitude. When this air moves out of its region of origin, it will carry these temperatures and moisture conditions elsewhere, eventually affecting a large portion of a continent (Figure 1).

An excellent example of the influence of an air mass is illustrated in Figure 2. Here a cold, dry mass from northern Canada moves southward. With a beginning temperature of

FIGURE 1   Bleak tundra scene in Canada's Yukon Territory. Northern Canada is the source region for cold, dry air masses. When these air masses move southward, they can have a significant impact on the weather. (Photo by Publiphoto/Photo Researchers)

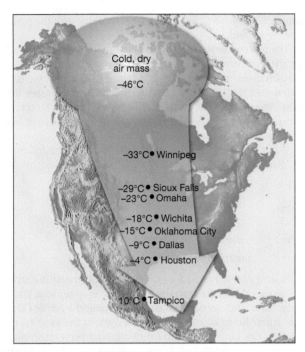

FIGURE 2 As this frigid Canadian air mass moved southward, it brought some of the coldest weather of the winter to the areas in its path. As it advanced out of Canada, the air mass slowly got warmer. Thus, the air mass was gradually modified at the same time that it modified the weather in the areas over which it moved. (After Tom L. McKnight, *Physical Geography*, 5th ed. Upper Saddle River, NJ: Prentice Hall, 1996, p. 174)

Map labels: Cold, dry air mass −46°C; −33°C Winnipeg; −29°C Sioux Falls; −23°C Omaha; −18°C Wichita; −15°C Oklahoma City; −9°C Dallas; −4°C Houston; 10°C Tampico

−46°C (−51°F), the air mass warms 13°C (24°F), to −33°C (−27°F), by the time it reaches Winnipeg. It continues to warm as it moves southward through the Great Plains and into Mexico. Throughout its southward journey, the air mass becomes warmer, but it also brings some of the coldest weather of the winter to the places in its path. Thus, the air mass is modified, but it also modifies the weather in the areas over which it moves.

The horizontal uniformity of an air mass is not complete because it may extend through 20 degrees or more of latitude and cover hundreds of thousands to millions of square kilometers. Consequently, small differences in temperature and humidity from one point to another at the same level are to be expected. Still, the differences observed within an air mass are small in comparison to the rapid rates of change experienced across air-mass boundaries.

Because it may take several days for an air mass to traverse an area, the region under its influence will probably experience generally constant weather conditions, a situation called **air-mass weather**. Certainly, some day-to-day variations may exist, but the events will be very unlike those in an adjacent air mass.

The air-mass concept is an important one because it is closely related to the study of atmospheric disturbances.

Many significant middle-latitude disturbances originate along the boundary zones that separate different air masses.

Source Regions

GE**O**De
THE ATMOSPHERE
Basic Weather Patterns
▸ Air Masses

Where do air masses form? What factors determine the nature and degree of uniformity of an air mass? These two basic questions are closely related, because the site where an air mass forms vitally affects the properties that characterize it.

Areas in which air masses originate are called **source regions**. Because the atmosphere is heated chiefly from below and gains its moisture by evaporation from Earth's surface, the nature of the source region largely determines the initial characteristics of an air mass. An ideal source region must meet two essential criteria. First, it must be an extensive and physically uniform area. A region having highly irregular topography or one that has a surface consisting of both water and land is not satisfactory.

The second criterion is that the area be characterized by a general stagnation of atmospheric circulation so that air will stay over the region long enough to come to some measure of equilibrium with the surface. In general, it means regions dominated by stationary or slow-moving anticyclones with their extensive areas of calms or light winds.

Regions under the influence of cyclones are not likely to produce air masses because such systems are characterized by converging surface winds. The winds in lows are constantly bringing air with unlike temperature and humidity properties into the area. Because the time involved is not long enough to eliminate these differences, steep temperature gradients result, and air-mass formation cannot take place.

Figure 3 shows the source regions that produce the air masses that most often influence North America. The waters of the Gulf of Mexico and Caribbean Sea and similar regions in the Pacific west of Mexico yield warm air masses, as does the land area that encompasses the southwestern United States and northern Mexico. In contrast, the North Pacific, the North Atlantic, and the snow- and ice-covered areas comprising northern North America and the adjacent Arctic Ocean are major source regions for cold air masses. It is also clear that the size of the source regions and the intensity of temperatures change seasonally.

Notice in Figure 3 that major source regions are not found in the middle latitudes but instead are confined to subtropical and subpolar locations. The fact that the middle latitudes are the site where cold and warm air masses clash, often because the converging winds of a traveling cyclone draw them together, means that this zone lacks the conditions necessary to be a source region. Instead, this latitude belt is one of the stormiest on the planet.

(a) **Winter pattern**

(b) **Summer pattern**

FIGURE 3 Air-mass source regions for North America. Source regions are largely confined to subtropical and subpolar locations. The fact that the middle latitudes are the site where cold and warm air masses clash, often because the converging winds of a traveling cyclone draw them together, means that this zone lacks the conditions necessary to be a source region. The differences between polar and arctic are relatively small and serve to indicate the degree of coldness of the respective air masses. By comparing the summer and winter maps, it is clear that the extent and temperature characteristics of source regions fluctuate.

Classifying Air Masses

GE●De Basic Weather Patterns
THE ATMOSPHERE ▶ Air Masses

The classification of an air mass depends on the latitude of the source region and the nature of the surface in the area of origin—ocean or continent. The latitude of the source region indicates the temperature conditions within the air mass, and the nature of the surface below strongly influences the moisture content of the air.

Air masses are identified by two-letter codes. With reference to latitude (temperature), air masses are placed into one of three categories: **polar (P)**, **arctic (A)**, or **tropical (T)**. The differences between polar and arctic are usually small and

simply serve to indicate the degree of coldness of the respective air masses.

The lowercase letter *m* (for **maritime**) or the lowercase letter *c* (for **continental**) is used to designate the nature of the surface in the source region and hence the humidity characteristics of the air mass. Because maritime air masses form over oceans, they have a relatively high water-vapor content compared to continental air masses that originate over landmasses (Figure 4).

When this classification scheme is applied, the following air masses can be identified:

cA	continental	arctic
cP	continental	polar
cT	continental	tropical
mT	maritime	tropical
mP	maritime	polar

Notice that the list does not include mA (maritime arctic). These air masses are not listed, because they seldom, if ever, form. Although arctic air masses form over the Arctic Ocean, this water body is ice-covered throughout the year. Consequently, the air masses that originate here consistently have the moisture characteristics associated with a continental source region.

Air-Mass Modification

After an air mass forms, it normally migrates from the area where it acquired its distinctive properties to a region with different surface characteristics. Once the air mass moves from its source region, it not only modifies the weather of the area it is traversing, but it is also gradually modified by the surface over which it is moving. This idea was clearly shown in Figure 2. Warming or cooling from below, the addition or loss of moisture, and vertical movements all act to bring about changes in an air mass. The amount of modification can be relatively small, or as the following example illustrates, the changes can be profound enough to alter completely the original identity of the air mass.

When cA or cP air moves over the ocean in winter, it undergoes considerable change. Evaporation from the water surface rapidly transfers large quantities of moisture to the once-dry continental air. Furthermore, because the underlying water is warmer than the air above, the air is also heated from below. This factor leads to instability and vertically ascending currents that rapidly transport heat and moisture to higher levels. In a matter of days, cold, dry, and stable continental air is transformed into an unstable mP air mass.

When an air mass is colder than the surface over which it is passing, as in the preceding example, the lowercase letter *k* is added after the air-mass symbol. If, however, an air mass is warmer than the underlying surface, the lowercase letter *w* is added. It should be remembered that the *k* or *w* suffix does not mean that the air mass itself is cold or warm. It means only that the air is *relatively* cold or warm in comparison with the underlying surface over which it is traveling. For example,

FIGURE 4 Air masses acquire their properties of temperature and moisture from extensive and physically uniform areas called *source regions*. When an air mass forms over the ocean, it is called *maritime*. Such air masses are relatively humid in contrast to *continental* air masses, which are dry. (Photo by iStockphoto)

an mT air mass from the Gulf of Mexico is usually classified as mTk as it moves over the southeastern states in summer. Although the air mass is warm, it is still cooler than the highly heated landmass over which it is passing.

The *k* or *w* designation gives an indication of the stability of an air mass and hence the weather that might be expected. An air mass that is colder than the surface is going to be warmed in its lower layers. This fact causes greater instability that favors the ascent of the heated lower air and creates the possibility of cloud formation and precipitation. Indeed, a *k* air mass is often characterized by cumulus clouds, and should precipitation occur, it will be of the shower or thunderstorm variety. Also, visibility is generally good (except in rain) because of the stirring and overturning of the air.

Conversely, when an air mass is warmer than the surface over which it is moving, its lower layers are chilled. A surface inversion that increases the stability of the air mass often develops. This condition does not favor the ascent of air, and so it opposes cloud formation and precipitation. Any clouds that do form will be stratus, and precipitation, if any, will be light to moderate. Moreover, because of the lack of vertical movements, smoke and dust often become concentrated in the lower layers of the air mass and cause poor visibility. During certain times of the year, fogs, especially the advection type, may also be common in some regions.

In addition to modifications resulting from temperature differences between an air mass and the surface below, upward and downward movements induced by cyclones and anticyclones or topography can also affect the stability of an air mass. Such modifications are often called *mechanical* or *dynamic* and are usually independent of the changes caused by surface cooling or heating. For example, significant modification can result when an air mass is drawn into a low. Here convergence and lifting dominate and the air mass is rendered more unstable. Conversely, the subsidence associated with anticyclones acts to stabilize an air mass. Similar alterations in stability occur when an air mass is lifted over highlands or descends the leeward side of a mountain barrier. In the first case, the air's stability is reduced; in the second case, the air becomes more stable.

Properties of North American Air Masses

Air masses frequently pass over us, which means that the day-to-day weather we experience often depends on the temperature, stability, and moisture content of these large bodies of air. In this section, we briefly examine the properties of the principal North American air masses. In addition, Table 1 serves as a summary.

TABLE 1	Weather Characteristics of North American Air Masses			
Air mass	Source Region	Temperature and moisture characteristics in source region	Stability in source region	Associated weather
cA	Arctic basin and Greenland ice cap	Bitterly cold and very dry in winter	Stable	Cold waves in winter
cP	Interior Canada and Alaska	Very cold and dry in winter	Stable entire year	a. Cold waves in winter b. Modified to cPk in winter over Great Lakes bringing "lake-effect" snow to leeward shores
mP	North Pacific	Mild (cool) and humid entire year	Unstable in winter Stable in summer	a. Low clouds and showers in winter b. Heavy orographic precipitation on windward side of western mountains in winter c. Low stratus and fog along coast in summer; modified to cP inland
mP	Northwestern Atlantic	Cold and humid in winter Cool and humid in summer	Unstable in winter Stable in summer	a. Occasional "nor'easter" in winter b. Occasional periods of clear, cool weather in summer
cT	Northern interior Mexico and southwestern U.S. (summer only)	Hot and dry	Unstable	a. Hot, dry, and cloudless, rarely influencing areas outside source region b. Occasional drought to southern Great Plains
mT	Gulf of Mexico, Caribbean Sea, western Atlantic	Warm and humid entire year	Unstable entire year	a. In winter it usually becomes mTw moving northward and bringing occasional widespread precipitation or advection fog b. In summer, hot and humid conditions, frequent cumulus development and showers or thunderstorms
mT	Subtropical Pacific	Warm and humid entire year	Stable entire year	a. In winter it brings fog, drizzle, and occasional moderate precipitation to N.W. Mexico and S.W. United States b. In summer this air mass occasionally reaches the western United States and is a source of moisture for infrequent convectional thunderstorms.

Continental Polar (cP) and Continental Arctic (cA) Air Masses

Continental polar and continental arctic air masses are, as their classification implies, cold and dry. Continental polar air originates over the often snow-covered interior regions of Canada and Alaska, poleward of the 50th parallel. Continental arctic air forms farther north, over the Arctic Basin and the Greenland ice cap (see Figure 3).

Continental arctic air is distinguished from cP air by its generally lower temperatures, although at times the differences may be slight. In fact, some meteorologists do not differentiate between cP and cA.

During the winter, both air masses are bitterly cold and very dry. Winter nights are long, and the daytime Sun is short-lived and low in the sky. Consequently, as winter advances, Earth's surface and atmosphere lose heat that, for the most part, is not replenished by incoming solar energy. Therefore, the surface reaches very low temperatures and the air near the ground is gradually chilled to heights of 1 kilometer (0.6 mile) or more. The result is a strong and persistent temperature inversion with the coldest temperatures near the ground. Marked stability is, therefore, the rule. Because the air is very cold and the surface below is frozen, the mixing ratio of these air masses is necessarily low, ranging from perhaps 0.1 gram per kilogram in cA up to 1.5 grams per kilogram in some cP air.

As wintertime cP or cA air moves outward from its source region, it carries its cold, dry weather to the United States, normally entering between the Great Lakes and the Rockies. Because there are no major barriers between the high-latitude source regions and the Gulf of Mexico, cP and cA air masses can sweep rapidly and with relative ease far southward into the United States. The winter cold waves experienced in much of the central and eastern United States are closely associated with such polar outbreaks. One such cold wave is described

Students Sometimes Ask . . .

When a cold air mass moves south from Canada into the United States, how rapidly can temperatures change?

When a fast-moving frigid air mass advances into the northern Great Plains, temperatures have been known to plunge 20° to 30°C (40°–50°F) in a matter of just a few hours. One notable example is a drop of 55.5°C (100°F), from 6.7°C to −48.8°C (44° to −56°F), in 24 hours at Browning, Montana, on January 23–24, 1916. Another remarkable example occurred on Christmas Eve, 1924, when the temperature at Fairfield, Montana, dropped from 17°C (63°F) at noon to −29°C (−21°F) at midnight—an amazing 46°C (83°F) change in just 12 hours.

BOX 1 ▶ THE SIBERIAN EXPRESS

The surface weather map for December 22, 1989, shows a very large high-pressure center covering the eastern two-thirds of the United States and a substantial portion of Canada (Figure A). As is usually the case in winter, a large anticyclone such as this is associated with a huge mass of dense and bitterly cold arctic air. After such an air mass forms over the frozen expanses near the Arctic Circle, the winds aloft sometimes direct it toward the south and east. When an outbreak takes place, it is popularly called the "Siberian Express" by the news media, even though the air mass did not originate in Siberia.

November 1989 was unusually mild for late autumn. In fact, across the United States, over 200 daily high-temperature

records were set. December, however, was different. East of the Rockies, the month's weather was dominated by two arctic outbreaks. The second brought record-breaking cold.

Between December 21–25, as the frigid dome of high pressure advanced southward and eastward, more than 370 record low temperatures were reported. On December 21, Havre, Montana, had an overnight low of −42.2°C (−44°F), breaking a record set in 1884. Meanwhile, Topeka's −32.2°C (−26°F) was that city's lowest temperature for any date since record keeping started 102 years earlier.

The three days that followed saw the arctic air migrate toward the south and east. By December 24, Tallahassee, Florida, had

a low temperature of −10°C (14°F). In the center of the state the daily minimum at Orlando was −5.6°C (22°F). It was actually warmer in North Dakota on Christmas Eve than in central and northern Florida!

As we would expect, utility companies in many states reported record demand. When the arctic air advanced into Texas and Florida, agriculture was especially hard hit. Some Florida citrus growers lost 40 percent of their crop, and many vegetable crops were wiped out completely (Figure B).

After Christmas the circulation pattern that brought this record-breaking Siberian Express from the arctic deep into the United States changed. As a result, temperatures for much of the country during January and February 1990 were well above normal. In fact, January 1990 was the second warmest January in 96 years. Thus, despite frigid December temperatures, the winter of 1989–1990 "averaged out" to be a relatively warm one.

FIGURE A A surface weather map for 7 AM EST, December 22, 1989. This simplified National Weather Service (NWS) map shows an intense winter cold wave caused by an outbreak of frigid continental arctic air. This event brought subfreezing temperatures as far south as the Gulf of Mexico. Temperatures on NWS maps are in degrees Fahrenheit.

FIGURE B When an arctic air mass invades the citrus regions of Florida and Texas, even modern freeze controls may not be able to prevent significant losses. (Photo courtesy of Florida Department of Citrus)

in Box 1. Usually, the last freeze in spring and the first in autumn can be correlated with outbreaks of polar or arctic air.

Because cA air is present principally in the winter, only cP air has any influence on our summer weather, and this effect is considerably reduced when compared with winter. During summer months, the properties of the source region for cP air are very different from those during winter. Instead of being chilled by the ground, the air is warmed from below as

the long days and higher Sun angle warm the snow-free land surface. Although summer cP air is warmer and has a higher moisture content than its wintertime counterpart, the air is still cool and relatively dry compared with areas farther south. Summer heat waves in the northern portions of the eastern and central United States are often ended by the southward advance of cP air, which for a day or two brings cooling relief and bright, pleasant weather.

Lake-Effect Snow: Cold Air over Warm Water

Continental polar air masses are not, as a rule, associated with heavy precipitation. Yet during late autumn and winter a unique and interesting weather phenomenon takes place along the downwind shores of the Great Lakes.* Periodically, brief, heavy snow showers issue from dark clouds that move onshore from the lakes (Box 2). Seldom do these storms move more than about 80 kilometers (50 miles) inland from the shore before the snows come to an end. These highly localized storms, occurring along the leeward shores of the Great Lakes, create what are known as **lake-effect snows**.

Lake-effect storms account for a high percentage of the snowfall in many areas adjacent to the lakes. The strips of land that are most frequently affected, called *snowbelts*, are shown in Figure 5. A comparison of average snowfall totals at Thunder Bay, Ontario, on the north shore of Lake Superior, and Marquette, Michigan, along the southern shore, provides another excellent example. Because Marquette is situated on the leeward shore of the lake, it receives substantial lake-effect snow and therefore has a much higher snowfall total than does Thunder Bay (Table 2).

What causes lake-effect snow? The answer is closely linked to the differential heating of water and land and to the concept of atmospheric instability. During the summer months, bodies of water, including the Great Lakes, absorb huge quantities of energy from the Sun and from the warm air that passes over them. Although these water bodies do not reach particularly high temperatures, they nevertheless represent huge reservoirs of heat. The surrounding land, in contrast, cannot store heat nearly as effectively. Consequently, during

---

*Actually, the Great Lakes are just the best-known example. Other large lakes can also experience this phenomenon.

TABLE 2	Monthly Snowfall at Thunder Bay, Ontario, and Marquette, Michigan

Thunder Bay, Ontario			
October	November	December	January
3.0 cm	14.9 cm	19.0 cm	22.6 cm
(1.2 in.)	(5.8 in.)	(7.4 in.)	(8.8 in.)

Marquette, Michigan			
October	November	December	January
5.3 cm	37.6 cm	56.4 cm	53.1 cm
(2.1 in.)	(14.7 in.)	(22 in.)	(20.7 in.)

autumn and winter, the temperature of the land drops quickly, whereas water bodies lose their heat more gradually and cool slowly.

From late November through late January the contrasts in average temperatures between water and land range from about 8°C in the southern Great Lakes to 17°C farther north. However, the temperature differences can be much greater (perhaps 25°C) when a very cold cP or cA air mass pushes southward across the lakes. When such a dramatic temperature contrast exists, the lakes interact with the air to produce major lake-effect storms. Figure 6 depicts the movement of a cP air mass across one of the Great Lakes. During its journey, the air acquires large quantities of heat and moisture from the relatively warm lake surface. By the time it reaches the opposite shore, this cPk air is humid and unstable and heavy snow showers are likely.

Maritime Polar (mP) Air Masses

Maritime polar air masses form over oceans at high latitudes. As the classification would indicate, mP air is cool to cold and humid, but compared with cP and cA air masses in winter, mP

FIGURE 5 Average annual snowfall. The snowbelts of the Great Lakes region are easy to pick out on this snowfall map. (Data from NOAA)

AVERAGE ANNUAL SNOWFALL	
cm	in.
>330	>130
250–329	100–129
150–249	60–99
90–149	36–59
60–89	24–35
<60	<24

BOX 2 ▶ ATMOSPHERIC HAZARD

An Extraordinary Lake-Effect Snowstorm

Northeastern Ohio is part of the Lake Erie snowbelt, a zone that extends eastward into northwestern Pennsylvania and western New York (see Figure 5). Here snowfall is enhanced when cold winds blow from the west or northwest across the relatively warm unfrozen waters of Lake Erie. Average annual snowfall in northeastern Ohio is between 200 and 280 centimeters (80 to 110 inches) and increases to 450 centimeters (175 inches) in western New York.

Although residents here are accustomed to abundant snow storms, even they were surprised in November 1996 by an especially early and strong storm. During a six-day span, from November 9–14, northeastern Ohio experienced record-breaking lake-effect snows. Rather than raking fall leaves, people were shoveling sidewalks and clearing snow from overloaded roofs (Figure C).

Persistent snow squalls (narrow bands of heavy snow) frequently produced accumulation rates of 5 centimeters (2 inches) per hour during the six-day siege. The snow was the result of especially deep and prolonged lower atmospheric instability created by the movement of cold air across a relatively warm Lake Erie. The surface temperature of the lake was 12°C (54°F), several degrees above normal. The air temperature at a height of 1.5 kilometers (nearly 5000 feet) was −5°C (23°F).

The northwest flow of cold air across Lake Erie and the 17°C lapse rate generated lake-effect rain and snow almost immediately.* During some periods loud thunder accompanied the snow squalls!

Data from the Cleveland National Weather Service Snow Spotters Network show 100 to 125 centimeters (39 to 49 inches) of snow through the core of the Ohio snowbelt (Figure D). The deepest accumulation was measured near Chardon, Ohio. Here the six-day total of 175 centimeters (68.9 inches) far exceeded the previous Ohio record of 107 centimeters (42 inches) set in 1901. In addition, the November 1996 snowfall total of 194.8 centimeters (76.7 inches) at the same site set a new monthly snowfall record for Ohio. The previous one-month record had been 176.5 centimeters (69.5 inches).

The impact of the storm was considerable. Ohio's governor declared a state of emergency on November 12, and National Guard troops were dispatched to assist in snow removal and aid in the rescue of snowbound residents. There was widespread damage to trees and shrubs across northeastern Ohio because the snow was particularly wet and dense and readily clung to objects. Press reports indicated that about 168,000 homes were without electricity, some for several days. Roofs of numerous buildings collapsed under the excessive snow loads. Although residents of the northeast Ohio snowbelt are winter storm veterans, the six-day storm in November 1996 will be long remembered as an extraordinary event.

---

*Thomas W. Schmidlin and James Kasarik, "A Record Ohio Snowfall during 9–14 November 1996," *Bulletin of the American Meteorological Society*, Vol. 80, No. 6, June 1999, p. 1109.

FIGURE C A six-day lake-effect snowstorm in November 1996 dropped 175 centimeters (nearly 69 inches) of snow on Chardon, Ohio, setting a new state record. (Photo by Tony Dejak/AP/Wide World Photos)

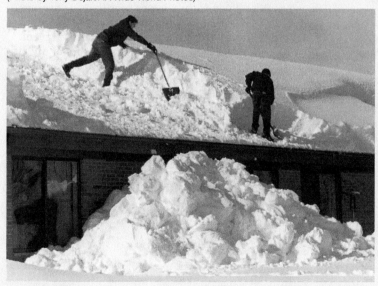

FIGURE D Snowfall totals (in inches) for northeastern Ohio for the November 9–14, 1996, lake-effect storm. The deepest accumulation, nearly 69 inches (175 centimeters), occurred near Chardon. (After National Weather Service)

(a)

(b)

FIGURE 6 (a) As continental polar air crosses the Great Lakes in winter, it acquires moisture and is made unstable because of warming from below. A "lake-effect" snow shower on the downwind side of the lakes is often the consequence of this air-mass modification. (b) This satellite image from December 27, 2001, shows thick bands of clouds extending from the eastern tip of Lake Erie to east of Buffalo, New York. Thick cloud bands also extend from the eastern margin of Lake Huron over southern Ontario. The arrows show the wind direction, which was blowing across the length of the lake. (Image courtesy of NASA GOES Project Science Office)

Students Sometimes Ask . . .

I know that Buffalo, New York, is famous for its lake-effect snows. Just how bad can it get?

Because of Buffalo's location along the eastern shore of Lake Erie, it does indeed receive a great deal of lake-effect snow (see Figures 5 and 6). One of the most memorable events took place between December 24, 2001, and January 1, 2002. This storm, which set a record as the longest-lasting lake-effect event, buried Buffalo with 207.3 centimeters (81.6 inches) of snow. Prior to this storm, the record for the *entire month* of December had been 173.7 centimeters (68.4 inches)! The eastern shore of Lake Ontario was also hard hit, with one station recording more than 317 centimeters (125 inches) of snow.

air is relatively mild because of the higher temperatures of the ocean surface as contrasted to the colder continents.

Two regions are important sources for mP air that influences North America: the North Pacific and the northwestern Atlantic from Newfoundland to Cape Cod (see Figure 3). Because of the general west-to-east circulation in the middle latitudes, mP air masses from the North Pacific source region usually influence North American weather more than mP air masses generated in the northwest Atlantic. Whereas air masses that form in the Atlantic generally move eastward toward Europe, mP air from the North Pacific has a strong influence on the weather along the western coast of North America, especially in the winter.

Pacific mP Air Masses During the winter, mP air masses from the Pacific usually begin as cP air in Siberia (Figure 7). Although air rarely stagnates over this area, the source region is extensive enough to allow the air moving across it to acquire its characteristic properties. As the air advances eastward over the relatively warm water, active evaporation and heating occur in the lower levels. Consequently, what was once a very cold, dry, and stable air mass is changed into one that is mild and humid near the surface and relatively unstable. As this mP air arrives at the western coast of North America, it is often accompanied by low clouds and shower activity. When the mP air advances inland against the western mountains, orographic uplift can produce heavy rain or snow on the windward slopes of the mountains.

Maritime Polar Air from the North Atlantic As is the case for mP air from the Pacific, air masses forming in the northwestern Atlantic source region were originally cP air masses that moved from the continent and were transformed over the ocean. However, unlike air masses from the North Pacific, mP air from the Atlantic only occasionally affects the weather of North America. Nevertheless, this air mass does have an effect when the northeastern United States is on the northern or northwestern edge of a passing low-pressure center. In winter, strong cyclonic winds can draw mP air into the region. Its influence is generally confined to the area east of the Appalachians and north of Cape Hatteras, North Carolina. The weather associated with a wintertime invasion of mP air from the Atlantic is known locally as a **nor'easter**. Strong northeast winds, freezing or near freezing temperatures, high relative humidity, and the likelihood of precipitation make this weather phenomenon an unwelcome event.

Summer brings a change in the characteristics of mP air masses from the North Pacific. During the warm season, the ocean is cooler than the surrounding continents. In addition, the Pacific high lies off the western coast of the United States.

FIGURE 7 During winter, maritime polar (mP) air masses in the North Pacific usually begin as continental polar (cP) air masses in Siberia. The cP air is modified to mP as it slowly crosses the ocean.

I once heard a weather report refer to some storms in California as being associated with the "Pineapple Express." What were they talking about?

Much of the precipitation along the western margin of North America occurs in winter when unstable mP air originating in the vicinity of the Gulf of Alaska is drawn into a cyclonic system and/or lifted orographically. Occasionally, however, storms approach the West Coast from the subtropical Pacific in the vicinity of the Hawaiian Islands. Because these storms advance from the direction of Hawaii, they are sometimes called the "Pineapple Express." These systems, with their associated mT air, sometimes yield torrential flood-producing rains.

Consequently, there is almost continuous southward flow of air having moderate temperatures. Although the air near the surface may often be conditionally unstable, the presence of the Pacific high means that there is subsidence and stability aloft. Thus, low stratus clouds and summer fogs characterize much of the western coast. Once summer mP air from the Pacific moves inland, it is heated at the surface over the hot and dry interior. The heating and resulting turbulence act to reduce the relative humidity in the lower layers, and the clouds dissipate.

Although mP air masses from the Atlantic may produce an occasional unwelcome nor'easter during the winter, summertime incursions of this air mass may bring pleasant weather. Like the Pacific source region, the northwestern Atlantic is dominated by high pressure during the summer. Thus, the upper air is stable because of subsidence and the lower air is essentially stable because of the chilling effect of the relatively cool water. As the circulation on the southern side of the anticyclone carries this stable and relatively dry mP air into New England, and occasionally as far south as Virginia, the region enjoys clear, cool weather and good visibility.

Maritime Tropical (mT) Air Masses

Maritime tropical air masses affecting North America most often originate over the warm waters of the Gulf of Mexico, the Caribbean Sea, or the adjacent western Atlantic Ocean (see Figure 3). The tropical Pacific is also a source region for mT air. However, the land area affected by this latter source is small compared with the size of the region influenced by air masses produced in the Gulf of Mexico and adjacent waters.

As expected, mT air masses are warm to hot, and they are humid. In addition, they are often unstable. It is through invasions of mT air masses that the subtropics export much heat and moisture to the cooler and drier areas to the north. Consequently, these air masses are important to the weather whenever present because they are capable of contributing significant precipitation.

North Atlantic mT Air   Maritime tropical air masses from the Gulf–Caribbean–Atlantic source region greatly affect the weather of the United States east of the Rocky Mountains. Although the source region is dominated by the North Atlantic subtropical high, the air masses produced are not stable but are neutral or unstable because the source region is located on the weak western edge of the anticyclone where pronounced subsidence is absent.

During winter, when cP air dominates the central and eastern United States, mT air only occasionally enters this part of the country. When an invasion does occur, the lower portions of the air mass are chilled and stabilized as it moves northward. Its classification is changed to mTw. As a result, the formation of convective showers is unlikely. Widespread precipitation does occur, however, when a northward-moving mT air mass is pulled into a traveling cyclone and forced to ascend. In fact, much of the wintertime precipitation over the eastern and central states results when mT air from the Gulf of Mexico is lifted along fronts in traveling cyclones.

Another weather phenomenon associated with a northward-moving wintertime mT air mass is advection fog. Dense fogs can develop as the warm, humid air is chilled as it moves over the cold land surface.

During the summer, mT air masses from the Gulf, Caribbean, and adjacent Atlantic affect a much wider area of North America and are present for a greater percentage of the time than during the winter. As a result, they exert a strong and often dominating influence over the summer weather of the United States east of the Rocky Mountains. This influence is due to the general sea-to-land (monsoonal) airflow over the eastern portion of North America during the warm months, which brings more frequent incursions of mT air that penetrate much deeper into the continent than during the winter months. Consequently, these air masses are largely responsible for the hot and humid conditions that prevail over the eastern and central United States.

Initially, summertime mT air from the Gulf is unstable. As it moves inland over the warmer land, it becomes an mTk air mass as daytime heating of the surface layers further increases the air's instability. Because the relative humidity is high, only modest lifting is necessary to bring about active convection, cumulus development, and thunderstorm or shower activity (Figure 8). This is, indeed, a common warm-weather phenomenon associated with mT air.

It should be also noted here that air masses from the Gulf–Caribbean–Atlantic region are the primary source of much, if not most, of the precipitation received in the eastern two-thirds of the United States. Pacific air masses contribute little to the water supply east of the Rockies because the western mountains effectively "drain" the moisture from the air by numerous episodes of orographic uplift.

Figure 9, which shows the distribution of average annual precipitation for the eastern two-thirds of the United States by using **isohyets** (lines connecting places having equal rainfall), illustrates this situation nicely. The pattern of isohyets shows the greatest rainfall in the Gulf region and a decrease in precipitation with increasing distance from the mT source region.

FIGURE 8 As mT air from the Gulf of Mexico moves over the heated land in summer, cumulus development and afternoon showers frequently result. (Photo by Rod Planck/Photo Researchers, Inc.)

North Pacific mT Air Compared to mT air from the Gulf of Mexico, mT air masses from the Pacific source region have much less of an impact on North American weather. In winter, only northwestern Mexico and the extreme southwestern United States are influenced by air from the tropical Pacific. Because the source region lies along the eastern side of the Pacific anticyclone, subsidence aloft produces upper-level stability. When the air mass moves northward, cooling at the surface also causes the lower layers to become more stable, often resulting in fog or drizzle. If lifted along a front or forced over mountains, moderate precipitation results.

For many years the summertime influence of air masses from the tropical Pacific source region on the weather of the southwestern United States and northern Mexico was believed to be minimal. It was thought that the moisture for the infrequent summer thunderstorms that occur in the region came from occasional westward thrusts of mT air from the Gulf of Mexico. However, the Gulf of Mexico is no longer believed to be the primary supplier of moisture for the area west of the Continental Divide. Rather, it has been demonstrated that the tropical North Pacific west of central Mexico is a more important source of moisture for this area.

In summer the mT air moves northward from its Pacific source region up the Gulf of California and into the interior of the western United States. This movement, which is confined largely to July and August, is essentially monsoonal in character. That is, the inflow of moist air is a response to thermally produced low pressure that develops over the heated landmass. The July–August rainfall maximum for Tucson is a response to this incursion of Pacific mT air (Figure 10). The chapter-opening photo relates to this phenomenon.

FIGURE 9 Average annual precipitation for the eastern two-thirds of the United States. Note the general decrease in yearly precipitation totals with increasing distance from the Gulf of Mexico, the source region for mT air masses. Isohyets are labeled in inches. (Courtesy of Environmental Data Service, NOAA)

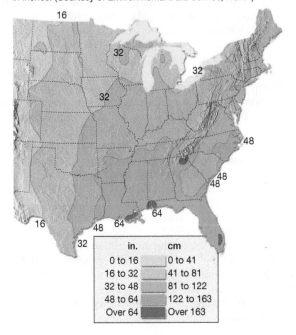

FIGURE 10 Monthly precipitation data for Tucson, Arizona. The July–August rainfall maximum in the desert Southwest results from the monsoonal flow of Pacific mT air into the region.

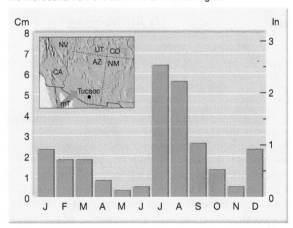

252

Continental Tropical (cT) Air Masses

North America narrows as it extends southward through Mexico; therefore, the continent has no extensive source region for continental tropical air masses. By checking the maps in Figure 3, you can see that only in summer do northern interior Mexico and adjacent parts of the arid southwestern United States produce hot, dry cT air. Because of the intense daytime heating at the surface, both a steep environmental lapse rate and turbulence extending to considerable heights are found. Nevertheless, although the air is unstable, it generally remains nearly cloudless because of extremely low humidity. Consequently, the prevailing weather is hot, with an almost complete lack of rainfall. Large daily temperature ranges are the rule. Although cT air masses are usually confined to the source region, occasionally they move into the southern Great Plains. If the cT air persists for long, drought may occur.

Chapter Summary

- In the middle latitudes many weather events are associated with the movements of air masses. An *air mass* is a large body of air, usually 1600 kilometers (1000 miles) or more across and perhaps several kilometers thick, that is characterized by homogeneous physical properties (in particular temperature and moisture content) at any given altitude. A region under the influence of an air mass will probably experience generally constant weather conditions, a situation referred to as *air-mass weather*.

- Areas in which air masses originate are called *source regions*. An ideal source region must meet two criteria. First, it must be an extensive and physically uniform area. The second criterion is that the area is characterized by a general stagnation of atmospheric circulation so that air will stay over the region long enough to come to some measure of equilibrium with the surface.

- The classification of an air mass depends on (1) the latitude of the source region, and (2) the nature of the surface in the area of origin—ocean or continent. Air masses are identified by two-letter codes. With reference to latitude (temperature), air masses are placed into one of three categories: *polar (P)*, *arctic (A)*, or *tropical (T)*. A lowercase letter (*m*, for *maritime*, or *c* for *continental*) is placed in front of the uppercase letter to designate the nature of the surface in the source region and therefore the humidity characteristics of the air mass. Using this classification scheme, the following air masses are identified: cA, cP, cT, mT, and mP.

- Once an air mass moves from its source region, it not only modifies the weather of the area it is traversing, but it is also gradually modified by the surface over which it is moving. Changes to the stability of an air mass can result from temperature differences between an air mass and the surface and/or vertical movements induced by cyclones, anticyclones, or topography.

- The day-to-day weather we experience depends on the temperature, stability, and moisture content of the air mass we are experiencing. *Continental polar* (cP) and *continental arctic* (cA) air masses are, as their classification implies, cold and dry. Although cP air masses are not, as a rule, associated with heavy precipitation, those that cross the Great Lakes during late autumn and winter sometimes bring *lake-effect snows* to the leeward shores. *Maritime polar* air masses (mP) form over oceans at high latitudes and are cool to cold and humid. The stormy winter weather associated with an invasion of mP air from the Atlantic into an area east of the Appalachians and north of Cape Hatteras is known as a *nor'easter*. *Maritime tropical* (mT) air masses affecting North America most often originate over the warm water of the Gulf of Mexico, the Caribbean Sea, or the adjacent western Atlantic Ocean. As expected, mT air masses are warm to hot, and they are humid. During winter, when cP air dominates the central and eastern United States, mT air only occasionally enters this part of the country. However, during the summer, mT air masses from the Gulf, Caribbean, and adjacent Atlantic are more common and cover a much wider area of the continent. The mT air masses from the Gulf–Caribbean–Atlantic source region are also the source of much, if not most, of the precipitation received in the eastern two-thirds of the United States. *Isohyets*, lines of equal rainfall drawn on a map, show that the greatest rainfall occurs in the Gulf region and decreases with increasing distance from the mT source region. Hot and dry *continental tropical* (cT) air is produced only in the summer in northern interior Mexico and adjacent parts of the arid southwestern United States.

Vocabulary Review

air mass	isohyet	polar (P) air mass
air-mass weather	lake-effect snow	source region
arctic (A) air mass	maritime (m) air mass	tropical (T) air mass
continental (c) air mass	nor'easter	

Review Questions

1. Define the terms *air mass* and *air-mass weather*.

2. What two criteria must be met for an area to be an air-mass source region?

3. Why are regions that have a cyclonic circulation generally not conducive to air-mass formation?

4. On what bases are air masses classified? Compare the temperature and moisture characteristics of the following air masses: cP, mP, mT, and cT.

5. Why is mA left out of the air-mass classification scheme?

6. What do the lowercase letters *k* and *w* indicate about an air mass? List the general weather conditions associated with *k* and *w* air masses.

7. During winter, polar air masses are cold. Which should be coldest, a wintertime mP air mass or a wintertime cP air mass? Explain your choice.

8. How might vertical movements induced by a pressure system or topography act to modify an air mass?

9. What two air masses are most important to the weather of the United States east of the Rocky Mountains? Explain your choice.

10. What air mass influences the weather of the Pacific Coast more than any other?

11. Why do cA and cP air masses often sweep so far south into the United States?

12. Describe the modifications that occur as a cP air mass moves across one of the Great Lakes in the winter.

13. Why do mP air masses from the North Atlantic source region seldom affect the eastern United States?

14. What air mass and source region provide the greatest amount of moisture to the eastern and central United States?

15. For each statement below, indicate which air mass is most likely involved and from what source region it came:
    a. summer drought in the southern Great Plains
    b. wintertime advection fog in the Midwest
    c. heavy winter precipitation in the western mountains
    d. summertime convectional showers in the Midwest and East
    e. a nor'easter

Problems

1. Figure 11 shows the distribution of air temperatures (top number) and dew-point temperatures (lower number) for a December morning. Two well-developed air masses are influencing North America at this time. The air masses are separated by a broad zone that is not affected by either air mass. Draw lines on the map that show the boundaries of each air mass. Label each air mass with the proper classification.

2. The Great Lakes are not the only water bodies associated with lake-effect snow. For example, large lakes in Canada also experience this phenomenon. Shown here are snowfall data (in centimeters) for two Canadian stations that receive significant lake-effect snow. Fort Resolution is on the southeastern shore of Great Slave Lake, and Norway House is at the northern end of Lake Winnipeg. During what month does each station have its snowfall

FIGURE 11 Map to accompany Problem 1.

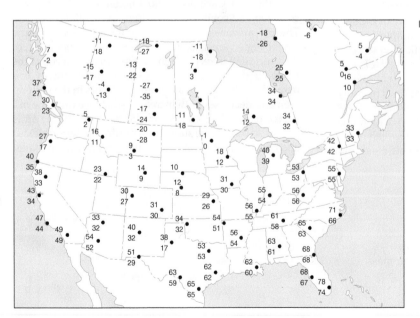

maximum? Suggest an explanation as to why the maximum occurs when it does.

	Sept.	Oct.	Nov.	Dec.	Jan.
Fort Resolution	2.5	13.7	36.6	19.6	15.4
Norway House	3.8	6.9	29.5	20.1	16.3

3. Refer to Figure 5. Notice the narrow, north–south-oriented zone of relatively heavy snowfall east of Pittsburgh and Charleston. This region is too far from the Great Lakes to receive lake-effect snows. Speculate on a likely reason for the higher snowfalls here. Does your explanation explain the shape of this snowy zone?

Atmospheric Science Online

The Atmosphere 11e website uses the resources and flexibility of the Internet to aid in your study of the topics in this chapter. Written and developed by meteorology instructors, this site will help improve your understanding of meteorology. Visit **www.mygeoscience.com** in order to:

• **Review** key chapter concepts

4. Albuquerque, New Mexico, is situated in the desert Southwest. Its annual precipitation is just 21.2 centimeters (8.3 inches). Month-by-month data (in centimeters) are as follows:

J	F	M	A	M	J	J	A	S	O	N	D
1.0	1.0	1.3	1.3	1.3	1.3	3.3	3.8	2.3	2.3	1.0	1.3

What are the two rainiest months? The pattern here is similar to other southwestern cities, including Tuscon, Arizona. Briefly explain why the rainiest months occur when they do.

• **Read** with links to the eBook and to chapter-specific web resources

• **Visualize** and comprehend challenging topics using learning activities in *GEODe: Atmosphere*

• **Test yourself** with online quizzes

GEODe: Atmosphere

GEODe: Atmosphere makes studying more effective by reinforcing key concepts using animation, video, narration, interactive exercises, and practice quizzes. Available at **www.mygeoscience.com.**

Weather Patterns

From Chapter 9 of *The Atmosphere: An Introduction to Meteorology*, Eleventh Edition, Frederick K. Lutgens, Edward J. Tarbuck, Dennis Tasa. Copyright © 2010 by Pearson Education, Inc. Published by Pearson Prentice Hall. All rights reserved.

Ominous storm clouds east of Kearney, Nebraska, May 29, 2008. (Photo by Ryan McGinnis/Alamy Images)

The winter of 1992–1993 came to a stormy conclusion in eastern North America during a weekend in mid-March. The daffodils were already out across the South, and people were thinking about spring when the Blizzard of '93 struck on March 13 and 14. The huge storm brought record-low temperatures, record-low barometric-pressure readings, and record-high snowfalls to an area that stretched from Alabama to the Maritime Provinces of eastern Canada (Table 1). The monster storm, with its driving winds and heavy snow, combined the attributes of both hurricane and blizzard as it moved up the spine of the Appalachians, lashing and burying a huge swatch of territory (Figure 1). Although the atmospheric pressure at the storm's center was lower than the pressures at the centers of some hurricanes and the winds were frequently as strong as those in a hurricane, this was definitely not a tropical storm but a classic winter cyclone (Figure 2).

The event quickly earned the title Storm of the Century. The name was well deserved. Although many notable storms occurred during the twentieth century, none could match the extreme dimensions of this event. A famous nineteenth-century storm known as the Blizzard of '88 was equally severe but affected a much smaller area.

Despite excellent forecasts that permitted timely warnings, at least 270 people died as a result of the storm, more than three times the combined death tolls of hurricanes Hugo and Andrew. In Florida severe weather that included 27 tornadoes killed 44 people. At one time or another, every major airport on the U.S. East Coast was closed, as were most highways. Hundreds of hikers were stranded in the mountains by the record snowfalls, and thousands of others were stranded away from home in a variety of settings. At one point, 3 million people were without electricity. As the blizzard buried the region, hundreds of roofs collapsed under the wet, heavy snow. The National Weather Service office in Asheville, North Carolina, reported an extraordinary snow-to-water ratio of 4.2 to 1. A general ratio of 10 units of snow to 1 unit of water is common. Meanwhile, storm-generated waves pounded the coast. About 200 homes along the Outer Banks of North Carolina were damaged, with many left uninhabitable, and on Long Island 18 houses succumbed to the surf.

In the aftermath of the storm, temperatures plunged to record low levels as a frigid continental arctic air mass spilled into the region. On Sunday, March 14, some 70 cities in the East and South experienced record low temperatures. The next day 75 more record-low daily minimums were established. Freezing temperatures that reached as far south as Orlando, Florida, and Birmingham, Alabama, set a new March record of −17°C (2°F). The Storm of the Century was truly an awesome event that inhabitants of eastern North America will not soon forget.

Polar-Front Theory (Norwegian Cyclone Model)

We are now ready to apply our knowledge of the basic elements of weather as well as the dynamics of atmospheric motions to an understanding of day-to-day weather patterns in the middle latitudes. For our purposes, *middle latitudes* refers to the region between southern Florida and Alaska, essentially the area of the westerlies. The primary weather producer here

TABLE 1	A Look at the Storm of the Century	
Snowfall totals		
City	(CM)	(IN)
Mount LeConte, TN	140	56
Mount Mitchell, NC	125	50
Syracuse, NY	108	43
Lincoln, NH	88	35
Mountain City, GA	60	24
Chattanooga, TN	50	20
Asheville, NC	48	19
Record-low temperatures in the South		
City	(°C)	(°F)
Mount LeConte, TN	−23	−10
Waynesville, NC	−20	−4
Birmingham, AL	−17	2
Knoxville, TN	−14	6
Atlanta, GA	−8	18
Daytona Beach, FL	−0.6	31
Strong wind gusts		
City	(KPH)	(MPH)
Mount Washington, NH	232	144
Flattop Mountain, NC	163	101
South Marsh Island, LA	148	92
Myrtle Beach, SC	145	90
Fire Island, NY	143	89
Boston, MA	130	81

FIGURE 1 One of the heaviest snowstorms to hit New York City since the Blizzard of '93, occurred on February 17, 2003. (Photo by Jasen Florio/CORBIS)

is the **mid-latitude** or **middle-latitude cyclone**.* These are the same phenomena that a TV weather reporter calls a *low-pressure system* or simply a *low*.

Mid-latitude cyclones are low-pressure systems with diameters often exceeding 1000 kilometers (600 miles) that travel from west to east across the planet (Figure 3). Lasting from a few days to more than a week, these weather systems have a counterclockwise circulation pattern with a flow inward toward their centers. Most mid-latitude cyclones have a cold front and a warm front extending from the central area of low pressure. Surface convergence and upward flow initiate cloud development that frequently produces precipitation.

As early as the 1800s, it was known that cyclones were the bearers of precipitation and severe weather. Thus, the barometer was established as the main tool in "forecasting" day-to-day weather changes. However, this early method of weather prediction largely ignored the role of air-mass interactions in the formation of these weather systems. Consequently, it was

not possible to determine the conditions under which cyclone development was favorable.

The first encompassing model to consider the development and intensification of a mid-latitude cyclone was constructed by a group of Norwegian scientists during World War I. The Norwegians were then cut off from weather reports, especially those from the Atlantic. To counter this deficiency, a closely spaced network of weather stations was established throughout the country. Using this network, several Norwegian-trained meteorologists made great advances in broadening our understanding of the weather and, in particular, our understanding of the middle-latitude cyclone. Included in this group were Vilhelm Bjerknes (pronounced *Bee-YURK-ness*), his son Jacob Bjerknes, Jacob's fellow student Halvor Solberg, and Swedish meteorologist Tor Bergeron. In 1921 the work of these scientists resulted in a publication outlining a compelling model of how mid-latitude cyclones progress through stages of birth, growth, and decay. These insights, which marked a turning point in atmospheric science, became known as the **polar-front theory**—also referred to as the **Norwegian cyclone model**.

---

*Mid-latitude cyclones go by a number of different names, including wave cyclones, frontal cyclones, extratropical cyclones, low-pressure systems, and, simply, lows.

(a) **Saturday, March 13, 1993**

(b) **Sunday, March 14, 1993**

FIGURE 2 These simplified weather maps show the positions of an enormous cyclonic storm on March 13 and 14, 1993. After the storm formed in the Gulf of Mexico, it moved northeastward, spawning tornadoes in Florida and dumping huge quantities of snow from Alabama to Canada's Maritime Provinces. The closely spaced isobars depict the steep pressure gradient that generated hurricane-force winds in many places. The strong winds caused extreme drifting of snow and created storm waves in the Atlantic that pounded the coast, causing much beach erosion and damage to shoreline homes. The colored areas indicate regions where precipitation occurred.

Even without the benefit of upper-air charts, these skilled meteorologists presented a working model that remains remarkably accurate to this day.

In the Norwegian cyclone model, middle-latitude cyclones develop in conjunction with the polar front. Recall that the polar front separates cold polar air from warm subtropical air. During cool months the polar front is generally well defined

Students Sometimes Ask ...

What is an extratropical cyclone?

Extratropical means "outside the tropics," so this is just another name for a mid-latitude cyclone. The term cyclone refers to the circulation around any low-pressure center, regardless of its size or intensity. Hence, hurricanes and mid-latitude cyclones are two types of cyclones. Whereas "extratropical cyclone" is another name for a mid-latitude cyclone, the name "tropical cyclone" is often used to describe a hurricane.

and forms a nearly continuous band around Earth that can be recognized on upper-air charts. At the surface, this frontal zone is often broken into distinct segments. These frontal segments are separated by regions of more gradual temperature change. It is along frontal zones where cold, equatorward-moving air collides with warm, poleward-moving air that most middle-latitude cyclones form.

Because mid-latitude cyclones develop in conjunction with fronts, we will first consider the nature of fronts and the weather associated with their movement and then apply what we learn to the model of cyclone development (Figure 3).

Fronts

 Weather Patterns
▶ **Fronts**

Fronts are boundary surfaces that separate air masses of different densities. One air mass is usually warmer and often contains more moisture than the other. However, fronts can

(a) **Map view**

(b) **Three-dimentional view from points A to B**

FIGURE 3   Idealized structure of a mid-latitude cyclone. (a) Map view showing fronts, air masses, and surface flow. (b) Three-dimensional view of the warm and cold fronts along a line from point A to point B.

form between any two contrasting air masses. When the vast sizes of air masses are considered, these 15- to 200-kilometer- (9- to 120-mile-) wide bands of discontinuity are relatively narrow. On the scale of a weather map, they are normally thin enough to represent as a broad line.

Above the ground the frontal surface slopes at a low angle so that warmer air overlies cooler air, as shown in Figure 4. In the ideal case the air masses on both sides of the front would move in the same direction and at the same speed. Under this condition the front would act simply as a barrier that travels along with the air masses. Generally, however, the distribution of pressure across a front is such that one air mass moves faster relative to the frontal boundary than does the other. Thus, one air mass actively advances into another and "clashes" with it. The Norwegian meteorologists visualized these zones of air-mass interactions as analogous to battle lines and tagged them "fronts," like battlefronts. It is along these zones of conflict that mid-latitude cyclones develop and produce much of the precipitation and severe weather in the belt of the westerlies.

As one air mass moves into another, limited mixing occurs along the frontal surface, but for the most part, the air masses retain their identity as one is displaced upward over the other.

No matter which air mass is advancing, it is always the warmer, less dense air that is forced aloft, whereas the cooler, denser air acts as a wedge on which lifting takes place. The term **overrunning** is generally applied to warm air gliding up along a cold air mass. We now shall look at five types of fronts—*warm, cold, stationary, occluded,* and *drylines.*

Warm Fronts

When the surface (ground) position of a front moves so that warm air occupies territory formerly covered by cooler air, it is called a **warm front** (Figure 4). On a weather map, the surface position of a warm front is shown by a red line with red semicircles protruding into the cooler air. East of the Rockies, maritime tropical (mT) air often enters the United States from the Gulf of Mexico and overruns receding cool air. As the colder air retreats, friction with the ground greatly slows the advance of the surface position of the front compared to its position aloft. Stated another way, less dense, warm air has a hard time displacing heavier, cold air. Consequently, the boundary separating these air masses acquires a very gradual slope. The slope of a warm front (height compared to

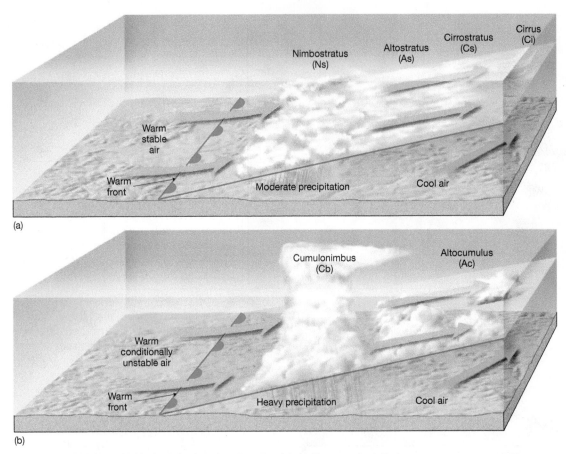

FIGURE 4 Warm fronts. (a) Idealized clouds and weather associated with a warm front. During most of the year, warm fronts produce light-to-moderate precipitation over a wide area. (b) During the warm season, when conditionally unstable air is forced aloft, cumulonimbus clouds and thunderstorms often arise.

horizontal distance) averages only about 1:200. This means that if you traveled 200 kilometers (120 miles) ahead of the surface location of a warm front, the frontal surface would be only 1 kilometer (0.6 miles) overhead.

As warm air ascends the retreating wedge of cold air, it expands and cools adiabatically, causing moisture in the ascending air to condense into clouds that often produce precipitation. The cloud sequence in Figure 4a typically precedes a warm front. The first sign of the approaching warm front is cirrus clouds. These high clouds form where the overrunning warm air has ascended high up the wedge of cold air, 1000 kilometers (600 miles) or more ahead of the surface front. Another indication of an approaching warm front is provided by aircraft contrails. On a clear day, when these condensation trails persist for several hours, you can be fairly certain that comparatively warm, moist air is ascending overhead.

As the front nears, cirrus clouds grade into cirrostratus that gradually blend into denser sheets of altostratus. About 300 kilometers (180 miles) ahead of the front, thicker stratus and nimbostratus clouds appear and precipitation commences.

Because of their slow rate of advance and very gentle slope, lifting associated with warm fronts has a large horizontal component. As a result, warm fronts tend to produce light-to-moderate precipitation over a wide area for an extended period (Figure 5). But this is not always the case. If, for example, the overriding air mass is relatively dry (low dew-point temperatures), there will be minimal cloud development, and no precipitation. By contrast, during the hot summer months, very moist air is commonly associated with an approaching warm front. If this conditionally unstable air is lifted sufficiently it will freely rise on its own, producing towering cumulonimbus clouds and thunderstorms (Figure 4b).

As you can see from Figure 4, the precipitation associated with a warm front occurs ahead of the surface position of the front. Some of the rain that falls through the cool air below the clouds evaporates. As a result, the air directly beneath the cloud base often becomes saturated and a stratus cloud deck develops. These clouds occasionally grow rapidly downward, which can cause problems for pilots of small aircraft that require visual landings. One minute pilots may have adequate visibility and the next be in a cloud mass (frontal fog) that has the landing strip "socked in." Occasionally during the winter, a relatively warm air mass is forced over a body of

FIGURE 5 Light rain associated with a warm front in late fall. (Photo by Miro Vintoniv/Stock Boston)

subfreezing air. When this occurs, it can create hazardous driving conditions. Raindrops become supercooled as they fall through the subfreezing air. Upon colliding with the road surface they flash-freeze to produce the icy layer called *glaze*.

When a warm front passes, temperatures gradually rise. As you would expect, the increase is most apparent when a large contrast exists between adjacent air masses. Moreover, a wind shift from the east to the southwest is generally noticeable. (The reason for this shift will become evident later.) The moisture content and stability of the encroaching warm air mass largely determine the time period required for clear skies to return. During the summer, cumulus and occasionally cumulonimbus clouds are embedded in the warm unstable air mass that follows the front. These clouds may produce precipitation, which can be heavy but is usually scattered and of short duration.

Cold Fronts

When cold, continental polar air actively advances into a region occupied by warmer air, the zone of discontinuity is called a **cold front** (Figure 6). As with warm fronts, friction slows the surface position of a cold front compared to its position aloft. Thus, the cold front steepens as it moves. On the average, cold fronts are about twice as steep as warm fronts, having a slope of perhaps 1:100. In addition, cold fronts advance at speeds around 35 to 50 kilometers (20 to 35 miles) per hour compared to 25 to 35 kilometers (15 to 20 miles) per hour for warm fronts. These two differences, steepness of slope and rate of movement, largely account for the more violent nature of cold-front weather, compared to the weather generally accompanying a warm front.

The arrival of a cold front is sometimes preceded by altocumulus clouds. As the front approaches, generally from the west or northwest, towering clouds can often be seen in the distance. Near the front, a dark band of ominous clouds foretells the ensuing weather. The forceful lifting of warm, moist air along a cold front is often so rapid that the released latent heat increases the air's buoyancy. The heavy downpours and vigorous wind gusts associated with mature cumulonimbus clouds frequently result. Because a cold front produces roughly the same amount of lifting as a warm front, but over a shorter distance, the precipitation intensity is greater but of shorter duration (Figure 7).

In addition, a marked temperature drop and wind shift from the southwest to the northwest usually accompany frontal passage. The reason for this shift will be explained later in this chapter. The sharp temperature contrast and

FIGURE 6 Fast-moving cold front and cumulonimbus clouds. Thunderstorms often occur if the warm air is unstable.

FIGURE 7 The forceful lifting of warm, moist air along a cold front is often associated with cumulonimbus clouds and thunderstorms. (Photo by David R. Frazier/Photolibrary/Alamy)

sometimes violent weather along cold fronts are symbolized on a weather map by a blue line with blue triangular points extending into the warm air mass (see Figure 6).

Most often the weather behind a cold front is dominated by subsiding air within a continental polar air mass. Thus, the drop in temperature is accompanied by clearing that begins soon after the front passes. Although subsidence causes adiabatic heating aloft, the effect on surface temperatures is minor. In winter the long, cloudless nights that often follow the passage of a cold front allow for abundant radiation cooling that reduces surface temperatures.

When a cold front moves over a relatively warm surface, radiation emitted from Earth can heat the lower atmosphere enough to produce shallow convection. This in turn may generate low cumulus or stratocumulus clouds behind the front. However, subsidence aloft renders these air masses quite stable. Any clouds that form will not develop great vertical thickness and will seldom produce precipitation. One exception is lake-effect snow where the cold air behind the front acquires both heat and moisture when it traverses a comparatively warm body of water.

Stationary Fronts

Occasionally, the airflow on both sides of a front is neither toward the cold air mass nor toward the warm air mass, but almost parallel to the line of the front. Consequently, the surface position of the front does not move, or moves very slowly. This condition is called a **stationary front.** On a weather map, stationary fronts are shown with blue triangular points on one side of the line and red semicircles on the other. Because overrunning usually occurs along stationary fronts, gentle to moderate precipitation is likely. Stationary fronts may remain over an area for several days, in which case flooding is possible.

Occluded Fronts

The fourth type of front is the **occluded front.** Here a rapidly moving cold front overtakes a warm front, as shown in Figure 8a. As the cold air wedges the warm front upward, a new front forms between the advancing cold air and the air over which the warm front is gliding (Figure 8b). The weather of an occluded front is generally complex. Most precipitation is associated with the warm air being forced aloft (Figure 8c). When conditions are suitable, however, the newly formed front is capable of initiating precipitation of its own.

As you might expect, there are cold-type occluded fronts and warm-type occluded fronts. In the occluded front shown in Figure 9a, the air behind the cold front is colder than the cool air it is overtaking. This is the most common type of occluded front east of the Rockies and is called a **cold-type occluded front.**

It is also possible for the air behind the advancing cold front to be warmer than the cold air it is overtaking. These

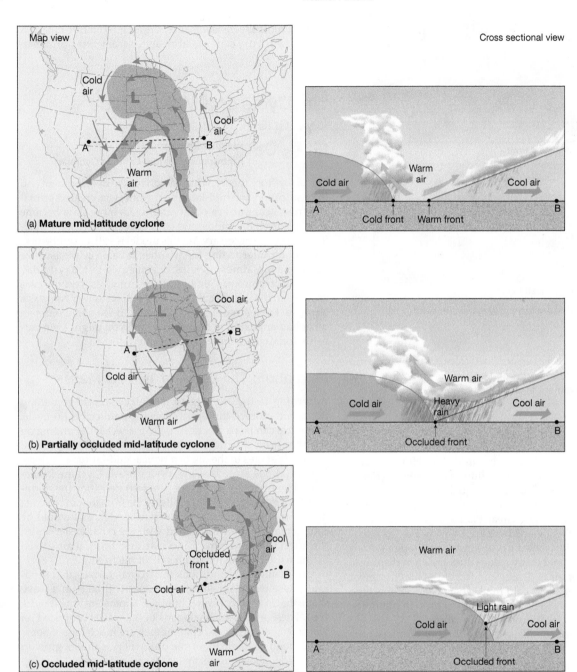

FIGURE 8 Stages in the formation of an occluded front and its relationship to an evolving mid-latitude cyclone. After the warm air has been forced aloft, the system begins to dissipate. The shaded areas indicate regions where precipitation is most likely to occur.

warm-type occluded fronts (Figure 9b) frequently occur along the Pacific Coast, where milder maritime polar air invades more frigid polar air that had its origin over the continent.

Notice in Figure 9 that in the warm-type occluded front, the warm air aloft (and hence the precipitation) often precedes the arrival of the surface front. This situation is reversed for the cold-type occluded front, where the front aloft (and its associated precipitation) lags behind the surface front. Also note that cold-type occluded fronts frequently resemble cold fronts in the type of weather generated.

Because of the complex nature of occluded fronts, they are often drawn on weather maps as either warm or cold fronts, depending on what kind of air is the aggressor. In those cases

(a) **Cold-type occluded front**

(b) **Warm-type occluded front**

FIGURE 9 Occluded fronts of (a) the cold type and (b) the warm type.

when they are drawn as an occluded front, a purple line with alternating purple triangles and semicircles pointing in the direction of movement is employed.

Drylines

Classifying fronts based only on the temperature differences across the frontal boundary can be misleading. Humidity also influences the density of air, with humid air being less dense than dry air, all other factors being equal. In the summer it is not unusual for a southeastward moving air mass that originated over the northern Great Plains to displace warm, humid air over the lower Mississippi Valley. The front that develops is usually labeled a cold front, even though the advancing air may not be any colder than the air it displaces. Simply, the drier air is denser and forcefully lifts the moist air in its path, just like a cold front. The passage of this type of frontal boundary is noticed as a sharp drop in humidity, without an appreciable drop in temperature.

A related type of boundary, called a **dryline,** develops over the southern Great Plains. This occurs when dry, continental tropical (cT) air originating over the American Southwest meets moist, maritime tropical (mT) air from the Gulf of Mexico. Basically a spring and summer phenomenon, drylines most often generate a band of severe thunderstorms along a line extending from Texas to Nebraska that moves eastward across the Great Plains. A dryline is easily identified by comparing the dew point temperatures of the cT air west of the boundary with the dew points of the mT air mass to the east.

In summary, because cold fronts are the aggressor, the lifting along a cold front tends to be more concentrated and forceful than along a warm front. Hence, the precipitation associated with a cold front usually occurs in a narrower zone and is more intense than that associated with a warm front.

Further, most severe weather occurs along cold fronts or drylines in which dry continental air aggressively lifts warm maritime air.

Life Cycle of a Mid-Latitude Cyclone

GE⬤De **Weather Patterns**
THE ATMOSPHERE ▶ Introducing Middle-Latitude Cyclones

The polar-front theory, which describes the development and intensification of a mid-latitude cyclone, was created primarily from near-surface observations. As more data became available from the middle and upper troposphere, some modifications were necessary. Yet this model is still a useful working tool for interpreting the weather. It helps us to visualize our dynamic atmosphere as it generates our day-to-day weather. If you keep this model in mind as you observe changes in the weather, the changes will no longer come as a surprise. Furthermore, you will begin to see some order in what had appeared to be disorder, and you might even correctly forecast the impending weather!

Formation: The Clash of Two Air Masses

According to the Norwegian model, cyclones form along fronts and proceed through a generally predictable life cycle. This cycle can last a few days to over a week, depending on whether atmospheric conditions are favorable. Figure 10 shows six stages in the life of a typical mid-latitude cyclone. In part (a), the stage is set for **cyclogenesis** (cyclone formation). Here two air masses of different densities (temperatures) are moving roughly parallel to the front, but in opposite directions. (In the classic polar-front model, this would be continental polar air associated with the polar easterlies on the north side of the front and maritime tropical air driven by the westerlies on the south side of the front.)

Under suitable conditions the frontal surface that separates these two contrasting air masses will take on a wave shape that is usually several hundred kilometers long (Figure 10b). These waves are analogous to the waves produced on water by moving air, except that they are much larger. Some waves tend to dampen, or die out, whereas others grow in amplitude. Those storms that intensify or "deepen" develop waves that change in shape over time, much like a gentle ocean swell does as it moves into shallow water and becomes a tall, breaking wave (Figure 10c).

Development of Cyclonic Flow

As the wave develops, warm air advances poleward invading the area formerly occupied by colder air, while cold air moves equatorward. This change in the direction of the surface flow is accompanied by a readjustment in the pressure pattern that results in nearly circular isobars, with the low pressure centered at the crest of the wave. The resulting flow is a counterclockwise cyclonic circulation that can be seen clearly on the

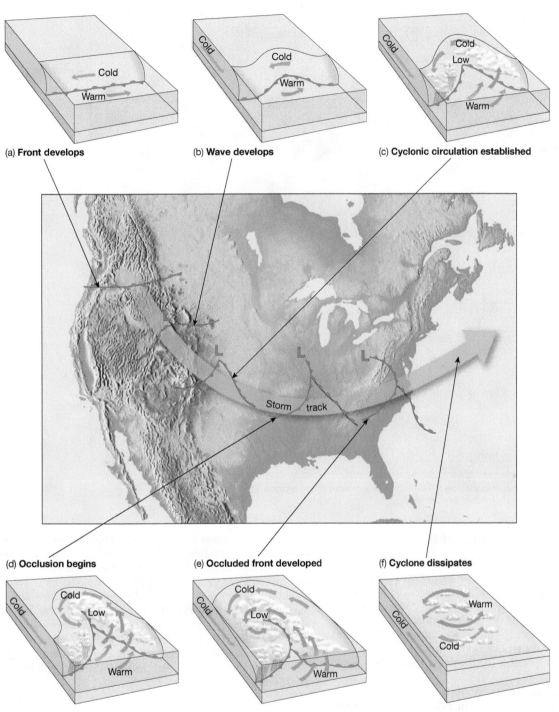

(a) **Front develops**

(b) **Wave develops**

(c) **Cyclonic circulation established**

Storm   track

(d) **Occlusion begins**

(e) **Occluded front developed**

(f) **Cyclone dissipates**

FIGURE 10   Stages in the life cycle of a middle-latitude cyclone, as proposed by J. Bjerknes.

weather map shown in Figure 11. Once the cyclonic circulation develops, we would expect general convergence to result in lifting, especially where warm air is overrunning colder air. You can see in Figure 11 that the air in the warm sector (over the southern states) is flowing northeastward toward colder air that is moving toward the northwest. Because the warm air is moving in a direction perpendicular to this front, we can conclude that the warm air is invading a region formerly occupied by cold air. Therefore, this must be a warm front. Similar reasoning indicates that to the left (west) of the cyclonic disturbance, cold air from the northwest is displacing the air of the warm sector and generating a cold front.

FIGURE 11 Simplified weather map showing the circulation of a middle-latitude cyclone. The colored areas indicate regions of probable precipitation.

Occlusion: The Beginning of the End

Usually, the position of the cold front advances faster than the warm front and begins to close (lift) the warm front, as shown in Figure 10c,d. This process, known as **occlusion**, forms an *occluded front,* which grows in length as it displaces the warm sector aloft. As occlusion begins, the storm often intensifies. Pressure at the storm's center falls, and wind speeds increase. In the winter, heavy snowfalls and blizzard-like conditions are possible during this phase of the storm's evolution.

As more of the sloping discontinuity (front) is forced aloft, the pressure gradient weakens. In a day or two the entire warm sector is displaced, and cold air surrounds the cyclone at low levels (see Figure 10f). Thus, the horizontal temperature (density) difference that existed between the two contracting air masses has been eliminated. At this point the cyclone has exhausted its source of energy. Friction slows the surface flow, and the once highly organized counterclockwise flow ceases to exist.

A simple analogy may help you visualize what is happening to the cold and warm air masses in the preceding discussion.

Imagine a large water trough that has a vertical divider separating the tank into two equal parts. Half of the tank is filled with hot water containing red dye, and the other half is filled with blue-colored ice water. Now imagine what happens when the divider is removed. The cold, dense water will flow under the less dense warm water, displacing it upward. This rush of water will come to a halt as soon as all of the warm water is displaced toward the top of the container. In a similar manner a middle-latitude cyclone dies once all of the warm air is displaced aloft and the horizontal discontinuity between the air masses no longer exists.

Idealized Weather of a Mid-Latitude Cyclone

GE⬤De **Weather Patterns**
THE ATMOSPHERE ▶ Introducing Middle-Latitude Cyclones

As stated earlier, the Norwegian model is a useful tool for examining weather patterns of the middle latitudes. Figure 12 illustrates a mature mid-latitude cyclone; note the distribution

FIGURE 12 Cloud patterns typically associated with a mature middle-latitude cyclone. The middle section is a map view. Note the cross-section lines (F–G, A–E). Above the map is a vertical cross section along line F–G. Below the map is a cross-section along A–E. For cloud abbreviations, refer to Figures 9–4 and 9–6.

of clouds and thus the regions of possible precipitation. Compare this map to the satellite image of a cyclone in Figure 23. It is easy to see why we often refer to the cloud pattern of a cyclone as having a "comma" shape.

Guided by the westerlies aloft, cyclones generally move eastward across the United States. Therefore, we can expect the first signs of a cyclone's arrival to appear in the western sky. In the region of the Mississippi Valley, however, cyclones often begin a more northeasterly trajectory and occasionally move directly northward. Typically, a mid-latitude cyclone requires two to four days to pass completely over a region. During that period, abrupt changes in atmospheric conditions may occur, particularly in the winter and spring when the greatest temperature contrasts occur across the middle latitudes.

Using Figure 12 as a guide, let us examine these weather producers and the changes you could expect if a mid-latitude cyclone passed over your area. To facilitate our discussion, profiles of the storm are provided above and below the map. They correspond to lines A–E and F–G on the map. (Remember, these storms move from west to east; therefore, the right side of the cyclone shown in Figure 12 will be the first to pass by.)

First, imagine the change in weather as you move from right to left along profile A–E (see bottom of Figure 12). At point A the sighting of high cirrus clouds is the first sign of the approaching cyclone. These high clouds can precede the surface front by 1000 kilometers (600 miles) or more, and they are normally accompanied by falling pressure. As the warm front advances, a lowering and thickening of the cloud deck is noticed. Within 12 to 24 hours after the first sighting of cirrus clouds, light precipitation usually commences (point B). As the front nears, the rate of precipitation increases, a rise in temperature is noticed, and winds begin to change from an easterly to a southerly flow.

With the passage of the warm front, the area is under the influence of the maritime tropical air mass of the warm sector (point C). Generally, the region affected by this part of the cyclone experiences relatively warm temperatures, southerly winds, and clear skies, although fair-weather cumulus or altocumulus clouds are not uncommon.

The rather pleasant weather of the warm sector passes quickly in the spring and is replaced by gusty winds and precipitation generated along the cold front. The approach of a rapidly advancing cold front is marked by a wall of rolling black clouds (point D). Severe weather accompanied by heavy precipitation and occasionally hail or a tornado is common at this time of year.

The passage of the cold front is easily detected by a wind shift. The warm flow from the south or southwest is replaced by cold winds from the west to northwest, resulting in a pronounced drop in temperature. Also, rising pressure hints of the subsiding cool, dry air behind the cold front. Once the front passes, the skies clear quickly as cooler air invades the region (point E). A day or two of almost cloudless deep blue skies are often experienced, unless another cyclone is edging into the region.

A very different set of weather conditions prevails in the portion of the cyclone that contains the occluded front along profile F–G (see top of Figure 12). Here temperatures remain cool during the passage of the storm. The first hints of the approaching low-pressure center are a continual drop in air pressure and increasingly overcast conditions. This section of the cyclone most often generates snow or icing storms during the coldest months. Moreover, the occluded front usually moves more slowly than the other fronts. Thus, the entire wishbone-shaped frontal structure shown in Figure 12 rotates counterclockwise so that the occluded front appears to "bend over backward." This effect adds to the misery of the region

influenced by the occluded front, for it remains over the area longer than the other fronts (Box 1).

Cyclone Formation

The polar-front model shows that cyclogenesis (cyclone formation) occurs where a frontal surface is distorted into a wave-shaped discontinuity. Several surface factors are thought to produce this wave in a frontal zone. Topographic irregularities (such as mountains), temperature contrasts (as between sea and land), or ocean-current influences can disrupt the general zonal flow sufficiently to produce a wave along a front. In addition, an intensification of the flow aloft frequently precedes the formation of a surface cyclone. This fact strongly suggests that upper-level flow contributes to the formation of these rotating storm systems.

When the earliest studies of cyclones were made, little data were available on airflow in the middle and upper troposphere. Since then, a close relationship has been established between surface disturbances and the flow aloft. Whenever the winds aloft exhibit a relatively straight zonal flow—that is, directly from west to east—little cyclonic activity occurs at the surface. However, when the upper air begins to meander widely from north-to-south, forming high-amplitude waves of alternating troughs (lows) and ridges (highs), cyclonic activity intensifies (Figure 13). Moreover, when surface cyclones form, almost invariably they are centered below the jet-stream axis and downwind from an upper-level trough (Figure 13).

Cyclonic and Anticyclonic Circulation

Before discussing how surface cyclones are generated and supported by the flow aloft, let us review the nature of cyclonic and anticyclonic winds. Recall that airflow about a surface low is inward, a fact that leads to mass convergence (coming together). Because accumulation of air is accompanied by a corresponding increase in surface pressure we might expect a surface low-pressure center to "fill" rapidly and be eliminated, just as the vacuum in a coffee can is quickly equalized when we open it. However, cyclones often exist for a week or longer. For this to happen, surface convergence must be offset by outflow aloft (Figure 13). As long as divergence (spreading out) aloft is equal to or greater than the surface inflow, the low pressure can be sustained.

Because cyclones are bearers of stormy weather, they have received far more attention than their counterparts, anticyclones. Yet the close relationship between them makes it difficult to totally separate a discussion of these two pressure systems. The surface air that feeds a cyclone, for example, generally originates as air flowing out of an anticyclone (Figure 13). Consequently, cyclones and anticyclones are typically found adjacent to one another. Like the cyclone, an anticyclone depends on the flow aloft to maintain its circulation. In the anticyclone, divergence at the surface is balanced by convergence aloft and general subsidence of the air column (Figure 13).

FIGURE 13 Idealized depiction of the support that divergence and convergence aloft provide to cyclonic and anticyclonic circulation at the surface.

Divergence and Convergence Aloft

Because divergence aloft is so important to cyclogenesis, we need a basic understanding of its role. Divergence aloft does not involve the outward flow in all directions as occurs about a surface anticyclone. Instead, the winds aloft flow generally from west to east along sweeping curves. How does zonal flow aloft cause upper-level divergence?

One mechanism responsible for divergence aloft is a phenomenon known as **speed divergence.** It has been known for some time that wind speeds can change dramatically in the vicinity of the jet stream. On entering a zone of high wind speed, air accelerates and stretches out (divergence). In contrast, when air enters a zone of slower wind speed, an air pile-up (convergence) results. Analogous situations occur every day on a toll highway. When exiting a toll booth and entering the zone of maximum speed, we find automobiles diverging (increasing the number of car lengths between them). As automobiles slow to pay the toll, they experience convergence (coming together).

In addition to speed divergence, several other factors contribute to divergence (or convergence) aloft. These include *directional divergence,* which is horizontal spreading of an air stream, and *vorticity,* which is the amount of rotation exhibited by a mass of moving air. Vorticity can either enhance or inhibit divergence aloft.

The combined effect of the phenomena that influence flow aloft is that an area of upper-air divergence and surface cyclonic circulation generally develop downstream from an upper-level trough, as illustrated in Figure 13. Consequently, in the United States surface cyclones generally form east of an upper-level trough. As long as divergence aloft exceeds convergence at ground level, surface pressures will fall and the cyclonic storm will intensify.

Conversely, the zone in the jet stream that experiences convergence and anticyclonic rotation is located downstream from a ridge (Figure 13). The accumulation of air in this region of the jet stream leads to subsidence and increased surface pressure. Hence, this is a favorable site for the development of a surface anticyclone.

Because of the significant role that the upper-level flow has on cyclogenesis, it should be evident that any attempt at weather prediction must take into account the airflow aloft. This is why television weather reporters frequently illustrate the flow within the jet stream.

In summary, the flow aloft contributes to the formation and intensification of surface low- and high-pressure systems. Areas of upper-level convergence and divergence are located in the vicinity of the jet stream, where dramatic changes in wind speeds cause air either to pile up (converge) or spread out (diverge). Upper-level convergence is favored downstream (east) of a ridge, whereas divergence occurs downstream of an upper-level trough. Below regions of upper-level convergence are areas of high pressure (anticyclones), whereas upper-level divergence supports the formation and development of cyclonic systems (lows).

BOX 1 ▶ WINDS AS A FORECASTING TOOL

Every Wind Has its Weather

Francis Bacon

People living in the middle latitudes know well that during the winter, northerly winds can chill you to the bone (Figure A). Conversely, a sudden change to a southerly flow can bring welcome relief from these frigid conditions. If you are more observant, you might have noticed that when the winds switch from a southerly flow to a more easterly direction, foul weather often follows.

By contrast, a change in wind direction from the southwest to the northwest is usually accompanied by clearing conditions. Just how are the winds and the forthcoming weather related?

Modern weather forecasts require the processing capabilities of high-speed computers as well as the expertise of people with considerable professional training.

Nevertheless, some reasonable insights into the impending weather can be gained through careful observation. The two most significant elements for this purpose are barometric pressure and wind direction. Recall that anticyclones (high-pressure cells) are associated with clear skies, and that cyclones (low-pressure cells) frequently bring clouds and precipitation. Thus, by noting whether the barometer is rising, falling, or steady, we have some indication of the forthcoming weather. For example, rising pressure indicates the approach of a high-pressure system and generally clearing conditions.

The use of winds in weather forecasting is also quite straightforward. Because cyclones are the "villains" in the weather game, we are most concerned with the circulation around these storm centers. In particular, changes in wind direction that occur with the passage of warm and cold fronts are useful in predicting the impending weather. Notice in Figure 12, that with the passage of both the warm and cold fronts, the wind arrows change positions in a clockwise manner. Specifically, with the passage of the cold front, the wind shifts from southwest to northwest. From nautical terminology, the word *veering* is applied to this clockwise wind shift. Because clearing conditions normally occur with the passage of

FIGURE A Wind blowing snow off mountain cabin, Alto Adige, Italian Alps. (Photo by AGRfoto/Alex Rowbotham/Alamy)

Traveling Cyclones

Cyclone development does not occur uniformly over Earth but tends to favor certain locations, such as the leeward sides of mountains and coastal regions. In general, cyclones form in areas where large temperature contrasts occur in the lower troposphere. Figure 14 shows areas of greatest cyclone development over North America and adjacent oceans. Notice that the main sites for cyclone formation occur along the lee side of the Rocky Mountains and along the Atlantic Coast east of the Appalachian Mountains. Other important sites are in the North Pacific and the North Atlantic.

Patterns of Movement

Once formed, cyclones tend to first travel in an easterly direction across North America and then follow a more northeasterly path into the North Atlantic (Figure 15). However, numerous exceptions to this general trend occur.

FIGURE 14 Major sites of cyclone formation.

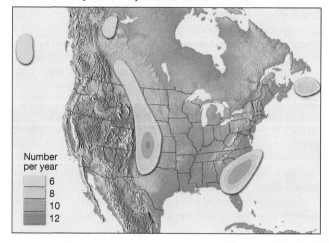

Number per year

6
8
10
12

either front, veering winds are indicators that the weather will improve.

In contrast, the area in the northern portion of the cyclone will experience winds that shift in a counterclockwise direction, as can be seen in Figure 12. Winds that shift in this manner are said to be *backing*. With the approach of a mid-latitude cyclone, backing winds indicate cool temperatures and continued foul weather.

A summary of the relationship among barometer readings, winds, and the impending weather is provided in Table A. Although this information is applicable in a very general way to much of the United States, local influences must be taken into account. For example, a rising barometer and a change in wind direction, from southwest to northwest, is usually associated with the passage of a cold front and indicates that

clearing conditions should follow. However, in the winter, residents of the southeast shore of one of the Great Lakes may not be so lucky. As cold, dry northwest winds cross large expanses of open water, they acquire heat and moisture from the relatively warm lake surface. By the time this air reaches the leeward shore, it is often humid and unstable enough to produce heavy lake-effect snow.

TABLE A Wind, Barometric Pressure, and Impending Weather

Changes in wind direction	Barometric pressure	Pressure tendency	Impending weather
Any direction	1023 mb and above (30.20 in.)	Steady or rising	Continued fair with no temperature change
SW to NW	1013 mb and below (29.92 in.)	Rising rapidly	Clearing within 12 to 24 hours and colder
S to SW	1013 mb and below (29.92 in.)	Rising slowly	Clearing within a few hours and fair for several days
SE to SW	1013 mb and below (29.92 in.)	Steady or slowly falling	Clearing and warmer, followed by possible precipitation
E to NE	1019 mb and above (30.10 in.)	Falling slowly	In summer, with light wind, rain may not fall for several days; in winter, rain within 24 hours
E to NE	1019 mb and above (10.10 in.)	Falling rapidly	In summer, rain probable within 12 to 24 hours; in winter, rain or snow with strong winds likely
SE to NE	1013 mb and below (29.92 in.)	Falling slowly	Rain will continue for 1 to 2 days
SE to NE	1013 mb and below (29.92 in.)	Falling rapidly	Stormy conditions followed within 36 hours by clearing and, in winter, colder temperatures

Source: Adapted from the National Weather Service.

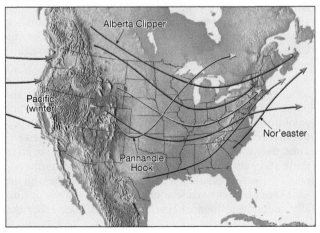

FIGURE 15 Typical paths of cyclonic storms that affect the lower 48 states.

One well-known example is a storm that goes by the name of *Panhandle Hook*. The "Hook" describes the curved path these storms follow (Figure 15). Developing in southern Colorado near Texas and Oklahoma panhandles, these cyclones first travel toward the southeast and then bend sharply northward traveling across Wisconsin and into Canada.

Cyclones that influence western North America originate over the North Pacific. Many of these systems move northeastward toward the Gulf of Alaska. However, during the winter months these storms travel farther southward and often reach the coast of the contiguous 48 states, occasionally traveling as far south as southern California. These cyclonic systems provide the winter rainy season that affects much of the West Coast.

Most Pacific storms do not cross the Rockies intact but may redevelop on the lee (eastward) side of these mountains. A favorite site for redevelopment is Colorado, but other common sites of formation exist as far south as Texas and as far north as Alberta. The cyclones that form in Canada tend to move southeastward toward the Great Lakes and then turn northeastward and move out into the Atlantic. Cyclones that redevelop over the Great Plains generally migrate eastward until they reach the central United States, where a northeastward or even northward trajectory is followed. Many of these cyclones traverse the Great Lakes region, making it the most storm-ridden portion of the country. Another area where cyclogenesis occurs is east of the southern Appalachians. These storms tend to move northward with the warm Gulf Stream and bring stormy conditions to the entire East Coast.

Alberta Clipper An *Alberta Clipper* is a cold, windy cyclonic storm that forms on the eastern side of the Canadian Rockies in the province of Alberta (see Figure 15). Noted for their speed, they are called "clippers" because in Colonial times the fastest vehicles were small ships by the same name. The average Alberta Clipper dives southeastward into Montana or the Dakotas and then tracks across the Great Lakes where it brings dramatically lower temperatures. Winds associated with Clippers frequently exceed 50 kilometers (30 miles) per hour. Because clippers move rapidly and remain a long way from the mild waters of the Gulf of Mexico they tend to be moisture deprived. As a result they do not drop large amounts of snow. Instead, they may leave a few inches in a narrow band from the Dakotas to New York over a span as short as two days. However, because these winter storms are relatively frequent occurrences, they make a significant contribution to the total winter snowfall in the northern tier of states.

Nor'easter From the Mid-Atlantic Coast to New England, the classic storm is called a *nor'easter* (see Figure 15). They are called nor'easters because the winds preceding the passage of these storms in coastal areas are from the northeast. They are most frequent and violent between September and April when cold air pouring south from Canada meets relatively warm humid air from the Atlantic. Once formed, nor'easters follow the coast, often bringing rain, sleet, and heavy snowfall to the Northeast. Because the circulation produces strong onshore winds, these storms can cause considerable coastal erosion, flooding, and property damage. The popular book and movie *The Perfect Storm* was based on a true story of a fishing boat that was caught in an intense nor'easter in October 1991.

Flow Aloft and Cyclone Migration

Recall that the wavy flow aloft is important to the development and evolution of a surface cyclonic storm. In addition, the flow in the middle and upper troposphere appears to strongly influence the rate at which these pressure systems advance and the direction they follow. As a general rule of thumb, surface cyclones move in the same direction as the

500-millibar wind, but at about half the speed. Normally these systems travel at 25 to 50 kilometers (15 to 30 miles) per hour so that distances of roughly 600 to 1200 kilometers (400 to 800 miles) are traversed each day. The faster speeds occur during the coldest months when temperature gradients are greatest.

One of the most exacting tasks in weather forecasting is predicting the paths of cyclonic storms. We have already seen that the flow aloft tends to steer developing pressure systems. Let us examine an example of this steering effect by seeing how changes in the upper-level flow correspond to changes in the path taken by a cyclone.

Figure 16a illustrates the changing position of a middle-latitude cyclone over a four-day period. Notice in Figure 16b that on March 21, the 500-millibar contours are relatively flat. Also notice that for the following two days, the cyclone moves in a rather straight southeasterly direction. By March 23 the 500-millibar contours make a sharp bend northward on the eastern side of a trough situated over Wyoming (Figure 16c). Likewise, the next day the path of the cyclone makes a similar northward migration.

Although this is an oversimplified example, it illustrates the "steering" effect of upper-level flow. Here we have examined the influence of upper airflow on cyclonic movement after the fact. To make useful predictions of future positions of cyclones, accurate appraisals of changes in the westerly flow aloft are required. For this reason, predicting the behavior of the wavy flow in the middle and upper troposphere is an important part of modern weather forecasting.

Anticyclonic Weather and Blocking Highs

Owing to the gradual subsidence within them, anticyclones generally produce clear skies and calm conditions. Because these high-pressure systems are not associated with stormy weather, both their development and movement have not been studied as extensively as that of mid-latitude cyclones. This does not imply, however, that anticyclones always bring desirable weather. Large anticyclones often develop over the Arctic during the winter. These cold high-pressure centers are known to migrate as far south as the Gulf Coast where they can impact the weather over as much as two-thirds of the United States (Figure 17). This dense frigid air often brings record-breaking cold temperatures.

Approximately one to three times each winter, and occasionally during other seasons, large anticyclones form and persist over the middle latitudes for nearly two weeks and sometimes longer than a month. These large highs deflect the nearly zonal west-to-east flow and send it poleward. Thus, they are sometimes called *blocking highs*. Once in place, these stagnant anticyclones block the eastward migration of cyclones. As a result, one section of the nation is kept dry for a week or more while another region remains continually under the influence of cyclonic storms. Such a situation

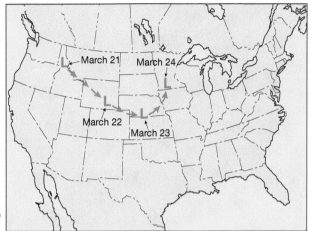

(a) **Movement of cyclone from March 21-24**

(b) **500-mb chart for March 21**

(c) **500-mb chart for March 23**

FIGURE 16 Steering of mid-latitude cyclones. (a) Notice that the cyclone (low) moved almost in a straight southeastward direction on March 21 and March 22. On the morning of March 23, it abruptly turned northward. This change in direction corresponds to the change from (b) rather straight contours on the upper-air chart for March 21 to (c) curved contours on the chart for March 23.

prevailed during the summer of 1993 when a strong high-pressure system became anchored over the southeastern United States and caused migrating storms to stall over the Midwest. The result was the most devastating flooding on record for the central and upper Mississippi Valley (Box 2). At the same time, the Southeast experienced severe drought.

Large stagnant anticyclones can also contribute to air-pollution episodes. The subsidence within an anticyclone can produce a temperature inversion that acts like a lid to trap pollutants. Further, the light winds associated with the center of an anticyclone do little to disperse polluted air. Both Los Angeles and Mexico City experience air pollution episodes when strong, stagnant high-pressure systems dominate their circulation for extended periods.

Case Study of a Mid-Latitude Cyclone

Weather Patterns
▶ In the Lab: Examining a Mature Middle-Latitude Cyclone

To give you a picture of the weather one might expect from a strong late-winter cyclonic storm we are going to look at an actual event. Our sample storm was one of three cyclones to migrate across the United States during the latter half of March. This cyclone reached the U.S. West Coast on March 21 a few hundred kilometers northwest of Seattle, Washington. Like many Pacific storms, this one rejuvenated over the western United States and moved eastward into the Plains states. By the morning of March 23, it was centered over the

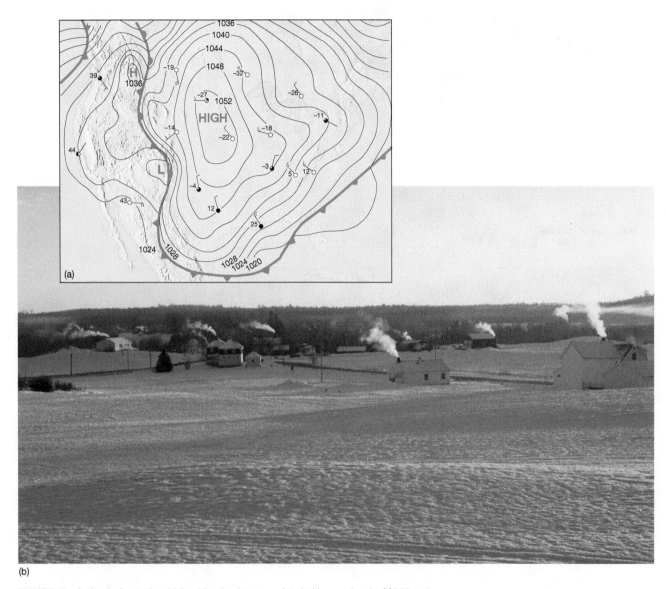

(a)

(b)

FIGURE 17 Anticyclonic weather. (a) A cold anticyclone associated with an outbreak of frigid arctic air impacts the eastern two-thirds of North America. Temperatures are shown in degrees Fahrenheit. (b) Cold outbreak of arctic air invades New England, bringing subzero temperatures and mostly clear skies. (Photo by Karen Thomas/Stock Boston Inc./PictureQuest)

Kansas–Nebraska border (Figure 18). At this time, the central pressure had reached 985 millibars, and its well-developed cyclonic circulation exhibited a warm front and a cold front.

During the next 24 hours, the forward motion of the storm's center became sluggish. It curved slowly northward through Iowa, and the pressure deepened to 982 millibars (Figure 19). Although the storm center advanced slowly, the associated fronts moved vigorously toward the east and somewhat northward. The northern sector of the cold front overtook the warm front and generated an occluded front, which by the morning of March 24 was oriented nearly east-west (Figure 19).

This period in the storm's history marked one of the worst blizzards ever to hit the north-central states. While the winter storm was brewing in the north, the cold front marched from northwestern Texas (on March 23) to the Atlantic Ocean (March 25). During its two-day trek to the ocean, this violent cold front generated numerous severe thunderstorms and 19 tornadoes.

By March 25 the low pressure had diminished in intensity (1000 millibars) and had split into two centers (Figure 20). Although the remnant low from this system, which was situated over the Great Lakes, generated some snow for the remainder of March 25, by the following day it had completely dissipated.

(a)

(b)

Atmosphere 09.18

FIGURE 18 Weather on March 23. (a) Surface weather map. (b) Satellite image showing the cloud patterns on that day. (Courtesy of NOAA/Seattle)

(a)

(b)

FIGURE 19 Weather on March 24. (a) Surface weather map. (b) Satellite image showing the cloud patterns on that day. (Courtesy of NOAA/Seattle)

(a)

(b)

FIGURE 20 Weather on March 25. (a) Surface weather map. (b) Satellite image showing the cloud patterns on that day. (Courtesy of NOAA/Seattle)

BOX 2 ▶ ATMOSPHERIC HAZARD

The Midwest Floods of 2008 and 1993

Floods are part of the natural behavior of streams. They are also among the most deadly and destructive of natural hazards. Most floods have a meteorological origin. Flash floods in small valleys are frequently triggered by torrential rains that last for just a few hours. By contrast, major regional floods in large river valleys are often the result of an extraordinary series of precipitation events over a broad region for an extended time span. The Midwest floods of 2008 and 1993 are examples of the latter situation.

Midwest Floods—June 2008

June 2008 saw record-breaking floods in many parts of the Midwest. June was a very wet month across a significant part of the region, with numerous heavy rain events that helped produce record flooding in Iowa, Wisconsin, Indiana, and Illinois (Figure B). Rainfall totals were more than two times the average in many places. Martinsville, Indiana, for example, reported a total of 20.11 inches of rain for the month—an amount equal to about half its annual rainfall and more than double its old record high for a single month.

For more than two months the jet stream had regularly been taking a major dip southward into the central United States, putting the favored storm track for rainy low pressure centers over the Midwest. As a result, at least 65 locations in the Midwest set new June rainfall records while more than 100 other stations had rainfall totals that ranked second to fifth on record. Prior to the heavy June rains, many of these stations had a very wet winter and spring. When soils are already waterlogged, there is no place for additional rain to go except to flow across the surface causing streams to rise.

The June 2008 floods represented the costliest weather disaster in Indiana history, but Iowa suffered even greater losses with 83 of its 99 counties declared disaster areas. Nine of the state's rivers were at or above previous record flood levels and millions of acres of productive farm land (an estimated 16 percent of the state's total) were submerged. Thousands of people were evacuated, mostly in Cedar Rapids where more than 400 city blocks were under water (Figure C). The list of towns and rural areas throughout the Midwest that were impacted is extraordinary. Many riverside communities were flooded when swollen

streams breached levees that were built to protect the towns (Figure D).

Overall crop losses were estimated to be $7 billion and property damages were expected to top $1 billion. Overall, the Midwest regional floods of 2008 were the worst in 15 years.

FIGURE B Nearly two weeks of intense rain is represented in this image that is based on satellite data. A string of storms brought rain and violent weather to the upper Midwest in early June 2008. Widespread flooding resulted. This image shows rainfall totals from June 2 through June 12. Red circles over parts of Indiana and Iowa indicate regions that received more than 16 inches of rain. Most of the Midwest received between 4 and 8 inches of rain (shown in dark green), with wide swaths of heavier rain measuring 8–12 inches (yellow). (NASA)

The Great Flood of 1993*

Although flood levels in some parts of the Midwest in June 2008 were the highest ever recorded, the overall impact of this event did not approach that of the *Great Flood of 1993*. Perhaps the country's worst nonhurricane

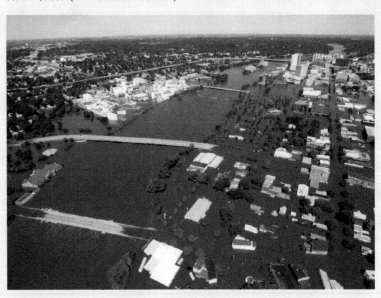

FIGURE C The flooding Cedar River covers a large portion of Cedar Rapids, Iowa, on June 14, 2008. (AP Photo/Jeff Roberson)

FIGURE D Water rushes through a break in an artificial levee in Monroe County, Illinois, in 1993. During the record-breaking floods of 2008 and 1993, many levees could not withstand the force of the floodwaters. Sections of many weakened structures were overtopped or simply collapsed. (Photo by James A. Finley/AP/Wide World Photos)

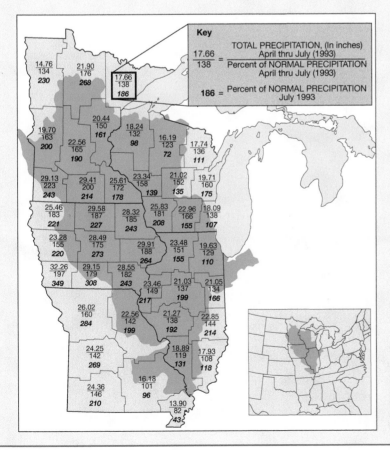

flooding disaster, the 1993 event caused an estimated $27 billion in damages (adjusted to 2007 dollars).

Unprecedented rainfall produced the wettest spring and early summer of the twentieth century for the Upper Mississippi River basin (Figure E). Soils throughout the Midwest were already saturated from ample rainfall in summer and fall 1992, and soils remained moist as winter began. This pattern continued into spring and summer 1993. Compared to the long-term average, rainfall in the Upper Mississippi River basin during April and May was 40 percent higher than average. As the deluge continued through July, much of the basin received between two and three times the norm.

A stationary weather pattern over the United States was responsible for the Midwest's persistent, drenching rains. Most of the showers and thunderstorms developed in the boundary area between cooler air over the Northern Plains and warm, very humid air over the South. This front oscillated north and south over the Midwest during much of June and July. Meanwhile, a strong high-pressure system (the "Bermuda High") became anchored over the southeastern United States, blocking the progression of weather systems through the eastern half of the nation.

Some of the individual station reports were nothing short of astounding. In northwestern Missouri, Skidmore reported 25.35 inches of rain in July. Normal July rainfall for this area is about 4 inches. Alton (northwestern Iowa) had July rains that totaled 20.41 inches, and Leon (south central Iowa) reported 20.68 inches. Rainfall totals such as these leave no doubt that the record-breaking flooding on the Mississippi and other rivers in the Midwest was directly related to the exceptional rainfall during the spring and early summer.

---

*Based on material prepared by Steven Hilberg, Center for Atmospheric Science, Illinois State Water Survey.

FIGURE E Precipitation data for the upper Mississippi River basin between April 1 and July 31, 1993. The magnitude of rainfall over such a large area resulted in flooding of extraordinary and catastrophic proportions on the Mississippi and many of its tributaries. (Data from the Illinois State Water Survey)

Violent Spring Weather

Now that you have read an overview of this storm, let us revisit this cyclone's passage in detail using the weather charts for March 23 through March 25 (see Figures 18 to 20). The weather map for March 23 depicts a classic developing cyclone. The warm sector of this system, as exemplified by Fort Worth, Texas, is under the influence of a warm, humid air mass having a temperature of 70°F and a dew-point temperature of 64°F. Notice in the warm sector that winds are from the south and are overrunning cooler air situated north of the warm front. In contrast, the air behind the cold front is 20° to 40°F cooler than the air of the warm sector and is flowing from the northwest, as depicted by the data for Roswell, New Mexico.

Prior to March 23, this system had generated some precipitation in the Northwest and as far south as California. On the morning of March 23, little activity was occurring along the fronts. As the day progressed, however, the storm intensified and changed dramatically. The map for March 24 illustrates the highly developed cyclone that evolved during the next 24 hours. The extent and spacing of the isobars indicate a strong system that affected the circulation of the entire eastern two-thirds of the United States. A glance at the winds reveals a robust counterclockwise flow converging on the low.

The activity in the cold sector of the storm just north of the occluded front produced one of the worst March blizzards ever to affect the northcentral United States. In the Duluth–Superior area of Minnesota and Wisconsin, winds of up to 81 miles per hour were measured. Unofficial estimates of wind speeds in excess of 100 miles per hour were made on the aerial bridge connecting these cities. Winds blew 12 inches of snow into 10- to 15-foot drifts, and some roads were closed for three days (Figure 21). One large supper club in Superior was destroyed by fire because drifts prevented firefighting equipment from reaching the blaze.

At the other extreme was the weather produced by the cold front as it closed in on the warm, humid air flowing into the warm sector. By the late afternoon of March 23, the cold front had generated a hailstorm in parts of eastern Texas. As the cold front moved eastward, it affected all of the southeastern United States except southern Florida. Throughout this region, numerous thunderstorms were spawned. Although high winds, hail, and lightning triggered extensive damage, the 19 tornadoes generated by the storm caused even greater death and destruction.

The path of the front can be easily traced from the reports of storm damage. By the evening of March 23, hail and wind damage were reported as far east as Mississippi and Tennessee. Early on the morning of March 24, golf ball size hail was reported in downtown Selma, Alabama. About 6:30 A.M. that day the "Governor's Tornado" struck Atlanta, Georgia. Here the storm displayed its worst temper. Damage was estimated at over $50 million, three lives were lost, and 152 people were injured. The 12-mile path of the "Governor's Tornado" cut through an affluent residential area of Atlanta

FIGURE 21 Paralyzing blizzard strikes the north-central United States. (Photo by Mike McCleary/Bismarck Tribune)

that included the governor's mansion (hence the name). (The official report on this tornado notes that no mobile homes lay in the tornado's path. Why was this fact worth noting?) The final damage along the cold front was reported at 4:00 A.M. on March 25 in northeastern Florida. Here hail and a small tornado caused minor damage. Thus, a day and a half and some 1200 kilometers (about 750 miles) after the cold front became active in Texas, it left the United States to vent its energy harmlessly over the Atlantic Ocean.

By the morning of March 24, you can see that cold polar air had penetrated deep into the United States behind the cold front (see Figure 19). Fort Worth, Texas, which just the day before was in the warm sector, now experienced cool northwest winds. Subfreezing temperatures had moved as far south as northern Oklahoma. Notice, however, that by March 25, Fort Worth was again experiencing a southerly flow. We can conclude that this was a result of the decaying cyclone that no longer dominated the circulation in the region. We can also safely assume that a warming trend was experienced in Fort Worth over the next day or so. Also notice on the map for March 25 that a high was situated over southwestern Mississippi. The clear skies and weak surface winds associated with the center of a subsiding air mass are well illustrated here.

You may have already noticed another cyclone moving in from the Pacific on March 25 as our storm exited to the east.

This storm developed in a similar manner, but was centered somewhat farther north. As you might guess, another blizzard hammered the northern Plains states and a few tornadoes spun through Texas, Arkansas, and Kentucky, while precipitation dominated the weather in the central and eastern United States.

Weather in Peoria

Having examined the general weather associated with the passage of this cyclone from March 23 through March 25, let us now look at the weather experienced at a single location during this time. We have selected Peoria, a city in central Illinois located just north of the Springfield station shown on the weather charts.

Before you read the description of Peoria's weather, try to answer the following questions by using Table 2, which provides weather observations at three-hour intervals during this time period. Also use the three weather charts (Figures 18 through 20) and recall the general wind and temperature changes expected with the passage of fronts.

1. What type of clouds were probably present in Peoria during the early morning hours of March 23?
2. At approximately what time did the warm front pass through Peoria?

TABLE 2	Weather Data for Peoria, Illinois, March 23 to 25				
	Temperature (°F)	Wind direction	Cloud coverage (tenths)	Visibility (miles)	Weather and precipitation
March 23					
00:00	43	ENE	5	15	
3:00 A.M.	43	ENE	8	15	
6:00 A.M.	42	E	5	12	
9:00 A.M.	50	ESE	10	10	
12:00 P.M.	61	SE	10	12	
3:00 P.M.	64	SE	10	10	Thunderstorm with rain showers
6:00 P.M.	64	SE	10	6	Haze
9:00 P.M.	65	S	10	10	Thunderstorm with rain
March 24					
00:00	57	WSW	10	15	
3:00 A.M.	47	SW	2	15	
6:00 A.M.	42	SW	6	15	
9:00 A.M.	39	SW	8	15	
12:00 P.M.	37	SSW	10	15	Snow showers
3:00 P.M.	33	SW	10	10	Snow showers
6:00 P.M.	30	WSW	10	10	Snow showers
9:00 P.M.	26	WSW	10	6	Snow showers
March 25					
00:00	26	WSW	10	15	
3:00 A.M.	25	WSW	10	8	Snow shower
6:00 A.M.	24	WSW	10	1	Snow
9:00 A.M.	26	W	10	3	Snow
12:00 P.M.	25	W	10	12	Snow
3:00 P.M.	27	WNW	10	12	Snow
6:00 P.M.	25	NW	9	12	
9:00 P.M.	24	NW	4	15	

3. List two lines of evidence indicating that a warm front did pass through Peoria.
4. How did the wind and temperature changes during the early morning hours of March 23 indicate the approach of a warm front?
5. Explain the slight temperature increases experienced between 6:00 P.M. and 9:00 P.M. on March 23.
6. By what time had the cold front passed through Peoria?
7. List some changes that indicate the passage of the cold front.
8. The cold front had already gone through Peoria by noon on March 24, so how do you account for the snow shower that occurred during the next 24 hours?
9. Did the thunderstorms in Peoria occur with the passage of the warm front, the cold front, or the occluded front?
10. Basing your answer on the apparent clearing skies late on March 25, would you expect the low temperature on March 26 to be lower or higher than on March 25? Explain.

Now read the following discussion to obtain a more complete description of the weather you just reviewed.

We begin our weather observations in Peoria just after midnight on March 23 (see Table 2). The sky contains cirrus and cirrocumulus clouds, and cool winds from the ENE dominate. As the early morning hours pass, we observe a slight wind shift toward the southeast and a very small drop in temperature. Three hours after sunrise, altocumulus clouds are replaced by stratus and nimbostratus clouds that darken the sky, yet the warm front passes without incident. The 20°F increase in temperature and the wind shift from an easterly to a southeasterly flow mark the passage of the warm front as the warm sector moves over Peoria. The pleasant 60°F temperatures are welcome in Peoria, which enjoys a day 14°F above normal.

But the mild weather is short-lived because the part of the cyclone that passed Peoria was near the apex of the storm, where the cold front is generally close behind the warm front. By afternoon the cold front generates numerous thunderstorms from cumulonimbus clouds embedded in the warm sector just ahead of the cold front. Strong winds, half-inch hail, and a tornado cause local damage. The temperature remains unseasonably warm during the thunderstorm activity.

Early on the morning of March 24 the passage of the cold front is marked by a wind shift, rapidly clearing skies, and a temperature drop of nearly 20°F, all in less than four hours. Throughout March 24 southwesterly winds bring cold air around the back (west) side of the intensifying storm (see Figure 19). Although the surface fronts have passed, this intense cyclone, with its occluded front aloft, is generating snowfall over a wide area. This is not unusual behavior. Occluding cyclones often slow their movement as this one did. For about 24 hours, snow flurries dominate Peoria's weather picture.

By noon on March 25 the storm has lost its punch and the pressure begins to climb. The skies start clearing and the winds become northwesterly as the once tightly wound storm weakens. The mean temperature on March 25 is 16°F below normal, and the ground is covered with snow.

This example demonstrates the effect of a spring cyclone on the weather of a mid-latitude location. Within just three days, Peoria's temperatures changed from unseasonably warm to unseasonably cold. Thunderstorms with hail were followed by snow showers. You can see how the north–south temperature gradient, which is most pronounced in the spring, generates these intense storms. Recall that it is the role of these storms to transfer heat from the tropics poleward. Because of Earth's rotation, however, this latitudinal heat exchange is complex, for the Coriolis force gives the winds a zonal (west-to-east) orientation. If Earth rotated more slowly or not at all, a more leisurely north-south flow would exist that might reduce the temperature gradient. Thus, the tropics would be cooler and the poles warmer, and the mid-latitudes would not be as stormy.

A Modern View: The Conveyor Belt Model

The Norwegian cyclone model has proven to be a valuable tool for describing the formation and development of mid-latitude cyclones. Although modern ideas have not replaced this model, a great deal more has been learned about the structure and evolution of these storm systems as a result of upper-air and satellite data. Armed with this additional information, meteorologists have developed another model to describe the circulation of a mid-latitude cyclone.

Along with this new way of describing the flow within a cyclone comes a new analogy. Recall that the Norwegian model describes cyclone development in terms of the interactions of air masses along frontal boundaries, similar to armies clashing along battlefronts. By contrast, the new model employs an example from industry—conveyor belts. Just as conveyor belts transport goods (or at airports, people) from one location to another, these atmospheric conveyor belts transport air with distinct characteristics from one location to another.

The modern view of cyclogenesis, called the **conveyor belt model**, provides a good picture of the airflow within a cyclonic system. It consists of three interacting airstreams: two that originate near the surface and ascend, and a third that originates in the uppermost troposphere. A schematic representation of these airstreams is shown in Figure 22.

The *warm conveyor belt* (shown in red) carries warm, moist air from the Gulf of Mexico into the warm sector of the mid-latitude cyclone (Figure 22). As this airstream flows northward, convergence causes it to slowly ascend. When it reaches the sloping boundary of the warm front, it rises even more rapidly over the cold air that lies beyond (north of) the front. During its ascent, the warm, humid air cools adiabatically and produces a wide band of clouds and precipitation. Depending on atmospheric conditions, drizzle, rain, freezing rain (glaze), and snow are possible. When this airstream reaches the middle troposphere, it begins to turn right (eastward) and eventually joins the general west-to-east flow aloft. The warm conveyor belt is the main precipitation producing air stream in a mid-latitude cyclone.

The *cold conveyor belt* (blue arrow) is airflow that starts at the surface ahead (north) of the warm front and flows westward toward the center of the cyclone (Figure 22). Flowing beneath

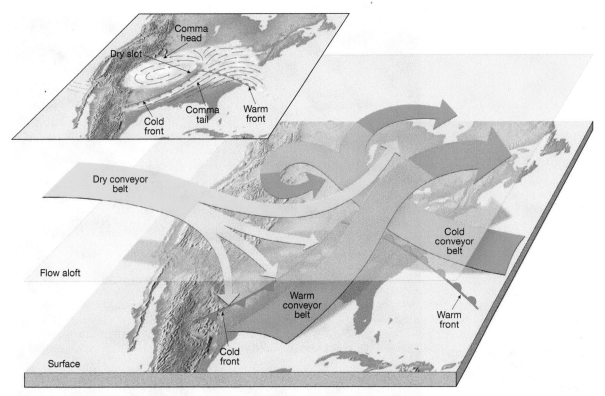

FIGURE 22 Schematic drawing of the circulation of a mature mid-latitude cyclone, showing the warm conveyor belt (red), cold conveyor belt (blue), and dry conveyor belt (yellow). The inset shows the cloud cover produced by the warm and cold conveyor belts and the dry slot produced by the dry conveyor belt.

the warm conveyor belt, this air is moistened by the evaporation of raindrops falling through it. (Near the Atlantic Ocean this conveyor belt has a marine origin and feeds significant moisture into the storm.) Convergence causes this air stream to rise as it nears the center of the cyclone. During its ascent, this air becomes saturated and contributes to the cyclone's precipitation. Upon reaching the middle troposphere, some of the flow rotates cyclonically around the low to produce the distinctive "comma head" of the mature storm system (Figure 23). The remaining flow turns right (clockwise) and becomes incorporated into the general westerly flow. Here it parallels the flow of the warm conveyor belt and may generate precipitation.

The third airstream, called the *dry conveyor belt*, is shown as a yellow arrow in Figure 22. Whereas the warm and cold conveyor belts begin at the surface, the dry airstream originates in the uppermost troposphere. Being part of the upper-level westerly flow, the dry conveyor belt is relatively cold and dry. As this air stream enters the cyclone, it splits. One branch descends behind the cold front. The result is the clear, cool conditions normally associated with the passage of a cold front. In addition, this flow maintains the strong temperature contrast observed across the cold front. The other branch of the dry conveyor belt maintains its westerly flow and forms the *dry slot* (cloudless area) that separates the head and tail of a comma cloud pattern (Figure 23).

In summary, the conveyor belt model of the mid-latitude cyclone provides a three dimensional picture of the major circulation of these storm systems. It also accounts for distribution of precipitation and the comma-shaped cloud pattern characteristic of mature cyclonic storms.

Students Sometimes Ask . . .

Sometimes when there is a major flood, it is described as a 100-year flood. What does that mean?

The phrase "100-year flood" is misleading because it leads people to believe that such an event happens only once every 100 years. The truth is that an uncommonly big flood can happen any year. The phrase "100-year flood" is really a statistical designation, indicating that there is a 1-in-100 chance that a flood this size will happen during any year. Perhaps a better term would be the "1-in-100-chance flood."

Many flood designations are reevaluated and changed over time as more data are collected or when a river basin is altered in a way that affects the flow of water. Dams and urban development are examples of some human influences in a basin that affect floods.

FIGURE 23 Satellite view of a mature mid-latitude cyclone over the eastern half of the United States. It is easy to see why we often refer to the cloud pattern of a cyclone as having a "comma" shape. (Courtesy of John Jensenius/National Weather Service)

Chapter Summary

- The primary weather producer in the middle latitudes (for our purposes, the region between southern Florida and Alaska, essentially the area of the westerlies) is the *middle-latitude* or *mid-latitude cyclone*. Mid-latitude cyclones are large, low pressure systems with diameters often exceeding 1000 kilometers (600 miles) that generally travel from west to east. They last a few days to more than a week, have a counterclockwise circulation pattern with a flow inward toward their centers, and have a cold front and frequently a warm front extending from the central area of low pressure. In the *polar front theory* (also called the *Norwegian cyclone model*), mid-latitude cyclones develop in conjunction with the *polar front*.

- *Fronts* are boundary surfaces that separate air masses of different densities, one usually warmer and more moist than the other. As one air mass moves into another, the warmer, less dense air mass is forced aloft in a process called *overrunning*. The five types of fronts are (1) *warm front*, which occurs when the surface (ground) position of a front moves so that warm air occupies territory formerly covered by cooler air, (2) *cold front*, where cold continental polar air actively advances into a region occupied by warmer air, (3) *stationary front*, which occurs when the airflow on both sides of a front is neither toward the cold air mass nor toward the warm air mass, (4) *occluded front*,

which develops when an active cold front overtakes a warm front and wedges the warm front upward, and (5) a *dryline,* a boundary between denser, dry air and less dense, humid air often associated with severe thunderstorms during the spring and summer. The two types of occluded fronts are the *cold-type occluded front,* where the air behind the cold front is colder than the cool air it is overtaking, and the *warm-type occluded front,* where the air behind the advancing cold front is warmer than the cold air it overtakes.

- According to the polar front model, mid-latitude cyclones form along fronts and proceed through a generally predictable life cycle. Along the polar front, where two air masses of different densities are moving parallel to the front and in opposite directions, *cyclogenesis* (cyclone formation) occurs and the frontal surface takes on a wave shape that is usually several hundred kilometers long. Once a wave forms, warm air advances poleward invading the area formerly occupied by colder air. This change in the direction of the surface flow causes a readjustment in the pressure pattern that results in almost circular isobars, with the low pressure centered at the apex of the wave. Usually, the position of the cold front advances faster than the warm front and gradually closes the warm sector and lifts the warm front. This process, known as *occlusion*, creates an occluded front. Eventually all the warm sector is forced aloft and cold air surrounds the cyclone at low levels. At this point, the cyclone has exhausted its source of energy and the once highly organized counterclockwise flow ceases to exist.

- Guided by the westerlies aloft, cyclones generally move eastward across the United States. As an idealized mid-latitude cyclone moves over a region, the passage of a warm front places the area under the influence of a maritime tropical air mass and its generally warm temperatures, southerly winds, and clear skies. The passage of a cold front is easily detected by a wind shift, the replacement of south or southwesterly winds with winds from the west or northwest. There is also a pronounced drop in temperature. A passing occluded front is often associated with cool, overcast conditions, and snow or glaze during the cool months.

- Airflow aloft (divergence and convergence) plays an important role in maintaining cyclonic and anticyclonic circulation. In a cyclone, divergence aloft does not involve the outward flow of air in all directions. Instead, the winds flow generally from west to east, along sweeping curves. Also, at high altitudes, speed variations within the jet stream cause air to converge in areas where the velocity slows, and to diverge where air is accelerating. In addition to *speed divergence*, *directional divergence* (the horizontal spreading of an air stream) and *vorticity* (the amount of rotation exhibited by a mass of moving air) also contribute to divergence (or convergence) aloft.

- During the colder months, when temperature gradients are steepest, cyclonic storms advance at their fastest rate.

Furthermore, the westerly airflow aloft tends to steer these developing pressure systems in a general west-to-east direction. Cyclones that influence western North America originate over the Pacific Ocean. Although most Pacific storms do not cross the Rockies intact, many redevelop on the lee (eastern) side of these mountains. Some cyclones that affect the United States form over the Great Plains and are associated with an influx of maritime tropical air from the Gulf of Mexico. Another area where cyclogenesis occurs is east of the southern Appalachians. These cyclones tend to migrate toward the northeast, impacting the Eastern Seaboard.

- Due to the gradual subsidence within them, anticyclones generally produce clear skies and calm conditions. One to three times each winter, large highs, called *blocking highs*, persist over the middle latitudes and deflect the nearly zonal west-to-east flow poleward. These stagnant anticyclones block the eastward migration of cyclones, keeping one section of the nation dry for a week or more while another region experiences one cyclonic storm after another. Also due to subsidence, large stagnant anticyclones can produce a temperature inversion that contributes to air pollution episodes.

- In the spring, Earth's pronounced north–south temperature gradient can generate intense cyclonic storms. At a mid-latitude location, as a spring cyclone with its associated fronts passes, temperatures can change quickly from unseasonably warm to unseasonably cold, and thunderstorms with hail can be followed by snow showers.

Vocabulary Review

cold front	front	occlusion	warm front
cold-type occluded front	middle-latitude	overrunning	warm-type occluded front
conveyor belt model	(mid-latitude) cyclone	polar-front theory	
cyclogenesis	Norwegian cyclone model	speed divergence	
dryline	occluded front	stationary front	

Review Questions

1. How did the early Norwegian meteorologists describe fronts?

2. If you were located 400 kilometers ahead of the surface position of a typical warm front, how high would the frontal surface be above you?

3. Compare the weather of a warm front with that of a cold front.

4. Why is cold-front weather usually more severe than warm-front weather?

5. Explain the basis for the following weather proverb:

   Rain long foretold, long last;

   Short notice, soon past.

6. How does a stationary front produce precipitation when its position does not change, or changes very slowly?

7. Distinguish between cold-type and warm-type occluded fronts.

8. Describe the initial stage in the formation of a mid-latitude cyclone.

9. Mid-latitude cyclones are sometimes called *wave cyclones.* Why do you think this is so?

10. Although the formation of an occluded front often represents a period of increased intensity for a mid-latitude cyclone, it also marks the beginning of the end of the system. Explain why such is the case.

11. For each of the weather elements listed here, describe the changes that an individual experiences when a middle-latitude cyclone passes with its center *north* of the observer. (*Hint:* See Figures 11 and 12)
    a. wind direction
    b. pressure tendency
    c. cloud type
    d. cloud cover
    e. precipitation
    f. temperature

12. Describe the weather conditions that an observer would experience if the center of a mid-latitude cyclone passed to the south.

13. Distinguish between veering and backing winds (see Box 1).

14. Briefly explain how the flow aloft maintains cyclones at the surface.

15. What is speed divergence? Speed convergence?

16. Given an upper-air chart, where do forecasters usually look to find favorable sites for cyclogenesis? Where do anticyclones usually form in relation to the upper-level flow?

17. What are two possible ways a blocking high might influence the weather?

18. Briefly describe the various weather phenomena that could be associated with a strong springtime cyclonic storm traveling across the United States.

Atmospheric Science Online

The Atmosphere 11e website uses the resources and flexibility of the Internet to aid in your study of the topics in this chapter. Written and developed by meteorology instructors, this site will help improve your understanding of meteorology. Visit **www.mygeoscience.com** in order to:

- **Review** key chapter concepts

- **Read** with links to the eBook and to chapter-specific web resources
- **Visualize** and comprehend challenging topics using learning activities in *GEODe: Atmosphere*
- **Test yourself** with online quizzes

GEODe: Atmosphere

GEODe: Atmosphere makes studying more effective by reinforcing key concepts using animation, video, narration, interactive exercises, and practice quizzes. Available at **www.mygeoscience.com**.

In much of the United States, a cold front usually represents the advancing boundary of a cold, dry continental polar air mass from Canada.

In the frames to follow you will be answering questions by referring to this weather map and by applying your knowledge of air masses, fronts, and cyclones.

Thunderstorms and Tornadoes

From Chapter 10 of *The Atmosphere: An Introduction to Meteorology*, Eleventh Edition, Frederick K. Lutgens, Edward J. Tarbuck, Dennis Tasa. Copyright © 2010 by Pearson Education, Inc. Published by Pearson Prentice Hall. All rights reserved.

This tornado near Mulvane, Kansas, was one of several to strike south-central Kansas on June 12, 2004. (Eric Nguyen/ Photo Researchers)

The subject of this and the following chapter, is severe weather. In this chapter we will examine the severe local weather produced in association with cumulonimbus clouds—namely, thunderstorms and tornadoes (Figure 1).

Occurrences of severe weather have a fascination that ordinary weather phenomena cannot provide. The lightning display generated by a thunderstorm can be a spectacular event that elicits both awe and fear. Of course, hurricanes and tornadoes also attract a great deal of much deserved attention. A single tornado outbreak or hurricane can cause billions of dollars in property damage as well as many deaths.

What's in a Name?

The use of the term "cyclone" is often confusing. For many people the term implies only an intense storm, such as a tornado or a hurricane. When a hurricane unleashes its fury on India, Bangladesh, or Myanmar, for example, it is usually reported in the media as a cyclone (the term denoting a hurricane in that part of the world). For example, in May 2008, the devastation caused when Cyclone Nargis struck Myanmar was a major news story (Figure 2a).

FIGURE 1 Summertime lightning display at Tucson, Arizona. (Photo by Kent Ward/Photo Researchers)

FIGURE 2(b)   In parts of the Great Plains, cyclone is a synonym for tornado. The nickname for the athlete teams at Iowa State University is the *Cyclones.** (Image courtesy of Iowa State University)

FIGURE 2(a)   Sometimes the use of the term *cyclone* can be confusing. In South Asia, the term cyclone is applied to tropical storms that are called hurricanes in the United States. This image shows Cyclone Nargis which devastated Myanmar (Burma) in May 2008. (Photo by AP Photo/NASA)

Similarly, tornadoes are referred to as cyclones in some places. This custom is particularly common in portions of the Great Plains of the United States. Recall that in the *Wizard of Oz*, Dorothy's house was carried from her Kansas farm to the land of Oz by a cyclone. Indeed, the nickname for the athletic teams at Iowa State University is the *Cyclones* (Figure 2b). Although hurricanes and tornadoes are, in fact, cyclones, the vast majority of cyclones are not hurricanes or tornadoes. The term "cyclone" simply refers to the circulation around any low-pressure center, no matter how large or intense it is.

Tornadoes and hurricanes are both smaller and more violent than middle-latitude cyclones. Middle-latitude cyclones may have a diameter of 1600 kilometers (1000 miles) or more. By contrast, hurricanes average only 600 kilometers (375 miles) across, and tornadoes, with a diameter of just 0.25 kilometer (0.16 mile), are much too small to show up on a weather map.

The thunderstorm, a much more familiar weather event, hardly needs to be distinguished from tornadoes, hurricanes, and mid-latitude cyclones. Unlike the flow of air about these storms, the circulation associated with thunderstorms is characterized by strong up-and-down movements. Winds in the vicinity of a thunderstorm do not follow the inward spiral of a cyclone, but they are typically variable and gusty.

Although thunderstorms form "on their own" away from cyclonic storms, they also form in conjunction with cyclones. For instance, thunderstorms are frequently spawned along the cold front of a mid-latitude cyclone, where on rare occasions a tornado may descend from the thunderstorm's cumulonimbus tower. Hurricanes also generate widespread thunderstorm activity. Thus, thunderstorms are related in some manner to all three types of cyclones mentioned here.

Thunderstorms

Almost everyone has observed various small-scale phenomena that result from the vertical movements of relatively warm, unstable air. Perhaps you have seen a dust devil over an open field on a hot day whirling its dusty load to great heights or maybe you have seen a bird glide effortlessly skyward on an invisible thermal of hot air. These examples illustrate the dynamic thermal instability that occurs during the development of a *thunderstorm*. A **thunderstorm** is simply a storm that generates lightning and thunder. It frequently produces gusty winds, heavy rain, and hail. A thunderstorm may be produced by a single cumulonimbus cloud and influence only a small area, or it may be associated with clusters of cumulonimbus clouds covering a large area.

Iowa State University is the only Division 1 school to use Cyclones as its team name. The pictured logo was created to better communicate the school's image by combining the mascot, a cardinal bird named Cy and the Cyclone team name, a swirling twister in the bird's tail.

Thunderstorms form when warm, humid air rises in an unstable environment. Various mechanisms can trigger the upward air movement needed to create thunderstorm producing cumulonimbus clouds. One mechanism, the unequal heating of Earth's surface, significantly contributes to the formation of *air-mass thunderstorms*. These storms are associated with the scattered puffy cumulonimbus clouds that commonly form *within* maritime tropical air masses and produce scattered thunderstorms on summer days. Such storms are usually short-lived and seldom produce strong winds or hail.

In contrast, thunderstorms in a second category not only benefit from uneven surface heating but are associated with the lifting of warm air, as occurs along a front or a mountain slope. Moreover, diverging winds aloft frequently contribute to the formation of these storms because they tend to draw air from lower levels upward beneath them. Some of the thunderstorms in this second category may produce high winds, damaging hail, flash floods, and tornadoes. Such storms are described as *severe*.

At any given time there are an estimated 2000 thunderstorms in progress. As we would expect, the greatest proportion occurs in the tropics, where warmth, plentiful moisture, and instability are always present. About 45,000 thunderstorms take place each day, and more than 16 million occur annually around the world. The lightning from these storms strikes Earth 100 times each second (Figure 3a).

Annually the United States experiences about 100,000 thunderstorms and millions of lightning strikes. A glance at Figure 3b shows that thunderstorms are most frequent in Florida and the eastern Gulf Coast region, where activity is recorded between 70 and 100 days each year. The region on the east side of the Rockies in Colorado and New Mexico is next, with thunderstorms occurring 60 to 70 days annually. Most of the rest of the nation experiences thunderstorms 30 to 50 days a year. Clearly, the western margin of the United States has little thunderstorm activity. The same is true for the northern tier of states and for Canada, where warm, moist, unstable mT air seldom penetrates.

Air-Mass Thunderstorms

In the United States **air-mass thunderstorms** frequently occur in maritime tropical (mT) air that moves northward from the Gulf of Mexico. These warm, humid air masses contain abundant moisture in their lower levels and can be rendered unstable when heated from below or lifted along a front. Because mT air most often becomes unstable in spring and

FIGURE 3 (a) Data from space-based optical sensors show the worldwide distribution of lightning, with color variations indicating the average annual number of lightning flashes per square kilometer. (NASA image) (b) Average number of days per year with thunderstorms. The humid subtropical climate that dominates the southeastern United States receives much of its precipitation in the form of thunderstorms. Most of the Southeast averages 50 or more days each year with thunderstorms. (Source: Environmental Data Service, NOAA)

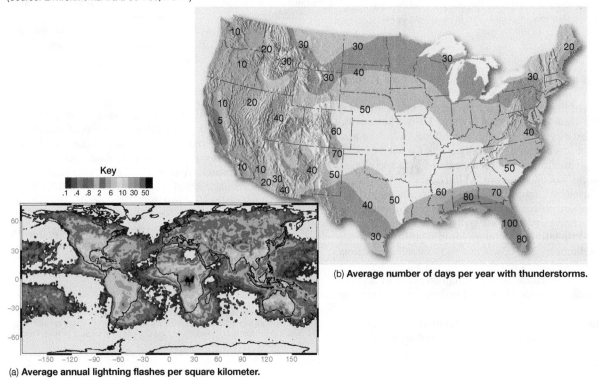

(b) **Average number of days per year with thunderstorms.**

Key

.1 .4 .8 2 6 10 30 50

(a) **Average annual lightning flashes per square kilometer.**

FIGURE 4 Stages in the development of a thunderstorm. During the cumulus stage, strong updrafts act to build the storm. The mature stage is marked by heavy precipitation and cool downdrafts in part of the storm. When the warm updrafts disappear completely, precipitation becomes light and the cloud begins to evaporate.

summer, when it is warmed from below by the heated land surface, it is during these seasons that air-mass thunderstorms are most frequent. They also have a strong preference for midafternoon, when surface temperatures are highest. Because local differences in surface heating aid the growth of air-mass thunderstorms, they generally occur as scattered, isolated cells instead of being organized in relatively narrow bands or other configurations.

Stages of Development

Important field experiments that were conducted in Florida and Ohio in the late 1940s probed the dynamics of air-mass thunderstorms. This pioneering work, known as the *Thunderstorm Project*, was prompted by a number of thunderstorm-related airplane crashes. It involved the use of radar, aircraft, radiosondes, and an extensive network of surface instruments. The research produced a three-stage model of the life cycle of an air-mass thunderstorm that remains basically unchanged after more than 60 years. The three stages are depicted in Figure 4.

Cumulus Stage Recall that an air-mass thunderstorm is largely a product of the uneven heating of the surface, which leads to rising currents of air that ultimately produce a cumulonimbus cloud. At first the buoyant thermals produce fair weather cumulus clouds that may exist for just minutes before evaporating into the drier, surrounding air (Figure 5a). This initial cumulus development is important because it moves water vapor from the surface to greater heights. Ultimately,

FIGURE 5 (a) At first, buoyant thermals produce fair weather cumulus clouds that soon evaporate into the surrounding air, making it more humid. As this process of cumulus development and evaporation continues, the air eventually becomes sufficiently humid so that newly forming clouds do not evaporate but continue to grow. (Photo by Henry Lansford/Photo Researchers, Inc.) (b) This developing cumulonimbus cloud became a towering August thunderstorm over central Illinois. (Photo by E. J. Tarbuck)

(a)

(b)

the air becomes sufficiently humid that newly forming clouds do not evaporate, but instead continue to grow vertically.

The development of a cumulonimbus tower requires a continuous supply of moist air. The release of latent heat allows each new surge of warm air to rise higher than the last, adding to the height of the cloud (Figure 5b). This phase in the development of a thunderstorm, called the **cumulus stage**, is dominated by updrafts (see Figure 4a).

Once the cloud passes beyond the freezing level, the Bergeron process begins producing precipitation. Eventually, the accumulation of precipitation in the cloud is too great for the updrafts to support. The falling precipitation causes drag on the air and initiates a downdraft.

The creation of the downdraft is further aided by the influx of cool, dry air surrounding the cloud, a process termed **entrainment**. This process intensifies the downdraft because the air added during entrainment is cool and therefore heavy; possibly of greater importance, it is dry. It thus causes some of the falling precipitation to evaporate (a cooling process), thereby cooling the air within the downdraft.

Mature Stage As the downdraft leaves the base of the cloud, precipitation is released, marking the beginning of the cloud's **mature stage** (see Figure 4b). At the surface the cool downdrafts spread laterally and can be felt before the actual precipitation reaches the ground. The sharp, cool gusts at the surface are indicative of the downdrafts aloft. During the mature stage, updrafts exist side by side with downdrafts and continue to enlarge the cloud. When the cloud grows to the top of the unstable region, often located at the base of the stratosphere, the updrafts spread laterally and produce the characteristic anvil top. Generally, ice-laden cirrus clouds make up the top and are spread downwind by strong winds aloft. The mature stage is the most active period of a thunderstorm. Gusty winds, lightning, heavy precipitation, and sometimes small hail are experienced.

Dissipating Stage Once downdrafts begin, the vacating air and precipitation encourage more entrainment of the cool, dry air surrounding the cell. Eventually, the downdrafts dominate throughout the cloud and initiate the **dissipating stage** (see Figure 4c). The cooling effect of falling precipitation and the influx of colder air aloft mark the end of the thunderstorm activity. Without a supply of moisture from updrafts, the cloud will soon evaporate. An interesting fact is that only a modest portion—on the order of 20 percent—of the moisture that condenses in an air-mass thunderstorm actually leaves the cloud as precipitation. The remaining 80 percent evaporates back into the atmosphere.

It should be noted that within a single air-mass thunderstorm there may be several individual *cells*—that is, zones of adjacent updrafts and downdrafts. When you view a thunderstorm, you may notice that the cumulonimbus cloud consists of several towers (See Figure 5b). Each tower may represent an individual cell that is in a somewhat different part of its life cycle.

To summarize, the stages in the development of an air-mass thunderstorm are as follows:

1. The *cumulus stage,* in which updrafts dominate throughout the cloud, and growth from a cumulus to a cumulonimbus cloud occurs.
2. The *mature stage,* the most intense phase, with heavy rain and possibly small hail, in which downdrafts are found side by side with updrafts.
3. The *dissipating stage,* dominated by downdrafts and entrainment, causing evaporation of the structure.

Occurrence

Mountainous regions, such as the Rockies in the West and the Appalachians in the East, experience a greater number of air-mass thunderstorms than do the Plains states. The air near the mountain slope is heated more intensely than air at the same elevation over the adjacent lowlands. A general upslope movement then develops during the daytime that can sometimes generate thunderstorm cells. These cells may remain almost stationary above the slopes below.

Although the growth of thunderstorms is aided by high surface temperatures, many thunderstorms are not generated solely by surface heating. For example, many of Florida's thunderstorms are triggered by the convergence associated with sea-to-land airflow. Many thunderstorms that form over the eastern two-thirds of the United States occur as part of the general convergence and frontal wedging that accompany passing mid-latitude cyclones. Near the equator, thunderstorms commonly form in association with the convergence along the equatorial low (also called the *intertropical convergence zone*). Most of these thunderstorms are not severe, and their life cycles are similar to the three-stage model described for air-mass thunderstorms.

Severe Thunderstorms

Severe thunderstorms are capable of producing heavy downpours and flash flooding as well as strong, gusty, straight-line winds, large hail, frequent lightning, and perhaps tornadoes (Box 1). For a thunderstorm to be officially classified as *severe* by the National Weather Service, it must have winds in excess of 93 kilometers (58 miles) per hour (50 knots) or produce hailstones with diameters larger than 1.9 centimeters (0.75 inch) or generate a tornado. Of the estimated 100,000 thunderstorms that occur annually in the United States, about 10 percent (10,000 storms) reach severe status.

As you learned in the preceding section, air-mass thunderstorms are localized, relatively short-lived phenomena that dissipate after a brief, well-defined life cycle. They actually extinguish themselves because downdrafts cut off the supply of moisture necessary to maintain the storm. For this reason, air-mass thunderstorms seldom if ever produce severe weather. By contrast, other thunderstorms do not quickly dissipate but instead may remain active for hours.

Some of these larger, longer-lived thunderstorms attain severe status.

Why do some thunderstorms persist for many hours? A key factor is the existence of strong vertical wind shear—that is, changes in wind direction and/or speed between different heights. When such conditions prevail, the updrafts that provide the storm with moisture do not remain vertical, but become tilted. Because of this, the precipitation that forms high in the cloud falls into the downdraft rather than into the updraft as occurs in air-mass thunderstorms. This allows the updraft to maintain its strength and continue to build upward. Sometimes the updrafts are sufficiently strong that the cloud top is able to push its way into the stable lower stratosphere, a situation called *overshooting* (Figure 6).

Beneath the cumulonimbus tower, where downdrafts reach the surface, the denser cool air spreads out along the ground. The leading edge of this outflowing downdraft acts like a wedge, forcing warm, moist surface air into the thunderstorm. In this way, the downdrafts act to maintain the updrafts, which in turn sustain the thunderstorm.

By examining Figure 6, you can see that the outflowing cool air of the downdraft acts as a "mini cold front" as it advances into the warmer surrounding air. This outflow boundary is called a **gust front**. As the gust front moves across the ground, the very turbulent air sometimes picks up loose dust and soil, making the advancing boundary visible. Frequently a *roll cloud* may form as warm air is lifted along the leading edge of the gust front (Figure 7). The advance of the gust front can provide the lifting needed for the formation of new thunderstorms many kilometers away from the initial cumulonimbus clouds.

Supercell Thunderstorms

Some of our most dangerous weather is caused by a type of thunderstorm called a **supercell**. Few weather phenomena are as awesome (Figure 8). An estimated 2000 to 3000 supercell thunderstorms occur annually in the United States. They represent just a small fraction of all thunderstorms, but they are responsible for a disproportionate share of the deaths, injuries, and property damage associated with severe weather. Less than half of all supercells produce tornadoes, yet virtually all of the strongest and most violent tornadoes are spawned by supercells.

A supercell consists of a single, very powerful cell that at times can extend to heights of 20 kilometers (65,000 feet) and persist for many hours. These massive clouds have diameters ranging between about 20 and 50 kilometers (12 and 30 miles).

Despite the single-cell structure of supercells, these storms are remarkably complex. The vertical wind profile may cause the updraft to rotate. For example, this could occur if the surface flow is from the south or southeast and the winds aloft increase in speed and become more westerly with height. If a thunderstorm develops in such a wind environment, the updraft is made to rotate. It is within this column of cyclonically rotating air, called the **mesocyclone**, that tornadoes often form (see Figure 8c)*

The huge quantities of latent heat needed to sustain a supercell require special conditions that keep the lower troposphere warm and moisture-rich. Studies suggest that the existence of an inversion layer a few kilometers above the surface helps to provide this basic requirement. Recall that temperature inversions represent very stable atmospheric conditions that restrict vertical air motions. The presence of an inversion seems to aid the production of a few very large thunderstorms by inhibiting the formation of many smaller ones (Figure 9). The inversion prevents the mixing of warm, humid air in the lower troposphere with cold, dry air above. Consequently, surface heating continues to increase the temperature and moisture content of the layer of air trapped below the inversion. Eventually, the inversion is locally

FIGURE 6 Diagram of a well-developed cumulonimbus tower showing updrafts, downdrafts, and an overshooting top. Precipitation forming in the tilted updraft falls into the downdraft. Beneath the cloud, the denser cool air of the downdraft spreads out along the ground. The leading edge of the outflowing downdraft acts to wedge moist surface air into the cloud. Eventually the outflow boundary may become a gust front that initiates new cumulonimbus development.

___
*More on mesocyclones can be found in the section on "Tornado Development."

BOX 1 ▶ ATMOSPHERIC HAZARD

Flash Floods—The Number One Thunderstorm Killer

Tornadoes and hurricanes are nature's most awesome storms. Because of this status, they are logically the focus of much well-deserved attention. Yet, surprisingly, in most years these dreaded events are not responsible for the greatest number of storm-related deaths. That distinction is reserved for floods (Figure A). For the ten-year period 1998–2007, the number of storm-related deaths in the United States from flooding averaged 71 per year. By contrast, tornado fatalities averaged 64 annually. The average number of fatalities for hurricanes was dramatically affected by Hurricane Katrina in 2005 (more than 1000). For all years other than 2005 represented in Figure A, the average number of hurricane fatalities was less than 20.

Floods are part of the *natural* behavior of streams. Most have a meteorological origin related to atmospheric processes that can vary greatly in both time and space. Major regional floods in large river valleys are often the result of an extraordinary series of precipitation events over a broad region for an extended time span. . By contrast, just an hour or two of intense thunderstorm activity can trigger flash floods in small valleys. Such situations are described here.

FIGURE A Average annual storm-related deaths in the United States for two time spans. The average number of hurricane fatalities was dramatically affected by a single event—Hurricane Katrina in 2005 (more than 1000 deaths). For all of the other years represented on this graph, the average number of hurricane-related fatalities was less than 20 per year. (Data from National Weather Service)

Flash floods are local floods of great volume and short duration. The rapidly rising surge of water usually occurs with little advance warning and can destroy roads, bridges, homes, and other substantial structures (Figure B). The amount of water flowing in the channel quickly reaches a maximum and then diminishes rapidly. Flood flows often contain large quantities of sediment and debris as they sweep channels clean.

Several factors influence flash flooding. Among them are rainfall intensity and duration, surface conditions, and topography. Urban areas are susceptible to flash floods because a high percentage of the surface area is composed of impervious roofs, streets, and parking lots, where runoff is very rapid (Figure C). In fact, a recent study indicated that the area of impervious surfaces in the United States (excluding Alaska and Hawaii) amounts to more than 112,600 square kilometers (nearly 44,000 square miles), which is slightly less than the area of the state of Ohio.*

Frequently, flash floods result from the torrential rains associated with a slow-moving severe thunderstorm or take place when a series of thunderstorms repeatedly pass

_____

*C. C. Elvidge, et al. "U.S. Constructed Area Approaches the Size of Ohio," in *EOS, Transactions, American Geophysical Union*, Vol. 85, No. 24 15 June 2004, p. 233.

FIGURE B The disastrous nature of flash floods is illustrated by the Big Thompson River flood of July 31, 1976, in Colorado. During a four-hour span more than 30 centimeters (12 inches) of rain fell on portions of the river's small drainage basin. This amounted to nearly three-quarters of the average yearly total. The flash flood in the narrow canyon lasted only a few hours but cost 139 lives. Damages were estimated at $39 million. (U. S. Geological Survey)

over the same location. Sometimes they are triggered by heavy rains from hurricanes and tropical storms. Occasionally, floating debris or ice can accumulate at a natural or artificial obstruction and restrict the flow of water. When such temporary dams fail, torrents of water can be released as a flash flood.

Flash floods can take place in almost any area of the country. They are particularly common in mountainous terrain, where steep slopes can quickly channel runoff into narrow valleys. The hazard is most acute when the soil is already nearly saturated from earlier rains or consists of impermeable materials. A disaster in Shadydale, Ohio, demonstrates what can happen when even moderately heavy rains fall on saturated ground with steep slopes.

On the evening of 14 June 1990, 26 people lost their lives as rains estimated to be in the range of 3 to 5 inches fell on saturated soil, which generated flood waves in streams that reached tens of feet in height, destroying near-bank residences and businesses. Preceding months of above-normal rainfall had generated soil moisture contents of near saturation. As a result, moderate amounts of rainfall caused large amounts of surface and near-surface runoff. Steep valleys with practically vertical walls channeled the floods, creating very fast, high, and steep wave crests.**

Why do so many people perish in flash floods? Aside from the factor of surprise (many are caught sleeping), people do not appreciate the power of moving water. A glance at Figure B helps illustrate the force of a flood wave. Just 15 centimeters (6 inches) of fast-moving flood water can knock a person down. Most automobiles will float and be swept away in only 0.6 meter (2 feet) of water. *More than half of all U.S. flash-flood fatalities are auto related!* Clearly, people should never attempt to drive over a flooded road. The depth of water is not always obvious. Also, the road bed may have been washed out under water. Present-day flash floods are calamities with potential for very high death tolls and huge property losses. Although efforts are being made to improve observations and warnings, flash floods remain elusive natural killers.

**"Prediction and Mitigation of Flash Floods: A Policy Statement of the American Meteorological Society." *Bulletin of the American Meteorological Society*, Vol. 74, No. 8 (Aug. 1993), p. 1586.

FIGURE C   Urban areas are susceptible to flash floods because runoff following heavy rains is rapid due to the high percentage of the surface that is impervious. The photo shows flash flooding in Las Vegas, Nevada, in August 2003. Parts of the city received nearly half the average annual rainfall in a matter of hours. Here firefighters are rescued from a fire truck that was caught in a torrent of water (Photo by John Locher/Las Vegas Review-Journal). The graphs demonstrate the effect of urbanization on streamflow in a hypothetical setting. Notice that the water level in the stream does not rise at the onset of precipitation, because time is required for water to move from the place where it fell to the stream. This span is called the *lag time*. Notice that when an area changes from rural to urban, the lag time is shortened and the flood peak gets higher. (After L. B. Leopold, U.S. Geological Survey)

FIGURE 7 Roll clouds, like this one at Miles City, Montana, are sometimes produced along a gust front in an eddy between the inflow and the downdraft. (Photo by National Science Foundation/ National Center for Atmospheric Research)

FIGURE 8 (a) Cross-section of a hypothetical supercell thunderstorm. (After National Weather Service) (b) This photo of a cluster of supercell thunderstorms along the Manitoba-Minnesota border in September 1994 was taken from space by an astronaut. (NASA) (c) View from ground level of a towering supercell thunderstorm that has produced a tornado. (Photo © Howard B. Bluestein, Professor of Meteorology)

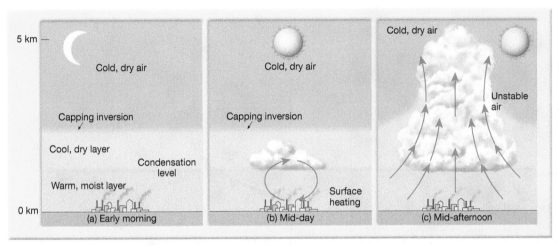

FIGURE 9 The formation of severe thunderstorms can be enhanced by the existence of a temperature inversion located a few kilometers above the surface.

Students Sometimes Ask . . .

What would it be like inside a towering cumulonimbus cloud?

The words violent and dangerous come to mind! Here is an example that involved a German paragliding champion who got pulled into an eruptig thunderstorm near Tamworth, New South Wales, Australia and blacked out.* Updrafts lofted her to 32,600 feet, covered her with ice and pelted her with hailstones. She finally regained consciousness around 22,600 feet. Her GPS equipment and a computer tracked her movements as the storm carried her away. Shaking vigorously and with lightning all around, she managed to slowly descend and eventually land 40 miles from where she started.

*Reported in the *Bulletin of the American Meteorological Society*, Vol. 88, No. 4, April 2007, p. 490.

eroded by strong mixing from below. The unstable air below "erupts" explosively at these sites, producing unusually large cumulonimbus towers. It is from such clouds, with their concentrated, persistent updrafts, that supercells form.

Squall Lines and Mesoscale Convective Complexes

Because the atmospheric conditions favoring the formation of severe thunderstorms often exist over a broad area, they frequently develop in groups that consist of many individual storms clustered together. Sometimes these clusters occur as elongate bands called *squall lines*. At other times the storms are organized into roughly circular clusters known as *mesoscale convective complexes*. No matter how the cells are arranged, they are not simply clusters of unrelated individual storms. Rather, they are related by a common origin, or they occur in a situation in which some cells lead to the formation of others.

Squall Lines A **squall line** is a relatively narrow band of thunderstorms, some of which may be severe, that develops in the warm sector of a middle-latitude cyclone, usually 100 to 300 kilometers (60 to 180 miles) in advance of the cold front. The linear band of cumulonimbus development might stretch for 500 kilometers (300 miles) or more and consist of many individual cells in various stages of development. An average squall line can last for 10 hours or more, and some have been known to remain active for more than a day. Sometimes the approach of a squall line is preceded by a *mammatus sky* consisting of dark cloud rolls that have downward pouches (Figure 10).

FIGURE 10 The dark overcast of a mammatus sky, with its characteristic downward bulging pouches, sometimes precedes a squall line. When a mammatus formation develops, it is usually after a cumulonimbus cloud reaches its maximum size and intensity. Its presence is generally a sign of an especially vigorous thunderstorm. (Photo by Wikipedia)

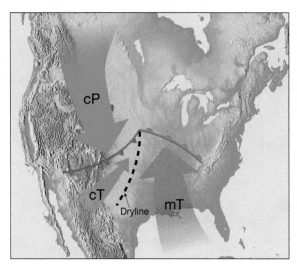

FIGURE 11 Squall-line thunderstorms frequently develop along a dryline, the boundary separating warm, dry continental tropical air and warm, moist maritime tropical air.

Most squall lines are not the product of forceful lifting along a cold front. Some develop from a combination of warm, moist air near the surface and an active jet stream aloft. The squall line forms when the divergence and resulting lift created by the jet stream is aligned with a strong, persistent low-level flow of warm, humid air from the south.

A squall line with severe thunderstorms can also form along a boundary called a **dryline**, a narrow zone along which there is an abrupt change in moisture. It forms when continental tropical (cT) air from the southwestern United States is pulled into the warm sector of a middle-latitude cyclone, as shown in Figure 11. The denser cT air acts to lift the less dense mT air with which it is converging.* By contrast, both cloud formation and storm development along the cold front are minimal because the front is advancing into dry cT air.

Drylines most frequently develop in the western portions of Texas, Oklahoma, and Kansas. Such a situation is illustrated by Figure 12. The dryline is easily identified by comparing the dew-point temperatures on either side of the squall line. The dew points in the mT air to the east are 30° to 45°F higher than those in the cT air to the west. Much severe weather was generated as this extraordinary squall line moved eastward, including 55 tornadoes over a six-state region.

Mesoscale Convective Complexes A **mesoscale convective complex (MCC)** consists of many individual thunderstorms organized into a large oval to circular cluster. A typical MCC is large, covering an area of at least 100,000 square kilometers

FIGURE 12 The squall line of this middle-latitude cyclone was responsible for a major outbreak of tornadoes. The squall line separates dry (cT) and very humid (mT) air. The dryline is easily identified by comparing dew-point temperatures on either side of the squall line. Dew point (°F) is the lower number at each station.

(39,000 square miles). The usually slow-moving complex may persist for 12 hours or more (Figure 13).

MCCs tend to form most frequently in the Great Plains. When conditions are favorable, an MCC develops from a group of afternoon air-mass thunderstorms. In the evening, as the local storms decay, the MCC starts developing. The transformation of afternoon air-mass thunderstorms into an MCC requires a strong low-level flow of very warm and moist air. This flow enhances instability, which in turn spurs convection

FIGURE 13 This satellite image shows a mesoscale convective complex (MCC) over the eastern Dakotas. (NOAA)

---

*Warm, dry air is more dense than warm, humid air, because the molecular weight of water vapor (H₂O) is only about 62 percent as great as the molecular weight of the mixture of gases that make up dry air.

and cloud development. As long as favorable conditions prevail, MCCs remain self-propagating as gust fronts from existing cells lead to the formation of new powerful cells nearby. New thunderstorms tend to develop near the side of the complex that faces the incoming low-level flow of warm, moist air.

Although mesoscale convective complexes sometimes produce severe weather, they are also beneficial because they provide a significant portion of the growing-season rainfall to the agricultural regions of the central United States.

Microbursts

Beneath some thunderstorms, strong localized downdrafts known as *downbursts* sometimes occur. When downbursts are small—that is, less than 4 kilometers (2.5 miles) across—they are called **microbursts**. These straight-line concentrated bursts of wind are often produced when downdrafts are accelerated by a great deal of evaporative cooling. (Remember, the colder the air, the denser it is, and the denser the air, the faster it will "fall.") Microbursts typically last just two to five minutes. Despite their small size and short duration, microbursts represent a significant atmospheric hazard.

Upon reaching the surface, the chilled air of the microburst pushes out in all directions from the center of the downdraft, similar to a jet of water from a faucet splashing in a sink. In this manner, microbursts can produce winds in excess of 160 kilometers (100 miles) per hour. Within minutes the source of the downdraft dissipates while the outflow at the ground continues to expand.

The violent winds of a microburst can cause a great deal of destruction. For example, in July 1993 millions of trees were uprooted by a microburst near Pak Wash, Ontario. In July 1984, 11 people drowned when a microburst caused a 28-meter- (90-foot-) long sternwheeler boat to capsize on the Tennessee River. Sometimes the damage associated with these violent outflows is mistaken for tornado damage. However, wind damage from microbursts occurs in straight lines, whereas a rotational circulation pattern is usually detectable along the damage path created by a tornado.

The wind shear associated with microbursts has been responsible for a number of airplane crashes. Imagine an aircraft attempting to land and being confronted by a microburst, as in Figure 14. As the airplane flies into the microburst, it initially encounters a strong headwind, which tends to carry it upward. To reduce the lift, the pilot points the nose of the aircraft downward. Then, just seconds later, a tailwind is encountered on the opposite side of the microburst. Here, because the wind is moving with the airplane, the amount of air flowing over the wings and providing lift is dramatically reduced, causing the craft to suddenly lose altitude and crash.

The number of aviation deaths due to microbursts has declined significantly as understanding of the event has increased. Systems to detect the wind shifts associated with microbursts have been installed at most major airports in the United States. Moreover, pilots now receive training on how to handle microbursts during takeoffs and landings.

FIGURE 14 The arrows in this sketch represent the movement of air in a microburst, a concentrated intense downdraft formed by extraordinary evaporative cooling that creates an outward wind burst at the surface. If you could see it leave the cloud and strike the ground, it might resemble a narrow stream of water "splashing" into a sink. Because of the extremely abrupt changes in wind direction within microbursts, they are a threat to aircraft during landings and takeoffs.

Lightning and Thunder

A storm is classified as a thunderstorm only after thunder is heard. Because thunder is produced by lightning, lightning must also be present (see Figure 1 and Figure 15). **Lightning** is similar to the electrical shock you may have experienced on touching a metal object on a very dry day. Only the intensity is different.

FIGURE 15 Multiple lightning stroke of a single flash as recorded by a moving-film camera. (Courtesy of E. J. Tarbuck)

During the formation of a large cumulonimbus cloud, a separation of charge occurs, which simply means that part of the cloud develops an excess negative charge, whereas another part acquires an excess positive charge. The object of lightning is to equalize these electrical differences by producing a negative flow of current from the region of excess negative charge to the region with excess positive charge or vice versa. Because air is a poor conductor of electricity (good insulator), the electrical potential (charge difference) must be very high before lightning will occur.

The most common type of lightning occurs between oppositely charged zones *within* a cloud or between clouds. About 80 percent of all lightning is of this type. It is often called *sheet lightning* because it produces a bright but diffuse illumination of those parts of the cloud in which the flash occurred. Sheet lightning is not a unique form; rather, it is ordinary lightning in which the flash is obscured by the clouds. The second type of lightning, in which the electrical discharge occurs between the cloud and Earth's surface, is often more dramatic (see Figure 1). This *cloud-to-ground lightning* represents about 20 percent of lightning strokes and is the most damaging and dangerous form.

What Causes Lightning?

The origin of charge separation in clouds, although not fully understood, must hinge on rapid vertical movements within, because lightning occurs primarily in the violent mature stage of a cumulonimbus cloud. In the midlatitudes the formation of these towering clouds is chiefly a summertime phenomenon, which explains why lightning is seldom observed there in the winter. Furthermore, lightning rarely occurs before the growing cloud penetrates the 5-kilometer level, where sufficient cooling begins to generate ice crystals.

Some cloud physicists believe that charge separation occurs during the formation of ice pellets. Experimentation shows that as droplets begin to freeze, positively charged ions are concentrated in the colder regions of the droplets, whereas negatively charged ions are concentrated in the warmer regions. Thus, as the droplets freeze from the outside in, they develop a positively charged ice shell and a negatively

charged interior. As the interior begins to freeze, it expands and shatters the outside shell. The small positively charged ice fragments are carried upward by turbulence, and the relatively heavy droplets eventually carry their negative charge toward the cloud base. As a result, the upper part of the cloud is left with a positive charge, and the lower portion of the cloud maintains an overall negative charge with small positively charged pockets (Figure 16).

As the cloud moves, the negatively charged cloud base alters the charge at the surface directly below by repelling negatively charged particles. Thus, the surface beneath the cloud acquires a net positive charge. These charge differences build to millions and even hundreds of millions of volts before a lightning stroke acts to discharge the negative region of the cloud by striking the positive area of the ground below, or, more frequently, the positively charged portion of that cloud, or a nearby cloud.

The Lightning Stroke

Cloud-to-ground strokes are of most interest and have been studied in detail (Box 2). Moving-film cameras have greatly aided in these studies (see Figure 15). They show that the lightning we see as a single flash is really several very rapid strokes between the cloud and the ground. We will call the total discharge—which lasts only a few tenths of a second and appears as a bright streak—the **flash**. Individual components that make up each flash are termed **strokes**. Each stroke is separated by roughly 50 milliseconds, and there are usually three to four strokes per flash.* When a lightning flash appears to flicker, it is because your eyes discern the individual strokes that make up this discharge. Moreover, each stroke consists of a downward propagating leader that is immediately followed by a luminous return stroke.

Each stroke is believed to begin when the electrical field near the cloud base frees electrons in the air immediately below, thereby ionizing the air (Figure 16). Once ionized, the air becomes a conductive path having a radius of roughly 10 centimeters and a length of 50 meters. This path is called a **leader**. During this electrical breakdown, the mobile electrons in the cloud base begin to flow down this channel. This flow increases the electrical potential at the head of the leader,

---

*One millisecond equals one one-thousandth $\left(1/1000\right)$ of a second.

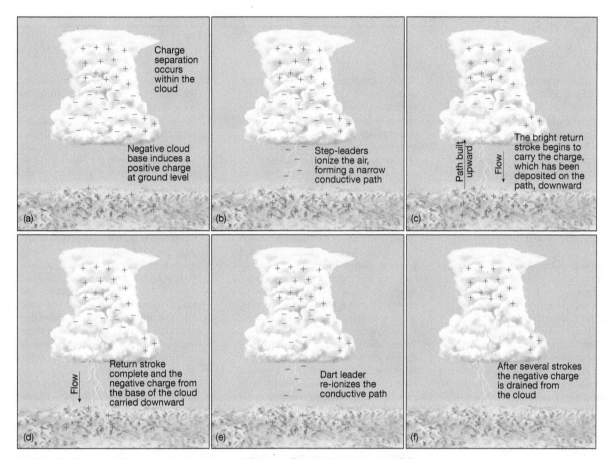

(a) Charge separation occurs within the cloud

Negative cloud base induces a positive charge at ground level

(b) Step-leaders ionize the air, forming a narrow conductive path

(c) Path built upward · Flow — The bright return stroke begins to carry the charge, which has been deposited on the path, downward

(d) Flow — Return stroke complete and the negative charge from the base of the cloud carried downward

(e) Dart leader re-ionizes the conductive path

(f) After several strokes the negative charge is drained from the cloud

FIGURE 16 Discharge of a cloud via cloud-to-ground lightning. Examine this drawing carefully while reading the text.

which causes a further extension of the conductive path through further ionization. Because this initial path extends itself earthward in short, nearly invisible bursts, it is called a **step leader.** Once this channel nears the ground, the electrical field at the surface ionizes the remaining section of the path. With the path completed, the electrons that were deposited along the channel begin to flow downward. The initial flow begins near the ground.

As the electrons at the lower end of the conductive path move earthward, electrons positioned successively higher up the channel begin to migrate downward. Because the path of electron flow is continually being extended upward, the accompanying electric discharge has been appropriately named a **return stroke**. As the wave front of the return stroke moves upward, the negative charge that was deposited on the channel is effectively lowered to the ground. It is this intense return stroke that illuminates the conductive path and discharges the lowest kilometer or so of the cloud. During this phase, tens of coulombs of negative charge are lowered to the ground.*

The first stroke is usually followed by additional strokes that apparently drain charges from higher areas within the

cloud. Each subsequent stroke begins with a **dart leader** that once again ionizes the channel and carries the cloud potential toward the ground. The dart leader is continuous and less branched than the step leader. When the current between strokes has ceased for periods greater than 0.1 second, further strokes will be preceded by a step leader whose path is different from that of the initial stroke. The total time of each flash consisting of three or four strokes is about 0.2 second.

Thunder

The electrical discharge of lightning superheats the air immediately around the lightning channel. In less than a second the temperature rises by as much as 33,000°C. When air is heated this quickly, it expands explosively and produces the sound waves we hear as **thunder.** Because lightning and thunder occur simultaneously, it is possible to estimate the distance to the stroke. Lightning is seen instantaneously, but the relatively slow sound waves, which travel approximately 330 meters (1000 feet) per second, reach us a little later. If thunder is heard five seconds after the lightning is seen, the lightning occurred about 1650 meters away (approximately 1 mile).

The thunder that we hear as a rumble is produced along a long lightning path located at some distance from the

---

*A coulomb is a unit of electrical charge equal to the quantity of charge transferred in 1 second by a steady current of 1 ampere.

BOX 2 ▶ ATMOSPHERIC HAZARD

Lightning Safety*

In most years, lightning ranks second only to floods in the number of storm-related deaths in the United States. Although the number of reported lightning deaths in the United States annually averages about 60, many go unreported. About 100 people are estimated to be killed and more than 1000 injured by lightning every year in the United States.

Warnings, statements, and forecasts are routinely issued for floods, tornadoes, and hurricanes, but not for lightning. Why is this the case? The answer relates to the wide geographic occurrence and frequency of lightning.

The magnitude of the cloud-to-ground lightning hazard is understood better today than ever before. Lightning occurs in the United States every day in summer and nearly every day during the rest of the year. Because lightning is so widespread and strikes the ground with such great frequency, it is not possible to warn each person of every flash. For this reason, lightning can be considered the most dangerous weather hazard that many people encounter each year.

Being aware of and following proven safety guidelines can greatly reduce the risk of injury or death. Individuals are ultimately responsible for their personal safety and should take appropriate action when threatened by lightning (Table A).

No place is absolutely safe from the threat of lightning, but some places are safer than others.

- Large enclosed structures (substantially constructed buildings) tend to be much safer than smaller or open structures.

The risk for lightning injury depends on whether the structure incorporates lightning protection, the types of construction materials used, and the size of the structure.

- In general, fully enclosed metal vehicles, such as cars, trucks, buses, vans, and fully enclosed farm vehicles, etc., with the windows rolled up, provide good shelter from lightning. Avoid contact with metal or conducting surfaces outside or inside the vehicle.
- Avoid being in or near high places and open fields, isolated trees, unprotected gazebos, rain or picnic shelters, baseball dugouts, communications towers, flagpoles, light poles, bleachers (metal or wood), metal fences, convertibles, golf carts, and water (ocean, lakes, swimming pools, rivers, etc.).
- When inside a building, avoid use of the telephone, taking a shower, washing your hands, doing dishes, or any contact with conductive surfaces with exposure to the outside, such as metal doorframes or window frames, electrical wiring, telephone wiring, cable TV wiring, plumbing, and so forth.

Safety guidelines for individuals include the following:

- Generally speaking, if individuals can see lightning and/or hear thunder, they are already at risk. Louder or more frequent thunder indicates that lightning activity is approaching, thus increasing the risk for lightning injury or death. If the time delay between seeing the flash (lightning) and hearing the bang (thunder) is less than 30 seconds, the individual should be in, or seek, a safer location. Be aware that this method of ranging has severe limitations, in part due to the difficulty of associating the proper thunder to the corresponding flash.
- High winds, rainfall, and cloud cover often act as precursors to actual cloud-to-ground strikes, and these should motivate individuals to take action. Many lightning casualties occur in the beginning, as the storm approaches, because people ignore these precursors. Also, many lightning casualties occur after the perceived threat has passed. Generally, the lightning threat diminishes with time after the last sound of thunder but may persist for more than 30 minutes. When thunderstorms are in the area but not overhead, the lightning threat can exist even when it is sunny, not raining, or when clear sky is visible.
- When available, pay attention to weather-warning devices such as NOAA (National Oceanic and Atmospheric Administration) weather radio and/or credible lightning-detection systems; however, do not let this information override good common sense.

*Material in this box is based in part on "Updated Recommendations for Lightning Safety—1998," in *Bulletin of the American Meteorological Society,* Vol. 80, No. 10, October 1999, pp. 2035–39.

TABLE A	Lightning Casualties in the U.S. by Location or Activity	
Rank	**Location/Activity**	**Relative Frequency**
1	Open Areas (including sports fields)	45%
2	Going Under Trees to Keep Dry	23%
3	Water Related Activities (swimming, boating, and fishing)	14%
4	Golfing (while in the open)	6%
5	Farm and Construction Vehicles (with open exposed cockpits)	5%
6	Corded Telephone (#1 indoor source of lightning casualties)	4%
7	Golfing (while mistakenly seeking "shelter" under trees)	2%
8	Using Radios and Radio Equipment	1%
Source: National Weather Service		

Students Sometimes Ask ...

About how many people who are struck by lightning are actually killed?

According to the National Weather Service, about 10 percent of lightning strike victims are killed; 90 percent survive. However, survivors are not unaffected. Many suffer severe, life-long injury and disability.

observer. The sound that originates along the path nearest the observer arrives before the sound that originated farthest away. This factor lengthens the duration of the thunder. Reflection of the sound waves by mountains or buildings further delays their arrival and adds to this effect. When lightning occurs more than 20 kilometers (12 miles) away, thunder is rarely heard. This type of lightning, popularly called *heat lightning*, is no different from the lightning that we associate with thunder.

Tornadoes

Tornadoes are local storms of short duration that must be ranked high among nature's most destructive forces. Their sporadic occurrence and violent winds cause many deaths each year. The nearly total destruction in some stricken areas has led many to liken their passage to bombing raids during war (Box 3).

Such was the case when devastating tornadoes hit portions of the South and lower Ohio Valley on February 5 and 6, 2008 (Figure 17). The event began on *Super Tuesday* as 24 states were holding primary elections and caucuses to select presidential candidates. Portions of Missouri, Illinois, Arkansas, Alabama, and Tennessee were among the areas in which primaries were being held. Eighty-four tornadoes were confirmed. Several strong tornadoes affected heavily populated areas—most notably in the Memphis metropolitan area, in Jackson, Tennessee, and the northern end of the Nashville metropolitan area. There were 59 confirmed fatalities across four states with hundreds of others injured. It was the deadliest outbreak in the United States in nearly 23 years and the worst in Tennessee and Kentucky since a historic outbreak in 1974.* In addition to spawning several killer tornadoes, the same weather system also produced significant straight-line wind damage, large hail (some the size of baseballs), and flooding. In colder parts of the storm, significant freezing rain and heavy snow were experienced across many parts of the eastern United States.

Tornadoes, sometimes called *twisters* or *cyclones*, are violent windstorms that take the form of a rotating column of air, or *vortex*, that extends downward from a cumulonimbus cloud. Pressures within some tornadoes have been estimated to be as much as 10 percent lower than immediately outside the storm. Drawn by the much lower pressure in the center of the vortex, air near the ground rushes into the tornado from all directions. As the air streams inward, it is spiraled upward around the core until it eventually merges with the airflow of the parent thunderstorm deep in the cumulonimbus tower.

Because of the rapid drop in pressure, air sucked into the storm expands and cools adiabatically. If the air cools below its dew point, the resulting condensation creates a pale and ominous-appearing cloud that may darken as it moves across the ground, picking up dust and debris (Figure 18). Occasionally, when the inward spiraling air is relatively dry, no condensation funnel forms because the drop in pressure is not

---

*For more about the record-setting 1974 "Super Tornado Outbreak" see Box 4 later in the chapter.

FIGURE 17   (a) Tornado damage on the campus of Union University in Jackson, Tennessee, February 6, 2008. The storm sent 50 students to the hospital, nine with severe injuries. (AP Photo/ Christopher Berkey) (b) Monroe County, Kentucky on February 6, 2008, showing the aftermath of the *Super Tuesday* tornado outbreak. (AP Photo/Hilly Schiffer, POOL)

(a)

(b)

BOX 3 ▶ ATMOSPHERIC HAZARD

Surviving a Violent Tornado

About 11 AM on Tuesday, July 13, 2004, much of northern and central Illinois was put on a tornado watch.* A large supercell had developed in the northwestern part of the state and was moving southeast into a very unstable environment (Figure D). A few hours later, as the supercell entered Woodford County, rain began to fall and the storm showed signs of becoming severe. The National Weather Service (NWS) issued a *severe thunderstorm warning* at 2:29 PM CDT. Minutes afterward a tornado developed. Twenty-three minutes later, the quarter-mile-wide twister had carved a 9.6-mile-long path across the rural Illinois countryside.

What, if anything, made this storm special or unique? After all, it was just one of a record-high 1819 tornadoes that were reported in the United States in 2004. For one, this tornado attained EF4 status for a portion of its life.** The NWS estimated that maximum winds reached 240 miles per hour. Fewer than 1 percent of tornadoes attain this level of severity. However, what was most remarkable is that no one was killed or injured when the Parsons Manufacturing facility west of the small town of Roanoke took a direct hit while the storm was most intense. At the time, 150 people were in three buildings that comprised the

FIGURE D   On July 13, 2004, an EF4 tornado cut a 23-mile path through the rural countryside near the Woodford County town of Roanoke, Illinois. The Parsons Manufacturing plant was just west of town.

plant. The 250,000-square-foot facility was flattened, cars were twisted into gnarled masses, and debris was strewn for miles (Figure E).

How did 150 people escape death or injury? The answer is foresight and planning. More than 30 years earlier, company owner Bob Parsons was inside his first factory when a small tornado passed close enough to blow windows out. Later, when he built a new plant, he made sure that the restrooms were constructed to double as tornado shelters with steel-reinforced concrete walls and eight-inch-thick concrete ceilings.

In addition, the company developed a severe weather plan. When the severe thunderstorm warning was issued at 2:29 PM on July 13, the emergency response team leader at the Parsons plant was immediately notified. A few moments later he went outside and observed a rotating wall cloud with a developing funnel cloud. He radioed back to the office to institute the company's severe weather plan. Employees were told to immediately go to their designated storm shelter. Everyone knew where to go and what to do because the plant conducted semi-annual tornado drills. All 150 people reached a shelter in less than four minutes. The emergency response team leader was the last person to reach shelter, less than two minutes before the tornado destroyed the plant at 2:41 PM

The total number of tornado deaths in 2004 for the entire United States was just 36. The toll could have been much higher. The building of tornado shelters and the development of an effective severe storm plan made the difference between life and death for 150 people at Parsons Manufacturing.

---

*Watches and warnings are discussed later in this chapter.

**EF4 is a reference to the Enhanced Fujita Scale of tornado intensity. See Table 2, p. 298.

FIGURE E   The quarter-mile-wide tornado had wind speeds reaching 240 miles per hour. The destruction at Parsons Manufacturing was devastating. (Photos courtesy of NOAA)

---

sufficient to cause the necessary adiabatic cooling. In such cases, the vortex is only made visible by the material that it vacuums from the surface and carries aloft.

Some tornadoes consist of a single vortex, but within many stronger tornadoes are smaller intense whirls called *suction vortices* that orbit the center of the larger tornado circulation (Figure 19). The tornadoes in this latter category are called

multiple vortex tornadoes. Suction vortices have diameters of only about 10 meters (30 feet) and usually form and die out in less than a minute. They can occur in all sorts of tornado sizes, from huge "wedges" to narrow "ropes." Suction vortices are responsible for most of the narrow, short swaths of extreme damage that sometimes are through tornado tracks. It is now believed that most reports of several tornadoes at once—from

FIGURE 18   A tornado is a violently rotating column of air in contact with the ground. The air column is visible when it contains condensation or when it contains dust and debris. Often the appearance is the result of both. When the column of air is aloft and does not produce damage, the visible portion is properly called a *funnel cloud*. This tornado in New Mexico near the Texas Panhandle touched down out of a rotating supercell thunderstorm. (Photo by A. T. Willett/Alamy)

For instance, the probability of a tornado striking a given point in the region most frequently subject to tornadoes is about once in 250 years. The development of Doppler radar, however, has increased our ability to study tornado-producing thunderstorms. As we shall see, the development of this technology is allowing meteorologists to gather important new data from a safe distance.

The Development and Occurrence of Tornadoes

Tornadoes form in association with severe thunderstorms that produce high winds, heavy (sometimes torrential) rainfall, and often damaging hail. Although hail may or may not precede a tornado, the portion of the thunderstorm adjacent to large hail is often the area where strong tornadoes are most likely to occur.

FIGURE 19   Some tornadoes have multiple suction vortices. These small and very intense vortices are roughly 10 meters (30 feet) across and move in a counterclockwise path around the tornado center. Because of this multiple vortex structure, one building might be heavily damaged and another one, just 10 meters away, might suffer little damage. (After Fujita)

news accounts and early-twentieth-century tornado tales—actually were multiple vortex tornadoes.

Because of the tremendous pressure gradient associated with a strong tornado, maximum winds can sometimes exceed 480 kilometers (300 miles) per hour. For example; using Doppler radar observations, scientists measured wind speeds of 510 kilometers (310 miles) per hour in a devastating tornado that struck Oklahoma City on May 3, 1999. Reliable wind-speed measurements using traditional anemometers are lacking. The changes that occur in atmospheric pressure with the passage of a tornado are largely estimates and are based on a few storms that happened to pass a nearby weather station. Thus, meteorologists have had to base their tornado models on a relatively scant observational foundation. Although additional data might be gathered if shelters and instruments capable of withstanding the fury of a tornado were placed in an area, such an effort would probably not be worthwhile. Tornadoes are highly localized and randomly distributed, and the probability of placing instruments at the right site would thus be infinitesimally small.

Fortunately, less than 1 percent of all thunderstorms produce tornadoes. Nevertheless, a much higher number must be monitored as potential tornado producers. Although meteorologists are still not sure what triggers tornado formation, it is apparent that they are the product of the interaction between strong updrafts in a thunderstorm and the winds in the troposphere.

Tornado Development

Tornadoes can form in any situation that produces severe weather, including cold fronts, squall lines, and tropical cyclones (hurricanes). Usually the most intense tornadoes are those that form in association with supercells. An important precondition linked to tornado formation in severe thunderstorms is the development of a mesocyclone. A *mesocyclone* is a vertical cylinder of rotating air, typically about 3 to 10 kilometers (2 to 6 miles) across, that develops in the updraft of a severe thunderstorm. The formation of this large vortex often precedes tornado formation by 30 minutes or so.

Mesocyclone formation depends on the presence of vertical wind shear. Moving upward from the surface, winds change direction from southerly to westerly and the wind speed increases. The speed wind shear (that is, stronger winds aloft and weaker winds near the surface) produces a rolling motion about a horizontal axis as shown in Figure 20a. If conditions are right, strong updrafts in the storm tilt the horizontally rotating air to a nearly vertical alignment (see Figure 20b). This produces the initial rotation within the cloud interior.

At first the mesocyclone is wider, shorter, and rotating more slowly than will be the case in later stages. Subsequently, the mesocyclone is stretched vertically and narrowed horizontally causing wind speeds to accelerate in an inward vortex (just as ice skaters accelerate while spinning or as a sink full of water accelerates when it spirals down a drain).

FIGURE 20 The formation of a mesocyclone often precedes tornado formation. (a) Winds are stronger aloft than at the surface (called *speed wind shear*), producing a rolling motion about a horizontal axis. (b) Strong thunderstorm updrafts tilt the horizontally rotating air to a nearly vertical alignment. (c) The mesocyclone, a vertical cylinder of rotating air, is established. (d) If a tornado develops it will descend from a slowly rotating wall cloud in the lower portion of the mesocyclone. This supercell tornado hit the Texas Panhandle in May 1996. (Photo by Warren Faidley/Weatherstock)

Next, the narrowing column of rotating air stretches downward until a portion of the cloud protrudes below the cloud base to produce a very dark, slowly rotating *wall cloud*. Finally, a slender and rapidly spinning vortex emerges from the base of the wall cloud to form a *funnel cloud*. If the funnel cloud makes contact with the surface, it is then classified as a *tornado* (Figure 20).

The formation of a mesocyclone does not necessarily mean that tornado formation will follow. Only about half of all mesocyclones produce tornadoes. The reason for this is not understood. Because this is the case, forecasters cannot determine in advance which mesocyclones will spawn tornadoes.

Tornado Climatology

Severe thunderstorms—and hence tornadoes—are most often spawned along the cold front or squall line of a middle-latitude cyclone or in association with supercell thunderstorms. Throughout the spring, air masses associated with mid-latitude cyclones are most likely to have greatly contrasting conditions. Continental polar air from Canada may still be very cold and dry, whereas maritime tropical air from the Gulf of Mexico is warm, humid, and unstable. The greater the contrast, the more intense the storm tends to be.

These two contrasting air masses are most likely to meet in the central United States because there is no significant natural barrier separating the center of the country from the arctic or the Gulf of Mexico. Consequently, this region generates more tornadoes than any other part of the country or, in fact, the world. Figure 21, which depicts the average annual tornado incidence in the United States over a 27-year period, readily substantiates this fact.

An average of about 1200 tornadoes were reported annually in the United States between 1990 and 2007. Still, the actual numbers that occur from one year to the next vary greatly. During the 18-year span just mentioned, for example, yearly totals ranged from a low of 941 in the year 2002 to a high of 1819 in 2004. Tornadoes occur during every month of the year. April through June is the period of greatest tornado frequency in the United States, and December and January are the months of lowest activity. Of the nearly 40,522 confirmed tornadoes reported over the contiguous 48 states during the 50-year period 1950–1999, an average of almost six per day occurred during May. At the other extreme, a tornado was reported only about every other day in December and January.

More than 40 percent of all tornadoes take place during the spring. Fall and winter, by contrast, together account for only 19 percent (Figure 21). In late January and February, when the incidence of tornadoes begins to increase, the center of maximum frequency lies over the central Gulf states. During March this center moves eastward to the southeastern Atlantic states, with tornado frequency reaching its peak in April.

During May and June the center of maximum frequency moves through the southern Great Plains and then to the northern Plains and Great Lakes area. This drift is due to the increasing penetration of warm, moist air while contrasting cool, dry air still surges in from the north and northwest. Thus, when the Gulf states are substantially under the influence of warm air after May, there is no cold-air intrusion to speak of, and tornado frequency drops. Such is the case across the country after June. Winter cooling permits fewer and fewer encounters between warm and cold air masses, and tornado frequency returns to its lowest level by December.

Profile of a Tornado

The average tornado has a diameter of between 150 and 600 meters (500 to 2000 feet), travels across the landscape at approximately 45 kilometers (30 miles) per hour, and cuts a path about 26 kilometers (16 miles) long. Because many tornadoes occur slightly ahead of a cold front, in the zone of southwest winds, most move toward the northeast. The Illinois example demonstrates this fact nicely (Figure 22). The figure also shows that many tornadoes do not fit the description of the "average" tornado.

FIGURE 21   The map shows average annual tornado incidence per 10,000 square miles (26,000 square kilometers) for a 27-year period. The graph shows average number of tornadoes and tornado days each month in the United States for the same period. (After NOAA)

- Beginning point
- Tornado aloft
- Tornado track on ground

kilometers
0   80

0   25   50
miles

Tri-state tornado

FIGURE 22 Paths of Illinois tornadoes (1916–1969). Because most tornadoes occur slightly ahead of a cold front, in the zone of southwest winds, they tend to move toward the northeast. Tornadoes in Illinois verify this. Over 80 percent exhibited directions of movement toward the northeast through east. (After John W. Wilson and Stanley A. Changnon, Jr., Illinois Tornadoes, Illinois State Water Survey Circular 103, 1971, pp. 10, 24)

Of the hundreds of tornadoes reported in the United States each year, over half are comparatively weak and short-lived. Most of these small tornadoes have lifetimes of three minutes or less and paths that seldom exceed 1 kilometer (0.6 mile) in length and 100 meters (330 feet) wide. Typical wind speeds are on the order of 150 kilometers (96 miles) per hour or less. On the other end of the tornado spectrum are the infrequent and often long-lived violent tornadoes (Table 1). Although large tornadoes constitute only a small percentage of the total reported, their effects are often devastating. Such tornadoes may exist for periods in excess of three hours and produce an essentially continuous damage path more than 150 kilometers (90 miles) long and perhaps a kilometer or more wide. Maximum winds range beyond 500 kilometers (310 miles) per hour (Figure 23).

Tornado Destruction

Because tornadoes generate the strongest winds in nature, they have accomplished many seemingly impossible tasks, such as driving a piece of straw through a thick wooden plank and uprooting huge trees (Figure 24). Although it may seem impossible for winds to cause some of the fantastic damage at-

TABLE 1	Tornado Extremes		
Tornado characteristic	**Value**	**Date**	**Location**
World's deadliest single tornado	1,300 killed–12,000 injured	26 Apr 1989	Salturia and Manikganj, Bangladesh
U.S. deadliest single tornado	695 dead	18 Mar 1925	MO-IL-IN
U.S. deadliest tornado outbreak	747 dead	18 Mar 1925	MO-IL-IN (includes the Tri-State Tornado deaths)
Biggest (numerical) tornado outbreak	147 tornadoes	3–4 Apr 1974	13 central U.S. states
Calendar month with greatest number of tornadoes[a]	543 tornadoes	May 2003	United States
Widest tornado (diameter*)	Nearly 4,000 m (2.5 miles) in width	22 May 2004	Hallam, NE. EF4 tornado
Highest recorded tornadic wind speed**	135 m s^{-1} (302 mph)	8 May 1999	Bridge Creek, OK
Highest elevation tornado	3650 m (12,000 ft)	7 Jul 2004	Sequoia National Park, CA
Longest tornado transport	A personal check carried 359 km (223 miles)	Apr 11 1991	Stockton, KS, to Winnetoon, NE

Source: National Weather Service, Storm Prediction Center as reported in *Bulletin of the American Meteorological Society*, Vol. 88, No. 6, June 2007, p. 857.
[a]Preliminary figure for May 2008 is 595 tornadoes. When final statistics are determined, the record for this category may change.
*"Widest" is now defined as maximum width of tornado damage by the NWS.
**By necessity this value is restricted to the small number of tornadoes sampled by mobile Doppler radars.

(a)

Tri-State Tornado

Wisconsin Michigan
Iowa
Illinois Indiana Ohio
Missouri
Kentucky
Tennessee

Olney

Veered 9° left and
3 funnels observed
for 9.6 km

541 killed and 1423
seriously injured in
40 minutes

Mt. Vernon

117 kph
1630
1600
Princeton
25%

97 kph
Griffin
100%

Owensville
85 farms
destroyed

97 kph
90 kph
1438
Parrish 90%
West Frankfort 20%
Murphysboro 40%

116
kph
108 kph
1400
Biehle
double funnel
track for 5.6 km

1301 1315
1305 Annapolis
90%

Cairo

Note:
Percentage refers to total number
of buildings and homes destroyed
in the community.

(b)

FIGURE 23   (a) "One tornado among the more than 13,000 which have occurred in the United States since 1915 easily ranks above all others as the single most devastating storm of this type. Shortly after its occurrence on 18 March 1925, the famed Tri-State tornado was recognized as the worst on record, and it still ranks as the nation's greatest tornado disaster. The tornado remained on the ground for 219 miles. The resulting losses included 695 dead, 2027 injured, and damages equal to $43 million in 1970 dollars. This represents the greatest death toll ever inflicted by a tornado and one of the largest damage totals." (Map and description from John W. Wilson and Stanley A. Changnon, Jr., Illinois Tornadoes, Illinois State Water Survey Circular 103, 1971, p. 32) (b) This historic image shows Murphysboro, Illinois, on March 21, 1925, three days after the Tri-State tornado devastated the community. (Bettmann/CORBIS)

FIGURE 24   (a) The force of the wind during a tornado near Wichita, Kansas, in April 1991 was enough to drive this piece of metal into a utility pole. (Photo by John Sokich/NOAA) (b) The remains of a truck wrapped around a tree in Bridge Creek, Oklahoma, on May 4, 1999, following a major tornado outbreak. (AP Photo/L. M. Otero)

(a)

(b)

tributed to tornadoes, tests in engineering facilities have repeatedly demonstrated that winds in excess of 320 kilometers (200 miles) per hour are capable of incredible feats.

There is a long list of documented examples. In 1931 a tornado actually carried an 83-ton railroad coach and its 117 passengers 24 meters (80 feet) through the air and dropped them in a ditch. A year later, near Sioux Falls, South Dakota, a steel beam 15 centimeters (6 inches) thick and 4 meters (13 feet) long was ripped from a bridge, flew more than 300 meters (nearly 1000 feet), and perforated a 35-centimeter- (14-inch-) thick hardwood tree. In 1970 an 18-ton steel tank was carried nearly 1 kilometer (0.6 mile) at Lubbock, Texas. Fortunately, the winds associated with most tornadoes are not this strong.

Most tornado losses are associated with a few storms that strike urban areas or devastate entire small communities. The amount of destruction wrought by such storms depends to a significant degree (but not completely) on the strength of the winds. A wide spectrum of tornado strengths, sizes, and lifetimes are observed. The commonly used guide to tornado intensity is the **Enhanced Fujita intensity scale** or the **EF-scale** for short (Table 2). Because tornado winds cannot be measured directly, a rating on the EF-scale is determined by assessing the damage produced by a storm. Although widely used, the EF-scale is not perfect. Estimating tornado intensity based on damage alone does not take into account the structural integrity of the objects hit by a tornado. A well-constructed building can withstand very high winds, whereas a poorly built structure can suffer devastating damage from the same or even weaker winds.

The drop in atmospheric pressure associated with the passage of a tornado plays a minor role in the damage process. Most structures have sufficient venting to allow for the sudden drop in pressure. Opening a window, once thought to be a way to minimize damage by allowing inside and outside atmospheric pressure to equalize, is no longer recommended. In fact, if a tornado gets close enough to a structure for the pressure drop to be experienced, the strong winds probably will have already caused significant damage.

Although the greatest part of tornado damage is caused by violent winds, most tornado injuries and deaths result from flying debris. On the average, tornadoes cause more deaths each year than any other weather events except lightning and flash floods. For the United States, the average annual death toll from tornadoes is about 60 people. However, the actual number of deaths each year can depart significantly from the average. On April 3–4, 1974, for example, an outbreak of 148 tornadoes brought death and destruction to a 13-state region east of the Mississippi River. More than 300 people died and nearly 5500 people were injured in this worst tornado disaster in half a century (Box 4).

The proportion of tornadoes that result in the loss of life is small. In 2007, there were 1080 tornadoes reported in the United States. Of this total, just 26 were "killer tornadoes," a number that is above the 30-year average of 20 for the span 1977–2006. Put another way, slightly less than 2 percent of all reported tornadoes in the United States during that period were "killers." Although the percentage of tornadoes that result in death is small, every tornado is potentially lethal. If you examine Figure 25, which compares tornado fatalities with storm intensities, the results are quite interesting. It is clear from this graph that the majority (63 percent) of all tornadoes are weak and that the number of storms decreases as tornado intensity increases. The distribution of tornado fatalities, however, is just the opposite. Although only 2 percent of tornadoes are classified as violent, they account for nearly 70 percent of the deaths.

If there is some question about the causes of tornadoes, there certainly is none about the destructive effects of these violent storms. A severe tornado leaves the affected area stunned and disorganized and may require a response of the magnitude demanded in war.

Tornado Forecasting

Because severe thunderstorms and tornadoes are small and short-lived phenomena, they are among the most difficult weather features to forecast precisely. Nevertheless, the prediction, the detection, and the monitoring of such storms are among the most important services provided by professional

TABLE 2	Enhanced Fujita Intensity Scale*		
	Wind Speed		
Scale	Km/Hr	Mi/Hr	Damage
EF-0	105–137	65–85	*Light*. Some damage to siding and shingles
EF-1	138–177	86–110	*Moderate*. Considerable roof damage. Winds can uproot trees and overturn single-wide mobile homes. Flagpoles bend.
EF-2	178–217	111–135	*Considerable*. Most single-wide homes destroyed. Permanent homes can shift off foundations. Flagpoles collapse. Softwood trees debarked.
EF-3	218–265	136–165	*Severe*. Hardwood trees debarked. All but small portions of houses destroyed.
EF-4	266–322	166–200	*Devastating*. Complete destruction of well-built residences, large sections of school buildings.
EF-5	>322	>200	*Incredible*. Significant structural deformation of mid- and high-rise buildings.

*The original Fujita scale was developed by T. Theodore Fujita in 1971 and put into use in 1973. The Enhanced Fujita Scale is a revision that was put into use in February 2007. Winds speeds are estimates (not measurements) based on damage, and represent 3-second gusts at the point of damage. More information about the criteria used to evaluate tornado intensity can be found at http://www.spc.noaa.gov/efscale/ and at http://www.spc.noaa.gov/faq/tornado/ef-scale.html.

FIGURE 25 Percentage of tornadoes in each intensity category (red) and percentage of fatalities associated with each category (orange). Because this study was completed prior to the adoption of the EF-scale, storm intensities are expressed using the F-scale. Wind speeds (mph) for this scale are: F0 (<72), F1 (72–112), F2 (113–157), F3 (158–206), F4 (207–260), F5 (>260). (From Joseph T. Schaefer et al., "Tornadoes—When, Where and How Often," Weatherwise, 33, no. 2 (1980), 57)

meteorologists. The timely issuance and dissemination of watches and warnings are both critical to the protection of life and property.

The Storm Prediction Center (SPC) located in Norman, Oklahoma, is part of the National Weather Service (NWS) and the National Centers for Environmental Prediction (NCEP). Its mission is to provide timely and accurate forecasts and watches for severe thunderstorms and tornadoes.

Severe thunderstorm outlooks are issued several times daily. *Day 1* outlooks identify those areas likely to be affected by severe thunderstorms during the next six to 30 hours, and *day 2* outlooks extend the forecast through the following day. Both outlooks describe the type, coverage, and intensity of the severe weather expected. Many local NWS field offices also issue severe weather outlooks that provide a more local description of the severe weather potential for the next 12 to 24 hours.

Tornado Watches and Warnings

Tornado watches alert the public to the possibility of tornadoes over a specified area for a particular time interval. Watches serve to fine-tune forecast areas already identified in severe weather outlooks. A typical watch covers an area of about 65,000 square kilometers (25,000 square miles) for a four- to six-hour period. A tornado watch is an important part of the tornado alert system because it sets in motion the procedures necessary to deal adequately with detection, tracking, warning, and response. Watches are generally reserved for organized severe weather events where the tornado threat will affect at least 26,000 square kilometers (10,000 square miles) and/or persist for at least three hours. Watches

typically are not issued when the threat is thought to be isolated and/or short-lived.

Whereas a tornado watch is designed to alert people to the possibility of tornadoes, a **tornado warning** is issued by local offices of the National Weather Service when a tornado has actually been sighted in an area or is indicated by weather radar. It warns of a high probability of imminent danger. Warnings are issued for much smaller areas than watches, usually covering portions of a county or counties. In addition, they are in effect for much shorter periods, typically 30 to 60 minutes. Because a tornado warning may be based on an actual sighting, warnings are occasionally issued after a tornado has already developed. However, most warnings are issued prior to tornado formation, sometimes by several tens of minutes, based on Doppler radar data and/or spotter reports of funnel clouds or cloud-base rotation.

If the direction and the approximate speed of the storm are known, an estimate of its most probable path can be made. Because tornadoes often move erratically, the warning area is fan-shaped downwind from the point where the tornado has been spotted. Improved forecasts and advances in technology have contributed to a significant decline in tornado deaths over the last 50 years. Figure 26 illustrates this trend. During a span when the United States population grew rapidly, tornado deaths trended downward.

As noted earlier, the probability of one place being struck by a tornado, even in the area of greatest frequency, is slight. Nevertheless, although the probabilities may be small, tornadoes have provided many mathematical exceptions. For example, the small town of Codell, Kansas, was hit three years in a row—1916, 1917, and 1918—and each time on the same date, May 20! Needless to say, tornado watches and warnings should never be taken lightly.

Doppler Radar

The installation of **Doppler radar** across the United States has significantly improved our ability to track thunderstorms and issue warnings based on their potential to produce

FIGURE 26 Number of tornado deaths in the United States by decade 1950–1999. Even though the population has risen sharply since 1950, there has been a general downward trend in tornado deaths. (Data from NOAA)

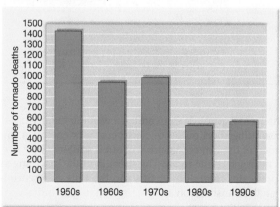

BOX 4 ▶ ATMOSPHERIC HAZARD

The April 1974 Super Tornado Outbreak

The dates April 3–4, 1974, are important in the tornado history of the United States. In a span of just 16 hours, 148 tornadoes hit 13 states and Canada—the largest and costliest outbreak ever recorded (Figure F). The storms killed 315 people and injured about 5500 more. Damages exceeded $600 million. Forty-eight tornadoes were killers, with seven rated F5 (the maximum possible on the Fujita Intensity Scale) and an additional 23 rated F4.* The town of Xenia, in southwestern Ohio, was especially hard hit—more than 1000 homes were destroyed, 34 people were killed, and 1100 were injured. Property damages exceeded $100 million.

Following this record-breaking event, extensive studies and surveys were conducted. The results of this work provided meteorologists with the evidence they needed to demonstrate that many of the notions about tornadoes held by the general public were incorrect. Here are some of the myths that were disproved:

MYTH: A tornado won't touch down at the confluence of major rivers. Fact: The town of Cairo, IL, located at the confluence of the Ohio and Mississippi Rivers was hit by a tornado that day.

MYTH: Tornadoes don't go up and down steep or high hills. Fact: A tornado that hit Guin, AL, stayed on the ground as it climbed the 1640-foot Monte Sano Mountain and grew in intensity as it descended the northeast slope. The Blue Ridge tornado of that day formed in the mountains at 1800 feet just east of Mulberry Gap and crossed a 3000-foot ridge before moving down to the bottom of the canyon. The tornado finally climbed to the 3300-foot top of Rich Nob before dissipating.

MYTH: Tornadoes will not follow terrain into steep valleys. Fact: The tornado that wiped out three schools in Monticello, IN, descended a 60-foot bluff over the Tippecanoe River as it moved out of the town and damaged homes at its base.**

FIGURE F Tracks of the 148 tornadoes that struck a 13-state area in the "super outbreak" of April 3–4, 1974. (After NOAA)

Engineering studies of damaged schools provided information that was later incorporated into construction designs that ensured greater safety. Evidence from damaged buildings showed that interior hallways provide the safest place and that classrooms with outside walls and gymnasiums with wide roof span were most dangerous.

What is the risk of another outbreak like the April 1974 event? We know such an occurrence is rare because it has only happened once since tornado records have been kept. However, there is no way to know if the odds are once in 50 years or once in 1000 years because we do not have a long enough record of accurate tornado statistics.

*This event took place when tornado intensities were described using the Fujita scale (F-scale), the predecessor of the EF-scale. Wind speeds (mph) for the F-scale are: F0 (<72), F1 (72–112), F2 (113–157), F3 (158–206), F4(207–260), F5 (>260).

**NOAA "Tornado Outbreak 1974: The Worst in U.S. History." This publication was prepared to mark the twenty-fifth anniversary of the April 3–4, 1974, super tornado outbreak. http://www.publicaffairs.noaa.gov/storms/

tornadoes (Figure 27). Conventional weather radar works by transmitting short pulses of electromagnetic energy. A small fraction of the waves that are sent out is scattered by a storm and returned to the radar. The strength of the returning signal indicates rainfall intensity, and the time difference between the transmission and return of the signal indicates the distance to the storm.

However, to identify tornadoes and severe thunderstorms, we must be able to detect the characteristic circulation patterns associated with them. Conventional radar cannot do so except occasionally when spiral rain bands occur in association with a tornado and give rise to a hook-shaped echo.

Doppler radar not only performs the same tasks as conventional radar but also has the ability to detect motion directly

(a)

(b)

(c)

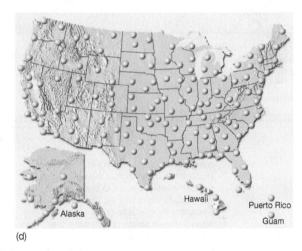

(d)

FIGURE 27 By using advanced Doppler radars, scientists are better able to estimate when and where thunderstorms will form, even in areas of seemingly clear air. Doppler radar installation (a) and advanced weather interactive processing system (b) at Sterling, Virginia, near Dulles International Airport. This is one of 115 state-of-the-art National Weather Service facilities shown on the map in (d). The equipment shown in (c), called *Doppler Radar on Wheels,* is scanning the skies of the Texas Panhandle on May 15, 2003. Portable units like this one are used by researchers to study severe weather events. (Photos (a) and (b) by Brownie Harris/The Stock Market; map after National Weather Service; photo (c) © University Corporation for Atmospheric Research)

Students Sometimes Ask . . .

Sometimes I hear the term "weather advisory" used in a report. How is that different from a warning?

A warning is issued when a hazardous weather event is occurring, is imminent, or has a very high probability of occurrence. Warnings are issued hours in advance for large-scale events such as hurricanes and winter storms, and minutes in advance for severe weather such as tornadoes and flash floods. Conditions *require* action to protect life and property. Advisories are similar to warnings except they are issued only for large-scale events and indicate that conditions *may require* immediate action to protect life and property. Impacts are generally not as severe as with a warning.

(Figure 28). The principle involved is known as the *Doppler effect* (Box 5). Air movement in clouds is determined by comparing the frequency of the reflected signal to that of the original pulse. The movement of precipitation toward the radar increases the frequency of reflected pulses, whereas motion away from the radar decreases the frequency. These frequency changes are then interpreted in terms of speed toward or away from the Doppler radar unit. It is this same principle that allows police radar to determine the speed of moving cars. Unfortunately, a single Doppler radar unit cannot detect air movements that occur parallel to it. Therefore, when a more complete picture of the winds within a cloud mass is desired, it is necessary to use two or more Doppler units.

Doppler radar can detect the initial formation and subsequent development of the mesocyclone within a severe

BOX 5 ▶ THE DOPPLER EFFECT

We have all heard the changes in the sounds that a car, truck, or train makes as it approaches and then passes by. As the vehicle moves toward us, the sound has a higher pitch, and after the vehicle passes, the pitch drops. The faster the car, truck, or train is moving, the more the pitch drops (Figure G). This phenomenon occurs not only in association with sound waves but also with electromagnetic waves. Known as the *Doppler effect*, it is named for Christian Johannn Doppler, the Austrian physicist who first explained it in 1842.

Why does the wave frequency appear to shift when the wave source is moving? Figure H(a) shows the pattern of wave crests generated by a source that is not moving. The distance between wave crests (the wavelength) is identical for each successive wave. If this were a source emitting sound, the pitch would be the same no matter where the listener was located. However, if the source were moving, the wave crests would no longer make a concentric pattern. Rather, they would become more closely spaced in the direction the source was advancing. Therefore, the wave frequency would be greater ahead of the source and lower behind the source. Figure H(b) illustrates this pattern.

Astronomers apply this principle when they wish to determine whether a light source such as a star is approaching or retreating relative to Earth. When the lines in the star's spectrum are shifted toward wavelengths that are shorter than those observed when such a source is at rest, the star is approaching. If the star is moving away from the observer, all of the spectral lines are shifted toward longer wavelengths. In meteorology, the new generation of weather radars use the Doppler principle to probe the circulation within a cloud by monitoring the movements of raindrops.

FIGURE G This everyday example of the Doppler effect illustrates the apparent lengthening and shortening of wavelengths caused by the relative movement between a source and an observer.

FIGURE H The Doppler effect is the change in the observed frequency of waves produced by the motion of the wave source and/or the wave receiver. In both parts of the diagram, the circles represent wave crests that travel at a constant speed. (a) When the wave source is stationary, the distance between waves is identical for all waves that are produced. The wave frequency (the pitch of the sound) at any point in this diagram is the same. (b) Here the source is moving toward the top of the page. Whenever the source (or the receiver) moves, the wave pattern becomes distorted. Wave 1 was produced when the source was at point 1; wave 2 was created when the source was at point 2; and wave 3 was emitted at point 3. Notice that even though the frequency emitted by the source remains the same as in part (a), a listener at location X would experience a higher frequency (higher-pitched sound) because each wave has a shorter distance to travel and therefore arrives at location X more frequently than would occur if the source were not moving. Conversely, a listener at location Y would experience a lower frequency.

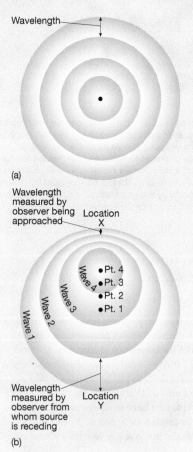

Thunderstorms and Tornadoes

FIGURE 28 This is a dual Doppler radar image of an EF5 tornado near Moore, Oklahoma, on May 3, 1999. The left image (reflectivity) shows precipitation in the supercell thunderstorm. The right image shows motion of the precipitation along the radar beam, that is, how fast rain or hail are moving toward or away from the radar. In this example, the radar was unusually close to the tornado—close enough to make out the signature of the tornado itself (most of the time only the weaker and larger mesocyclone is detected). (After NOAA)

Reflectivity   Storm-relative velocity

thunderstorm that frequently precedes tornado development. Almost all (96 percent) mesocyclones produce damaging hail, severe winds, or tornadoes. Those that produce tornadoes (about 50 percent) can sometimes be distinguished by their stronger wind speeds and their sharper gradients of wind speeds. Mesocyclones can sometimes be identified within parent storms 30 minutes or more before tornado formation, and if a storm is large, at distances up to 230 kilometers (140 miles). In addition, when close to the radar, individual tornado circulations may sometimes be detected. Ever since the implementation of the national Doppler network, the average lead time for tornado warnings has increased from less than 5 minutes in the late 1980s to nearly 11 minutes today.

Doppler radar is not without problems. One concern relates to the weak tornadoes that rank at or near the bottom of the Enhanced Fujita Intensity Scale. The nature of this problem has been summarized as follows:

Presently, all tornadoes are treated in the same manner by the NWS (National Weather Service); a tornado warning is issued, and local governments usually respond by activating their emergency procedures. Doppler radar makes forecasting and detection of these tornadoes possible in real-time operations. Thus, the potential exists for numerous warnings being issued for tornadoes which do little or no damage. This could desensitize the public to the dangers of more rare, life-threatening tornadoes. A future research goal should be the development of techniques that enable forecasting of tornado intensity.*

It should also be pointed out that not all tornado-bearing storms have clear-cut radar signatures and that other storms can give false signatures. Detection, therefore, is sometimes a subjective process and a given display could be interpreted in several ways. Consequently, trained observers will continue to form an important part of the warning system in the foreseeable future.

Although some operational problems exist, the benefits of Doppler radar are many. As a research tool, it is not only providing data on the formation of tornadoes but is also helping meteorologists gain new insights into thunderstorm development, the structure and dynamics of hurricanes, and air-turbulence hazards that plague aircraft. As a practical tool for tornado detection, it has significant advantages over a system that uses conventional radar.

———
*Lawrence B. Dunn, "Two Examples of Operational Tornado Warnings Using Doppler Radar Data," *Bulletin of the American Meteorological Society,* 71, no. 2 (February 1990), 152.

Chapter Summary

- Although tornadoes and *hurricanes* are, in fact, cyclones, the vast majority of cyclones are not hurricanes or tornadoes. The term "cyclone" simply refers to the circulation around any low-pressure center, no matter how large or intense it is. *Thunderstorms,* storms containing lightning and thunder, are related in some manner to tornadoes, hurricanes, and mid-latitude cyclones.
- Dynamic thermal instability occurs during the development of thunderstorms, which form when warm, humid air rises in an unstable environment. A number of mechanisms, such as unequal heating of Earth's surface or lifting

of warm air along a front or mountain slope, can trigger the upward air movement needed to create thunderstorm-producing cumulonimbus clouds. Severe thunderstorms produce high winds, damaging hail, flash floods, and tornadoes.
- In the United States, *air-mass thunderstorms* frequently occur in maritime tropical (mT) air that moves northward from the Gulf of Mexico. During the spring and summer, when the air is heated from below by the warmer land surface, the warm, humid air mass becomes unstable and thunderstorms develop. Generally, three stages are

involved in the development of a thunderstorm. The *cumulus stage* is dominated by rising currents of air (updrafts) and the formation of a towering cumulonimbus cloud. Falling precipitation within the cloud causes drag on the air and initiates a downdraft that is further aided by the influx of cool, dry air surrounding the cloud, a process termed *entrainment*. The beginning of the *mature stage* is marked by the downdraft leaving the base of the cloud and the release of precipitation. With gusty winds, lightning, heavy precipitation, and sometimes hail, the mature stage is the most active period of a thunderstorm. Marking the end of the storm, the *dissipating stage* is dominated by downdrafts and entrainment. Without a supply of moisture from updrafts, the cloud soon evaporates. It should be noted that within a single air-mass thunderstorm there may be several individual *cells*—that is, zones of adjacent updrafts and downdrafts.

- Mountainous regions, such as the Rockies in the West and the Appalachians in the East, experience a greater number of air-mass thunderstorms than do the Plains states. Many thunderstorms that form over the eastern two-thirds of the United States occur as part of the general convergence and frontal wedging that accompany passing mid-latitude cyclones.
- *Severe thunderstorms* are capable of producing heavy downpours and flash flooding as well as strong, gusty, straight-line winds. They are influenced by strong vertical wind shear—that is, changes in wind direction and/or speed between different heights, and updrafts that become tilted and continue to build upward. Downdrafts from the thunderstorm cells reach the surface and spread out to produce an advancing wedge of cold air, called a *gust front*, which may form a *roll cloud* as warm air is lifted along its leading edge.
- Some of the most dangerous weather is produced by a type of thunderstorm called a *supercell*, a single, very powerful thunderstorm cell that at times may extend to heights of 20 kilometers (65,000 feet) and persist for many hours. The vertical wind profile of these cells may produce a *mesocyclone*, a column of cyclonically rotating air, within which tornadoes sometimes form. Supercells appear to form as inversion layers are eroded locally and unstable air "erupts" from below to form unusually large cumulonimbus clouds with concentrated, persistent updrafts.
- *Squall lines* are relatively narrow, elongated bands of thunderstorms that develop in the warm sector of a middle-latitude cyclone, usually in advance of a cold front. Some develop when divergence and lifting created by an active jet stream aloft is aligned with a strong, persistent low-level flow of warm, humid air from the south. A squall line with severe thunderstorms can also form along a boundary called a *dryline*, a narrow zone along which there is an abrupt change in moisture.
- A *mesoscale convective complex* (MCC) consists of many individual thunderstorms that are organized into a large oval to circular cluster. They form most frequently in the Great Plains from groups of afternoon air-mass thunderstorms. Although MCCs sometimes produce severe weather, they also provide a significant portion of the growing-season rainfall to the agricultural regions of the central United States.
- *Microbursts* are small, short-lived localized downdrafts of wind that occur beneath some thunderstorms and can reach speeds of 160 kilometers (100 miles) per hour. Microbursts are not only destructive, but the wind shear associated with them is a significant airport hazard.
- *Thunder* is produced by *lightning*. The object of lightning is to equalize the electrical difference associated with the formation of a large cumulonimbus cloud by producing a negative flow of current from the region of excess negative charge to the region with excess positive charge, or vice versa. The most common type of lightning, often called *sheet lightning*, occurs within and between clouds. The less common, but more dangerous, type of lightning is *cloud-to-ground lightning*.
- The origin of charge separation in clouds, although not fully understood, must hinge on rapid vertical movements within the cloud. The lightning we see as some single flashes are really several very rapid strokes between the cloud and the ground. When air is heated by the electrical discharge of lightning, it expands explosively and produces the sound waves we hear as thunder. The thunder we hear as a rumble is produced by a long lightning flash at some distance from the observer.
- *Tornadoes*, sometimes called twisters, or cyclones, are violent windstorms that take the form of a rotating column of air, or *vortex*, that extends downward from a cumulonimbus cloud. Some tornadoes consist of a single vortex. Within many stronger tornadoes, called *multiple vortex tornadoes*, are smaller intense whirls called *suction vortices* that rotate within the main vortex. Pressures within some tornadoes have been estimated to be as much as 10 percent lower than immediately outside the storm. Because of the tremendous pressure gradient associated with a strong tornado, maximum winds approach 480 kilometers (300 miles) per hour.
- Tornadoes form in association with severe thunderstorms that produce high winds, heavy rainfall, and often damaging hail. They form in any situation that produces severe weather including cold fronts, squall lines, and tropical cyclones (hurricanes). An important precondition linked to tornado formation in severe thunderstorms is the development of a mesocyclone that forms in the updraft of the thunderstorm. As the narrowing column of rotating air stretches downward, a rapidly spinning *funnel cloud* may emerge from a slowly rotating *wall cloud*. If the funnel cloud makes contact with the surface, it is then classified as a tornado.
- Severe thunderstorms, and hence tornadoes, are most often spawned along the cold front or squall line of a middle-latitude cyclone or in association with supercell thunderstorms. Although April through June is the period of greatest tornado activity, tornadoes occur during

every month of the year. The average tornado has a diameter of between 150 and 600 meters, travels across the landscape toward the northeast at approximately 45 kilometers per hour, and cuts a path about 26 kilometers long.

- Most tornado damage is caused by tremendously strong winds. One commonly used guide to tornado intensity is the *Enhanced Fujita Intensity Scale*, or simply *EF-scale*. A rating on the EF-scale is determined by assessing damages produced by a storm. Whereas most tornado damage is done by violent winds, most tornado injuries and deaths result from flying debris.

- Because severe thunderstorms and tornadoes are small and short-lived phenomena, they are among the most difficult weather features to forecast precisely. When necessary, the Storm Prediction Center of the National Weather Service issues severe thunderstorm outlooks several times daily. When weather conditions favor the formation of tornadoes, a *tornado watch* is issued to alert the public to the possibility of tornadoes over a specified area for a particular time interval. A *tornado warning* is issued by local offices of the National Weather Service when a tornado has been sighted in an area or is indicated by weather radar. With its ability to detect the movement of precipitation within a cloud, *Doppler radar* technology has greatly advanced the accuracy of tornado warnings. Using the principle known as the *Doppler effect*, Doppler radar can identify the initial formation and subsequent development of the mesocyclone within a thunderstorm that frequently precedes tornado development.

Vocabulary Review

air-mass thunderstorm	gust front	severe thunderstorm
cumulus stage	leader	squall line
dart leader	lightning	step leader
dissipating stage	mature stage	stroke
Doppler radar	mesocyclone	supercell
dryline	mesoscale convective	thunder
entrainment	complex (MCC)	thunderstorm
flash	microburst	tornado
Enhanced Fujita Intensity	multiple vortex tornado	tornado warning
Scale (EF-scale)	return stroke	tornado watch

Review Questions

1. If you hear that a cyclone is approaching, should you immediately seek shelter?

2. Compare the wind speeds and the sizes of middle-latitude cyclones, tornadoes, and hurricanes.

3. Although tornadoes and hurricanes are dangerous storms, in most years they are not responsible for the greatest number of storm-related deaths in the United States. What is the deadliest storm phenomenon? (See Box 1.)

4. What are the primary requirements for the formation of thunderstorms?

5. Where would you expect thunderstorms to be most common on Earth? In the United States?

6. During what season and at what time of day is air-mass thunderstorm activity greatest? Why?

7. Why does entrainment intensify thunderstorm downdrafts?

8. Describe how downdrafts in a severe thunderstorm act to maintain updrafts. What is a *gust front?*

9. Briefly describe the formation of a squall line along a dry line.

10. How is thunder produced?

11. Which is more common, sheet lightning or cloud-to-ground lightning?

12. What is heat lightning?

13. Why do tornadoes have such high wind speeds?

14. What general atmospheric conditions are most conducive to the formation of tornadoes?

15. When is the "tornado season"? Can you explain why it occurs when it does? Why does the area of greatest tornado frequency migrate?

16. Distinguish between a tornado watch and a tornado warning.

17. A vehicle with its horn sounding moves away from an observer at point *A* and toward an observer at point *B*. Should the pitch of the horn at point *B* be higher or lower than at point *A*? What effect explains the difference in pitch experienced at points *A* and *B*? (See Box 5.)

18. What advantages does Doppler radar have over conventional radar?

Problems

1. If thunder is heard 15 seconds after lightning is seen, about how far away was the lightning stroke?

2. Examine the upper left portion of Figure 22 and determine the percentage of tornadoes that exhibited directions of movement toward the E through NNE.

3. Figures 29 and 30 represent two common ways that United States tornado statistics are graphically presented to the public. Which four states experience the greatest number of tornadoes? Are these the states with the greatest tornado threat? Which map is most useful for depicting the tornado hazard in the United States? Does the map in Figure 21 have an advantage over either or both of these maps?

4. Table 3 lists the total number of tornadoes reported in the United States by decade. Propose a reason that might explain why the total for the 1990s was so much higher than for the 1950s.

TABLE 3	Number of U.S. Tornadoes Reported by Decade*
1950–59	4796
1960–69	6813
1970–79	8579
1980–89	8196
1990–99	12,138
*Data from Storm Prediction Center, NOAA	

5. Figure 26 shows that the number of tornado deaths in the United States in the 1990s was less than half the number that occurred in the 1950s, even though there was a significant rise in the population during that span. To what can you attribute this decline in the death toll?

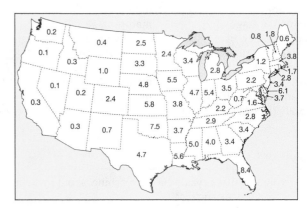

FIGURE 29 Annual average number of tornadoes by state for a 45-year period.

FIGURE 30 Annual average number of tornadoes per 10,000 square miles by state for a 45-year period.

Atmospheric Science Online

The Atmosphere 11e website uses the resources and flexibility of the Internet to aid in your study of the topics in this chapter. Written and developed by meteorology instructors, this site will help improve your understanding of meteorology. Visit **www.mygeoscience.com** in order to:

- **Review** key chapter concepts

- **Read** with links to the eBook and to chapter-specific web resources
- **Visualize** and comprehend challenging topics using learning activities in *GEODe: Atmosphere*
- **Test yourself** with online quizzes

Hurricanes

From Chapter 11 of *The Atmosphere: An Introduction to Meteorology*, Eleventh Edition, Frederick K. Lutgens, Edward J. Tarbuck, Dennis Tasa. Copyright © 2010 by Pearson Education, Inc. Published by Pearson Prentice Hall. All rights reserved.

Tropical Storms Boris (right) and Christina (left) appeared together in the eastern Pacific several hundred kilometers off the coast of Mexico on June 28, 2008. The two spiral storms took westerly tracks away from land. Tropical storms have sustained winds of 61–119 kilometers per hour and are the stage that precedes hurricanes. It is during the tropical storm phase that a name is given. (NASA)

The whirling tropical cyclones that occasionally have wind speeds exceeding 300 kilometers (185 miles) per hour are known in the United States as **hurricanes**—the greatest storms on Earth. Hurricanes are among the most destructive of natural disasters. When a hurricane reaches land, it is capable of annihilating low-lying coastal areas and killing thousands of people.

Fortunately, when Hurricane Ike made landfall along the Texas coast near Galveston on September 13, 2008, loss of life was relatively small. Because forecasts were accurate and warnings were timely, tens of thousands were safely evacuated from the most vulnerable areas before the storm arrived. Nevertheless, damages to the coastal zone and inland areas were substantial and costly (Figure 1).

On the positive side, hurricanes provide essential rainfall over many areas they cross. Consequently, a resort owner along the Florida coast may dread the coming of hurricane season, whereas a farmer in Japan may welcome its arrival.

The vast majority of hurricane-related deaths and damage are caused by relatively infrequent yet powerful storms. Table 1 lists the deadliest hurricanes to strike the United States between 1900 and 2008. The storm that pounded an unsuspecting Galveston, Texas, in 1900 was not just the deadliest U.S. hurricane ever, but the deadliest natural disaster *of any kind* to affect the United States. Of course, the deadliest and most costly storm in recent memory occurred in August 2005, when Hurricane Katrina devastated the Gulf Coast of Louisiana, Mississippi, and Alabama.* Although hundreds of thousands fled before the storm made landfall, thousands of others were caught by the storm. In addition to the human suffering and tragic loss of life that were left in the wake of Hurricane Katrina, the financial losses caused by the storm are practically incalculable. Up until August 2005, the $25 billion in damages associated with Hurricane Andrew in 1992 represented the costliest natural disaster in U.S. history. This figure was exceeded many times over when Katrina's economic impact was

calculated. Although imprecise, some suggest that the final accounting could exceed $100 billion.

The devastating hurricane season of 2005 came on the heels of an extraordinary 2004 season. Storms claimed more than 3100 lives (mostly in Haiti), and property losses in the United States topped $44 billion. The most notable storms were hurricanes Charley, Frances, Ivan, and Jeanne, all of which struck the state of Florida in August and September. Three of the storm tracks (Charley, Frances, and Jeanne) intersected in central Florida, whereas Hurricane Ivan struck the state's panhandle as it made landfall along the gulf Coast (Figure 2). The Bahamas and many Caribbean islands were also hit hard. Each hurricane season, storms like those just described remind us of our vulnerability to these great forces of nature.

Profile of A Hurricane

Most of us view the weather in the tropics with favor. Places like Hawaii and the islands of the Caribbean are known for their lack of significant day-to-day variations. Warm breezes,

*Many images of this storm can be seen in Box 3 "Atmospheric Hazard: Examining Hurricane Katrina from Space."

TABLE 1	The 10 Deadliest Hurricanes to Strike the U.S. Mainland 1900–2008			
Rank	Hurricane	Year	Category	Deaths
1.	Texas (Galveston)	1900	4	8000*
2.	SE Florida (Lake Okeechobee)	1928	4	2500–3000
3.	Katrina	2005	4	1833
4.	Audrey	1957	4	At least 416
5.	Florida Keys	1935	5	408
6.	Florida (Miami)/Mississippi/Alabama/Florida (Pensacola)	1926	4	372
7.	Louisiana (Grande Isle)	1909	4	350
8.	Florida Keys/South Texas	1919	4	287
9. (tie)	Louisiana (New Orleans)	1915	4	275
9. (tie)	Texas (Galveston)	1915	4	275

Source: National Weather Service/National Hurricane Center NOAA Technical Memorandum NWS TPC-5.
*This number may actually have been as high as 10,000–12,000.

FIGURE 1　Crystal Beach, Texas, on September 16, 2008, three days after Hurricane Ike came ashore. At landfall the storm had sustained winds of 165 kilometers (105 miles) per hour. The extraordinary storm surge caused much of the damage pictured here. (Photo by Earl Nottingham/ Associated Press)

steady temperatures, and rains that come as heavy but brief tropical showers are expected. It is ironic that these relatively tranquil regions sometimes produce the most violent storms on Earth.

Most hurricanes form between the latitudes of 5° and 20° over all the tropical oceans except the South Atlantic and the eastern South Pacific (Figure 3). The North Pacific has the greatest number of storms, averaging 20 per year. Fortunately for those living in the coastal regions of the southern and eastern United States, fewer than five hurricanes, on the average, develop each year in the warm sector of the North Atlantic.

These intense tropical storms are known in various parts of the world by different names. In the western Pacific, they are called *typhoons,* and in the Indian Ocean, including the Bay of Bengal and Arabian Sea, they are simply called *cyclones.* In the following discussion, these storms will be referred to as hurricanes. The term *hurricane* is derived from Huracan, a Carib god of evil.

Although many tropical disturbances develop each year, only a few reach hurricane status. By international agreement a hurricane has sustained wind speeds of at least 119 kilometers (74 miles) per hour and a rotary circulation.* Mature hurricanes average about 600 kilometers (375 miles) across,

---

Sustained winds are defined as the wind averaged over a one-minute interval.

although they can range in diameter from 100 kilometers (60 miles) up to about 1500 kilometers (930 miles). From the outer edge of the hurricane to the center, the barometric pressure has sometimes dropped 60 millibars, from 1010 to 950 millibars. The lowest pressures ever recorded in the Western Hemisphere are associated with these storms.

A steep pressure gradient like that shown in Figure 4 generates the rapid, inward spiraling winds of a hurricane. As the air moves closer to the center of the storm, its velocity increases. This acceleration is explained by the law of conservation of angular momentum (Box 1).

As the inward rush of warm, moist surface air approaches the core of the storm, it turns upward and ascends in a ring of cumulonimbus towers (Figure 5a). This doughnut-shaped wall of intense convective activity surrounding the center of the storm is called the **eye wall**. It is here that the greatest wind speeds and heaviest rainfall occur. Surrounding the eye wall are curved bands of clouds that trail away in spiral fashion. Near the top of the hurricane the airflow is outward, carrying the rising air away from the storm center, thereby providing room for more inward flow at the surface.

At the very center of the storm is the **eye** of the hurricane. This well-known feature is a zone where precipitation ceases and winds subside. The graph in Figure 5(b) shows changes in wind speed and air pressure as Cyclone Monty came

FIGURE 2 Tracks of the four major hurricanes to hit Florida in 2004. Hurricanes Charley, Frances, and Jeanne intersected over Polk County, Florida (see inset). Ivan made landfall near Mobile, Alabama, but greatly affected Florida's western panhandle. Each solid line shows the path of a storm when it had hurricane status. The dashed portion of each line traces the storm's path before and after hurricane stage. (After National Hurricane Center)

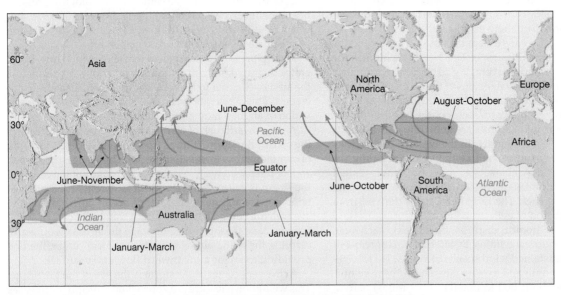

FIGURE 3 This world map shows the regions where most hurricanes form as well as their principal months of occurrence and the most common tracks they follow. Hurricanes do not develop within about 5° of the equator because the Coriolis force is too weak. Because warm surface ocean temperatures are necessary for hurricane formation, they seldom form poleward of 20° latitude nor over the cool waters of the South Atlantic and the eastern South Pacific.

Thursday, September 5, 1996

Friday, September 6, 1996

FIGURE 4 Weather maps showing Hurricane Fran at 7 AM, EST, on two successive days, September 5 and 6, 1996. On September 5, winds exceeded 190 kph. As the storm moved inland, heavy rains caused flash floods, killed 30 people, and caused more than $3 billion in damages. The station information plotted off the Gulf and Atlantic coasts is from data buoys, which are remote floating instrument packages.

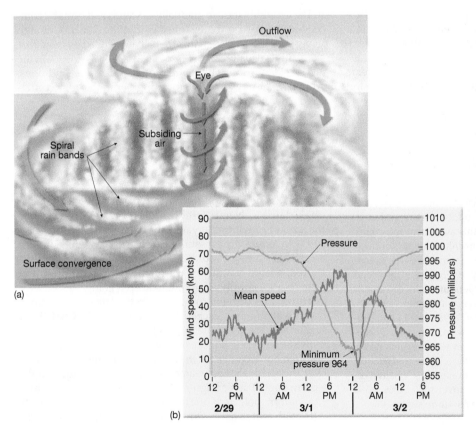

FIGURE 5 (a) Cross section of a hurricane. Note that the vertical dimension is greatly exaggerated. The eye, the zone of relative calm at the center of the storm, is a distinctive hurricane feature. Sinking air in the eye warms by compression. Surrounding the eye is the eye wall, the zone where winds and rain are most intense. Tropical moisture spiraling inward creates rain bands that pinwheel around the storm center. Outflow of air at the top of the hurricane is important because it prevents the convergent flow at lower levels from "filling in" the storm. (After NOAA) (b) Measurements of surface pressure and wind speed during the passage of Cyclone Monty at Mardie Station in Western Australia between February 29 and March 2, 2004. The strongest winds are associated with the eye wall, and the weakest winds and lowest pressure are found in the eye. In this part of the world the term *cyclone* is used instead of hurricane. (Data from World Meteorological Organization)

BOX 1 ▶ THE CONSERVATION OF ANGULAR MOMENTUM

Why do winds blowing around a storm move faster near the center and more slowly near the edge? To understand this phenomenon, we must examine the *law of conservation of angular momentum*. This law states that the product of the velocity of an object around a center of rotation (axis) and the distance of the object from the axis is constant.

Picture an object on the end of a string being swung in a circle. If the string is pulled inward, the distance of the object from the axis of rotation decreases and the speed of the spinning object increases. The change in radius of the rotating mass is balanced by a change in its rotational speed.

Another common example of the conservation of angular momentum occurs when a figure skater starts whirling on the ice with both arms extended (Figure A). Her arms are traveling in a circular path about an axis (her body). When the skater pulls her arms inward, she decreases the radius of the circular path of her arms. As a result,

her arms go faster and the rest of her body must follow, thereby increasing her rate of spinning.

In a similar manner, when a parcel of air moves toward the center of a storm, the product of its distance and velocity must remain unchanged. Therefore, as air moves inward from the outer edge, its rotational velocity must increase.

Let us apply the law of conservation of angular momentum to the horizontal movement of air in a hypothetical hurricane. Assume that air with a velocity of 5 kilometers per hour begins 500 kilometers from the center of the storm. By the time it reaches a point 100 kilometers from the center, it will have a velocity of 25 kilometers per hour (assuming there is no friction). If this same parcel of air were to continue to advance toward the storm's center until its radius was just 10 kilometers, it would be traveling at 250 kilometers per hour. Friction reduces these values somewhat.

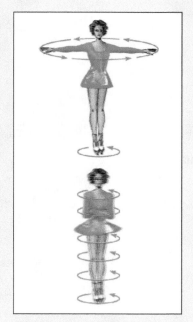

FIGURE A When the skater's arms are extended, she spins slowly. When her arms are pulled in, she spins much faster.

ashore at Mardie Station in Western Australia between February 29 and March 2, 2004. The very steep pressure gradient and strong winds associated with the eye wall are evident, as is the relative calm of the eye.

The eye offers a brief but deceptive break from the extreme weather in the enormous curving wall clouds that surround

it. The air within the eye gradually descends and heats by compression, making it the warmest part of the storm. Although many people believe that the eye is characterized by clear blue skies, this is usually not the case because the subsidence in the eye is seldom strong enough to produce cloudless conditions. Although the sky appears much brighter in this region, scattered clouds at various levels are common.

Students Sometimes Ask . . .

Why do hurricanes hit the Gulf and Atlantic coasts but not the Pacific Coast?

There are two main reasons. One is that after hurricanes form in the subtropics, they tend to move toward the west or northwest. In the Atlantic and Gulf of Mexico, this movement sometimes brings storms into the vicinity of the mainland. In the northeast Pacific, however, a west or northwest track moves hurricanes farther offshore, away from the coast (see Figure 3). The second factor is the difference in water temperatures between America's coasts. Along the Gulf and Atlantic, water temperatures in summer and fall are warm (more than 27°C or 80°F) and provide the needed heat and moisture to sustain hurricanes. By contrast, along the U.S. West Coast, ocean temperatures rarely exceed the low 20s Celsius (70s Fahrenheit). These cool temperatures are not sufficient to sustain a hurricane. Thus, when an occasional northeast Pacific hurricane moves toward the West Coast, the cool waters quickly reduce the storm's strength.

Hurricane Formation and Decay

A hurricane is a heat engine that is fueled by the latent heat liberated when huge quantities of water vapor condense. The amount of energy produced by a typical hurricane in just a single day is truly immense. The release of latent heat warms the air and provides buoyancy for its upward flight. The result is to reduce the pressure near the surface, which in turn encourages a more rapid inflow of air. To get this engine started, a large quantity of warm, moist air is required, and a continuous supply is needed to keep it going.

Hurricanes develop most often in the late summer when ocean waters have reached temperatures of 27°C (80°F) or higher and are thus able to provide the necessary heat and moisture to the air (Figure 6). This ocean-water temperature requirement accounts for the fact that hurricanes do not form over the relatively cool waters of the South Atlantic and the eastern South Pacific (Figure 7). For the same reason, few hurricanes form poleward of 20 degrees of latitude (see Figure 3). Although water temperatures are sufficiently high, hurri-

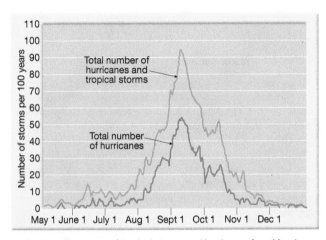

FIGURE 6 Frequency of tropical storms and hurricanes from May 1 through December 31 in the Atlantic Basin. The graph shows the number of storms to be expected over a span of 100 years. The period from late August through October is clearly the most active. (After National Hurricane Center/NOAA)

canes do not form within 5 degrees of the equator, because the Coriolis force is too weak to initiate the necessary rotary motion.

Hurricane Formation

Many tropical storms achieve hurricane status in the western parts of oceans, but their origins often lie far to the east. In such locations, disorganized arrays of clouds and

FIGURE 7 Since the beginning of the satellite era in the mid-1960s, no hurricane had ever been observed in the South Atlantic—that is, until March 2004. On the morning of March 28, 2004, a Category 1 hurricane, with winds between 121–129 kilometers (75–80 miles) per hour, struck the east coast of Brazil. (For an explanation of hurricane categories, see Table 2.) Although there was minimal loss of life, coastal property damage approached $330 million. The clouds show the clockwise spiral associated with Southern Hemisphere storms. (NASA image)

thunderstorms, called **tropical disturbances,** sometimes develop and exhibit weak pressure gradients and little or no rotation. Most of the time these zones of convective activity die out. However, occasionally tropical disturbances grow larger and develop a strong cyclonic rotation.

Several different situations can trigger tropical disturbances. They are sometimes initiated by the powerful convergence and lifting associated with the intertropical convergence zone (ITCZ). Others form when a trough from the middle latitudes intrudes into the tropics. Tropical disturbances that produce many of the strongest hurricanes that enter the western North Atlantic and threaten North America often begin as large undulations or ripples in the trade winds known as **easterly waves,** so named because they gradually move from east to west.

Figure 8 illustrates an easterly wave. The lines on this simple map are not isobars. Rather, they are *streamlines*, lines drawn parallel to the wind direction used to depict surface airflow. When middle-latitude weather is analyzed, isobars are usually drawn on the weather map. By contrast, in the tropics the differences in sea-level pressure are quite small, so isobars are not always useful. Streamlines are helpful because they show where surface winds converge and diverge.

To the east of the wave axis the streamlines move poleward and get progressively closer together, indicating that the surface flow is convergent. Convergence, of course, encourages air to rise and form clouds. Therefore, the tropical disturbance is located on the east side of the wave. To the west of the wave axis, surface flow diverges as it turns toward the equator. Consequently, clear skies are the rule here.

Easterly waves frequently originate as disturbances in Africa. As these storms head westward with the prevailing

FIGURE 8 Easterly wave in the subtropical Atlantic. Streamlines show low-level airflow. To the east of the wave axis, winds converge as they move slightly poleward. To the west of the axis, flow diverges as it turns toward the equator. Tropical disturbances are associated with the convergent flow of the easterly wave. Easterly waves extend for 2000 to 3000 kilometers (1200 to 1800 miles) and move from east to west with the trade winds at rates between 15 and 35 kilometers (10 and 20 miles) per hour. At this rate, it takes an imbedded tropical disturbance a week or 10 days to move across the North Atlantic.

trade winds, they encounter the cold Canary Current. If the disturbance survives the trip across the cold stabilizing waters of the current, it is rejuvenated by the heat and moisture of the warmer water of the mid-Atlantic. From this point on, a small percentage may develop into more intense and organized systems, some of which may reach hurricane status.

Even when conditions seem to be right for hurricane formation, many tropical disturbances do not strengthen. One circumstance that may inhibit further development is a temperature inversion called the *trade wind inversion*. It forms in association with the subsidence that occurs in the region influenced by the subtropical high.* A strong inversion diminishes air's ability to rise and thus inhibits the development of strong thunderstorms. Another factor that works against the strengthening of tropical disturbances is strong upper-level winds. When present, a strong flow aloft disperses the latent heat released from cloud tops, heat that is essential for continued growth and development.

What happens on those occasions when conditions favor hurricane development? As latent heat is released from the clusters of thunderstorms that make up the tropical disturbance, areas within the disturbance get warmer. As a consequence, air density lowers and surface pressure drops, creating a region of weak low pressure and cyclonic circulation. As pressure drops at the storm center, the pressure gradient steepens. In response, surface wind speeds increase and bring additional supplies of moisture to nurture storm growth. The water vapor condenses, releasing latent heat, and the heated air rises. Adiabatic cooling of rising air triggers more condensation and the release of more latent heat, which causes a further increase in buoyancy. And so it goes.

Meanwhile, higher pressure develops at the top of the developing tropical depression. This causes air to flow outward (diverge) from the top of the storm. Without this outward flow up top, the inflow at lower levels would soon raise surface pressures and thwart further storm development.

Although many tropical disturbances occur each year, only a few develop into full-fledged hurricanes. Recall that tropical cyclones are called hurricanes only when their winds reach 119 kilometers (74 miles) per hour. By international agreement, lesser tropical cyclones are given different names based on the strength of their winds. When a cyclone's strongest winds do not exceed 61 kilometers (37 miles) per hour, it is called a **tropical depression.** When sustained winds are between 61 and 119 kilometers (37 and 74 miles) per hour, the cyclone is termed a **tropical storm.** It is during this phase that a name is given (Andrew, Fran, Opal, etc.). Should the tropical storm become a hurricane, the name remains the

*In the troposphere, a temperature inversion exists when temperatures in a layer of air increase with an increase in altitude rather than decrease with height, which is usually the case.

Students Sometimes Ask . . .

When is hurricane season?

Hurricane season is different in different parts of the world. People in the United States are usually most interested in Atlantic storms. The Atlantic hurricane season officially extends from June through November. More than 97 percent of tropical activity in that region occurs during this six-month span. The "heart" of the season is August through October (see Figure 6). During these three months, 87 percent of the minor hurricane (category 1 and 2) days and 96 percent of the major hurricane (category 3, 4, and 5) days occur. Peak activity is in early to mid-September.

same (Box 2). Each year between 80 and 100 tropical storms develop around the world. Of them, usually half or more eventually reach hurricane status.

Hurricane Decay

Hurricanes diminish in intensity whenever they (1) move over ocean waters that cannot supply warm, moist tropical air, (2) move onto land, or (3) reach a location where the large-scale flow aloft is unfavorable. Richard Anthes describes the possible fate of hurricanes in the first category as follows:

> Many hurricanes approaching the North American or Asian continents from the southeast are turned toward the northeast, away from the continents, by the steering effect of an upper-level trough. This recurvature carries the storms toward higher latitudes where the ocean temperatures are cooler and an encounter with cool, dry polar air masses is more likely. Often the tropical cyclone and a polar front interact, with cold air entering the tropical cyclone from the west. As the release of latent heat is diminished, the upper-level divergence weakens, mean temperatures in the core fall and the surface pressure rises.*

Whenever a hurricane moves onto land, it loses its punch rapidly. For example, in Figure 4 notice how the isobars show a much weaker pressure gradient on September 6 after Hurricane Fran moved ashore than on September 5 when it was over the ocean. The most important reason for this rapid demise is the fact that the storm's source of warm, moist air is cut off. When an adequate supply of water vapor does not exist, condensation and the release of latent heat must diminish.

In addition, the increased surface roughness over land results in a rapid reduction in surface wind speeds. This factor causes the winds to move more directly into the center of the low, thus helping to eliminate the large pressure differences.

*Tropical Cyclones: Their Evolution, Structure, and Effects, Meteorological Monographs, Vol. 19, no. 41 (1982), p. 61. Boston: American Meteorological Society.

BOX 2 ▶ NAMING TROPICAL STORMS AND HURRICANES

Tropical storms are named to provide ease of communication between forecasters and the general public regarding forecasts, watches, and warnings. Tropical storms and hurricanes can last a week or longer, and two or more storms can be occurring in the same region at the same time. Thus, names can reduce the confusion about what storm is being described.

During World War II, tropical storms were informally assigned women's names (perhaps after wives and girlfriends) by U.S. Army Corps and Navy meteorologists who were monitoring storms over the Pacific. From 1950 to 1952, tropical storms in the North Atlantic were identified by the phonetic alphabet—Able, Baker, Charlie, and so forth. In 1953 the U.S. Weather Bureau (now the National Weather Service) switched to women's names.

The practice of using feminine names continued until 1978, when a list containing both male and female names was adopted for tropical cyclones in the eastern Pacific. In the same year a proposal that both male and female names be adopted for Atlantic hurricanes, beginning with the 1979 season, was accepted by the World Meteorological Organization (WMO).

The WMO has created six lists of names for tropical storms over ocean areas. The names used for Atlantic, Gulf of Mexico, and Caribbean hurricanes are shown in Table A. The names are ordered alphabetically and do not contain names that begin with the letters Q, U, X, Y, and Z because of the scarcity of names beginning with those letters. When a tropical depression reaches tropical storm status, it is assigned the next unused name on the list. At the beginning of the next hurricane season, names from the next list are selected even though many names may not have been used the previous season.

The names for Atlantic storms are used over again at the end of each six-year cycle unless a hurricane was particularly noteworthy. This is to avoid confusion when storms are discussed in future years. For example, five names from the list for the extraordinary 2005 Atlantic hurricane season were retired—Dennis, Katrina, Rita, Stan, and Wilma. They were replaced by Don, Katia, Rina, Sean, and Whitney on the list for the year 2011.

TABLE A   Tropical Storm and Hurricane Names for the Atlantic, Gulf of Mexico, and Caribbean Sea*

2008	2009	2010	2011	2012	2013
Arthur	Ana	Alex	Arlene	Alberto	Andrea
Bertha	Bill	Bonnie	Bret	Beryl	Barry
Cristobal	Claudette	Colin	Cindy	Chris	Chantal
Dolly	Danny	Danielle	Don	Debby	Dorian
Edouard	Erika	Earl	Emily	Ernesto	Erin
Fay	Fred	Fiona	Franklin	Florence	Fernand
Gustav	Grace	Gaston	Gert	Gordon	Gabrielle
Hanna	Henri	Hermine	Harvey	Helene	Humberto
Ike	Ida	Igor	Irene	Isaac	Ingrid
Josephine	Joaquin	Julia	Jose	Joyce	Jerry
Kyle	Kate	Karl	Katia	Kirk	Karen
Laura	Larry	Lisa	Lee	Leslie	Lorenzo
Marco	Mindy	Matthew	Maria	Michael	Melissa
Nana	Nicholas	Nicole	Nate	Nadine	Nestor
Omar	Odette	Otto	Ophelia	Oscar	Olga
Paloma	Peter	Paula	Philippe	Patty	Pablo
Rene	Rose	Richard	Rina	Rafael	Rebekah
Sally	Sam	Shary	Sean	Sandy	Sebastien
Teddy	Teresa	Tomas	Tammy	Tony	Tanya
Vicky	Victor	Virginie	Vince	Valerie	Van
Wilfred	Wanda	Walter	Whitney	William	Wendy

*If the entire alphabetical list of names for a given year is exhausted, the naming system moves on to using letters of the Greek alphabet (alpha, beta, gamma, etc). This issue never arose until the record-breaking 2005 hurricane season when Tropical Storm Alpha, Hurricane Beta, tropical storms Gamma and Delta, Hurricane Epsilon, and Tropical Storm Zeta occurred after Hurricane Wilma.

Hurricane Destruction

Although the amount of damage caused by a hurricane depends on several factors, including the size and population density of the area affected and the nearshore bottom configuration, certainly the most significant factor is the strength of the storm itself.

Saffir–Simpson Scale

Based on the study of past storms, the **Saffir–Simpson scale** was established to rank the relative intensities of hurricanes (Table 2). Predictions of hurricane severity and damage are usually expressed in terms of this scale. When a tropical storm becomes a hurricane, the National Weather Service assigns it

TABLE 2 Saffir-Simpson Hurricane Scale

Scale Number (category)	Central Pressure (millibars)	Winds (km/hr)	Storm Surge (meters)	Damage
1	≥980	119–153	1.2–1.5	Minimal
2	965–979	154–177	1.6–2.4	Moderate
3	945–964	178–209	2.5–3.6	Extensive
4	920–944	210–250	3.7–5.4	Extreme
5	<920	>250	>5.4	Catastrophic

Students Sometimes Ask . . .

Are larger hurricanes stronger than smaller hurricanes?

Not necessarily. Actually, there is very little correlation between intensity (either measured by maximum sustained winds or by central pressure) and size (either measured by the radius of gale force winds or the radius of the outer closed isobar). Hurricane Andrew is a good example of a very intense storm (recently reevaluated and upgraded to the most intense category 5 level) that was also relatively small (gale-force winds extended only 150 kilometers/90 miles from the eye). Research has shown that changes in intensity and size are essentially independent of one another.

a scale (category) number. Category assignments are based on observed conditions at a particular stage in the life of a hurricane and are viewed as estimates of the amount of damage a storm would cause if it were to make landfall without changing size or strength. As conditions change, the category of a storm is reevaluated so that public-safety officials can be kept informed. By using the Saffir–Simpson scale, the disaster potential of a hurricane can be monitored and appropriate precautions can be planned and implemented.

A rating of 5 on the scale represents the worst storm possible, and a 1 is least severe. Storms that fall into Category 5 are rare. Only three storms this powerful are known to have hit the continental United States: Andrew struck Florida in 1992, Camille pounded Mississippi in 1969, and a Labor Day hurricane struck the Florida Keys in 1935. Damage caused by hurricanes can be divided into three classes: (1) storm surge, (2) wind damage, and (3) inland freshwater flooding.

Storm Surge

Without question, the most devastating damage in the coastal zone is caused by the storm surge. It not only accounts for a large share of coastal property losses but is also responsible for 90 percent of all hurricane-caused deaths. A **storm surge** is a dome of water 65 to 80 kilometers (40 to 50 miles) wide that sweeps across the coast near the point where the eye makes landfall. If all wave activity were smoothed out, the storm surge would be the height of the water above normal tide level (Figure 9). In addition, tremendous wave activity is superimposed on the surge. We can easily imagine the dam-

age that this surge of water could inflict on low-lying coastal areas (Figure 10). The worst surges occur in places like the Gulf of Mexico, where the continental shelf is very shallow and gently sloping (see Figure 1). In addition, local features such as bays and rivers can cause the surge height to double and increase in speed.

In the delta region of Bangladesh, for example, most of the land is less than 2 meters (6.5 feet) above sea level. When a storm surge superimposed on normal high tide inundated that area on November 13, 1970, the official death toll was 200,000; unofficial estimates ran to 500,000. It was one of the worst natural disasters of modern times. In May 1991 a similar event again struck Bangladesh. This time the storm took the lives of at least 143,000 people and devastated coastal towns in its path.

A common misconception about the cause of hurricane storm surges is that the very low pressure at the center of the storm acts as a partial vacuum that allows the ocean to rise up in response. However, this effect is relatively insignificant. The most important factor responsible for the development

FIGURE 9 Superimposed upon high tide, a storm surge can devastate a coastal area. The worst storm surges occur in coastal areas where there is a very shallow and gently sloping continental shelf extending from the beach. The Gulf Coast is such a place.

(a)

(b)

FIGURE 10 Storm surge damage along the Mississippi coast caused by Hurricane Katrina. At some locations the surge exceeded 7.5 meters (25 feet). (a) This concrete slab was all that remained of an apartment house in Biloxi. (Photo by Barry Williams/Getty Images) (b) Houses and vehicles litter the railway near Pass Christian. (AP Photo/Phil Coale)

of a storm surge is the piling up of ocean water by strong onshore winds. Gradually the hurricane's winds push water toward the shore, causing sea level to elevate while also churning up violent wave activity.

As a hurricane advances toward the coast in the Northern Hemisphere, storm surge is always most intense on the right side of the eye where winds are blowing *toward* the shore. In addition, on this side of the storm the forward movement of the hurricane also contributes to the storm surge. In Figure 11, assume a hurricane with peak winds of 175 kilometers (109 miles) per hour is moving toward the shore at 50 kilometers (31 miles) per hour. In this case, the net wind speed on the right side of the advancing storm is 225 kilometers (140 miles) per hour. On the left side, the hurricane's winds are blowing opposite the direction of storm movement, so the net winds are *away* from the coast at 125 kilometers (78 miles) per hour. Along the shore facing the left side of the oncoming hurricane, the water level may actually decrease as the storm makes landfall.

Wind Damage

Destruction caused by wind is perhaps the most obvious of the classes of hurricane damage. Debris such as signs, roofing materials, and small items left outside become dangerous flying missiles in hurricanes. For some structures, the force of the wind is sufficient to cause total ruin. Mobile homes are particularly vulnerable. High-rise buildings are also susceptible to hurricane-force winds. Upper floors are most vulnerable because wind speeds usually increase with height. Recent research suggests that people should stay below the tenth floor but remain above any floors at risk for flooding. In regions with good building codes, wind damage is usually not as catastrophic as storm-surge damage. However, hurricane-force winds affect a much larger area than storm surge and can cause huge economic losses. For example, in 1992 it was largely the winds associated with Hurricane Andrew that produced more than $25 billion of damage in southern Florida and Louisiana.

Hurricanes sometimes produce tornadoes that contribute to the storm's destructive power. Studies have shown that more than half of the hurricanes that make landfall produce at least one tornado. In 2004 the number of tornadoes associated with tropical storms and hurricanes was extraordinary. Tropical Storm Bonnie and five landfalling hurricanes—Charley, Frances, Gaston, Ivan, and Jeanne—produced nearly 300 tornadoes that affected the southeast and mid-Atlantic states (Table 3). Hurricane Frances produced the most tornadoes ever reported from one hurricane. The large number of hurricane-generated tornadoes in 2004 helped make this a record-breaking year—surpassing the previous record by more than 300.*

---

*K. L. Gleason, et al. "U.S. Tornado Records" in Bulletin of the American Meteorological Society, Vol. 86, No. 6, June 2005, p. 551.

FIGURE 11 Winds associated with a Northern Hemisphere hurricane that is advancing toward the coast. This hypothetical storm, with peak winds of 175 kilometers (109 miles) per hour, is moving toward the coast at 50 kilometers (31 miles) per hour. On the right side of the advancing storm, the 175-kilometer-per-hour winds are in the same direction as the movement of the storm (50 kilometers per hour). Therefore, the *net* wind speed on the right side of the storm is 225 kilometers (140 miles) per hour. On the left side, the hurricane's winds are blowing opposite the direction of storm movement, so the *net* winds of 125 kilometers (78 miles) per hour are away from the coast. Storm surge will be greatest along that part of the coast hit by the right side of the advancing hurricane.

Heavy Rains and Inland Flooding

The torrential rains that accompany most hurricanes represent a third significant threat—flooding. The 2004 hurricane season was very deadly, with a loss of life that exceeded 3000 people. Nearly all of the deaths occurred in Haiti as a result of flash floods and mudflows caused by the heavy rains associated with then Tropical Storm Jeanne.

Hurricane Agnes (1972) illustrates that even modest storms can have devasting results. Although it was only a category 1 storm on the Saffir–Simpson scale, it was one of the costliest hurricanes of the twentieth century, creating more than $2 billion in damage and taking 122 lives. The greatest destruction was attributed to flooding in the northeastern portion of the United States, especially in Pennsylvania, where record

TABLE 3	Number of Tornadoes Spawned by Hurricanes and Tropical Storms in the United States, 2004	
Tropical Storm Bonnie		30
Hurricane Charley		25
Hurricane Frances		117
Hurricane Ivan		104
Hurricane Jeanne		16

rainfalls occurred. Harrisburg received nearly 32 centimeters (12.5 inches) in 24 hours and western Schuykill County measured more than 48 centimeters (19 inches) during the same span. Agnes's rains were not as devastating elsewhere. Prior to reaching Pennsylvania, the storm caused some flooding in Georgia, but most farmers welcomed the rain because dry conditions had been plaguing them earlier. In fact, the value of the rains to crops in the region far exceeded the losses caused by flooding.

Another well-known example is Hurricane Camille (1969). Although this storm is best known for its exceptional storm surge and the devastation it brought to coastal areas, the greatest number of deaths associated with this storm occurred in the Blue Ridge Mountains of Virginia two days after Camille's landfall. Here many places received more than 25 centimeters (10 inches) of rain and severe flooding took more than 150 lives.

To summarize, extensive damage and loss of life in the coastal zone can result from storm surge, strong winds, and torrential rains. When loss of life occurs, it is commonly caused by the storm surge, which can devastate entire barrier islands or zones within a few blocks of the coast. Although wind damage is usually not as catastrophic as the storm surge, it affects a much larger area. Where building codes are inadequate, economic losses can be especially severe. Because hurricanes weaken as they move inland, most wind damage occurs within 200 kilometers (125 miles) of the coast. Far from the coast, a weakening storm can produce extensive flooding long after the winds have diminished below hurricane levels. Sometimes the damage from inland flooding exceeds storm-surge destruction.

Cyclone Nargis—May 2008

All three classes of hurricane damage came into play in May 2008 when the first cyclone of the season in the northern Indian Ocean struck Myanmar (also called Burma). Figure 12a is a satellite image showing the storm over the Bay of Bengal and Figure 12b shows the path of the storm and the rainfall it produced. The storm devastated much of the fertile Irrawaddy Delta. According to a United Nations estimate, more than 90 percent of the dwellings were destroyed in the hardest hit areas. In addition, death and destruction also occurred in portions of Yangon, the nation's largest city. In all, about 30,000 square kilometers (nearly 11,600 square miles) were significantly affected—an area that was home to nearly one-quarter of Myanmar's 57 million people.

A storm surge of 3.6 meters (12 feet) and torrential rains (up to 600 mm [2feet] in some places) brought widespread flooding. Powerful winds contributed to the destruction. The

FIGURE 12 (a) Cyclone Nargis hovers over the Bay of Bengal on May 1, 2008. At one point Nargis was a Category 4 storm on the Saffir–Simpson scale with winds of 210 kilometers (131 miles) per hour. Although it lost strength before coming ashore on May 2 as a Category 2 storm, Nargis still had powerful winds and torrential rains. The storm surge and heavy rains combined to cause extensive floods on the low-lying Irrawaddy Delta, killing thousands and displacing as many as 2 million people. (NASA) (b) This image shows rainfall accumulations along the path of Cyclone Nargis between April 27 and May 4, 2008, using data from the Tropical Rainfall Measuring Mission satellite. Rainfall totals range up to 600 millimeters (nearly 2 feet). The path of the storm and its strength on various dates are shown as colored line segments. (NASA)

fact that this low-lying region was densely populated and had a high proportion of poorly constructed dwellings exacerbated the situation. The government reported the official death toll to be nearly 85,000 with an additional 54,000 people unaccounted for. It is likely that more than 100,000 perished. It was the deadliest cyclone to hit Asia since 1991 when 143,000 people died in Bangladesh. Many who survived the storm lost their homes—an estimated 2 million people were displaced.

Estimating the Intensity of a Hurricane

The Saffir–Simpson Hurricane Scale appears to be a straightforward tool. However, the accurate observations needed to correctly portray hurricane intensity at the surface are sometimes difficult to obtain. Estimating hurricane intensity is difficult because direct surface observations in the eye wall are rarely available. Therefore, winds in this most intense part of the storm have to be estimated. One of the best ways to estimate surface intensity is to adjust the wind speeds measured by reconnaissance aircraft.

Winds aloft are stronger than winds at the surface. Therefore, the adjustment of values determined for winds aloft to values expected at the surface involves *reducing* the measurements made aloft. However, until the late 1990s, determining the proper adjustment factor was problematic because surface observations in the eye wall were too limited to establish a broadly accepted relationship between flight-level and surface winds. In the early 1990s the reduction factors commonly used ranged from 75 to 80 percent (that is, surface wind speeds were assumed to be between 75 and 80 percent of the speed at 3000 meters/10,000 feet). Some scientists and engineers even maintained that surface winds were as low as 65 percent of flight-level winds.

Beginning in 1997 a new instrument, called a *Global Positioning System (GPS) dropwindsonde*, came into use (sometimes just called a *dropsonde*). After being released from the aircraft, this package of instruments, slowed by a small parachute, drifts downward through the storm (Figure 13). During the descent, it continuously transmits data on temperature, humidity, air pressure, wind speed, and wind direction. The development of this technology provided, for the first time, a way to accurately measure the strongest winds in a hurricane from flight level all the way to the surface.

Over a span of several years, hundreds of GPS dropwindsondes were released in hurricanes. The data accumulated from these trials showed that the speed of surface winds in the eye wall averaged about 90 percent of the flight-level winds, not 75 to 80 percent. Based on this new understanding, the National Hurricane Center now uses the 90 percent figure to estimate a hurricane's maximum surface winds from flight-level observations. This means that the winds in some storms in the historical record were underestimated.

For example, in 1992 the surface winds in Hurricane Andrew were estimated to be 233 kilometers (145 miles) per hour. This was 75 to 80 percent of the value measured at 3000 meters by the reconnaissance aircraft. When scientists at the National Hurricane Center reevaluated the storm using the 90 percent value, they concluded that the maximum-sustained surface winds had been 266 kilometers (165 miles) per hour—33 kilometers (20 miles) per hour faster than the original 1992 estimate. Consequently, in August 2002 the intensity of Hurricane Andrew was officially changed from Category 4 to Category 5. The upgrade makes Hurricane Andrew only the third Category 5 storm on record to strike the continental United States. (The other two were the "Florida Keys 1935 Hurricane" and Hurricane Camille in 1969.)

FIGURE 13 The Global Positioning System (GPS) dropwindsonde is frequently just called a dropsonde. This cylindrical instrument package is roughly 7 cm (2.75 in) in diameter, 40 cm (16 in) long, and weighs about 0.4 kg (0.86 lb). The instrument package is released from the aircraft and falls through the storm via a parachute, making and transmitting measurements of temperature, pressure, winds, and humidity every half-second. (After NASA)

Detecting, Tracking, and Monitoring Hurricanes

By examining Figures 2 and 3, you can see some of the typical paths followed by tropical storms and hurricanes in the North Atlantic. What determines these tracks? The storms

Students Sometimes Ask . . .

If a Category 1 hurricane produces only "minimal" damage, are tropical storms any sort of significant weather threat?

The answer is a definite yes. Although tropical storm winds are less intense than winds in a hurricane, rainfall amounts can be prodigious. For example, in June 2001, Tropical Storm Allison dropped 93.95 centimeters (36.99 inches) of rain at the Port of Houston, Texas. At Houston Intercontinental Airport, 41.83 centimeters (16.47 inches) fell on June 10, 2001—roughly four times the normal June precipitation—making it the wettest June on record. The previous wettest June occurred in 1989 when 41.35 centimeters (16.28 inches) of rain fell, mostly from another tropical storm, named Allison! The 2001 storm caused nearly $5 billion in damages in the Houston area, making it the costliest tropical storm in U.S. history. In addition, the flooding, lightning, and tornadoes associated with Allison claimed more than 40 lives.

can be thought of as being steered by the surrounding environmental flow throughout the depth of the troposphere. The movement of hurricanes has been likened to a leaf being carried along by the currents in a stream, except that for a hurricane the "stream" has no set boundaries.

In the latitude zone equatorward of about 25° north, tropical storms and hurricanes commonly move to the west with a slight poleward component. (Look at the storm tracks in Figure 2 and in Figure G, for example.) This occurs because of the semipermanent cell of high pressure (called the *Bermuda High*) that is positioned poleward of the storm. On the equatorward side of this high-pressure center, easterly winds prevail that guide the storms westward. If this high-pressure center is weak in the western Atlantic, the storm often turns northward. On the poleward side of the Bermuda High, westerly winds prevail that steer the storm back toward the east. Often it is difficult to determine whether the storm will curve back out to sea or whether it will continue straight ahead and make landfall.

A location only a few hundred kilometers from a hurricane—just a day's striking distance away—may experience clear skies and virtually no wind. Before the age of weather satellites, such a situation made it difficult to warn people of impending storms. The worst natural disaster in U.S. history came as a result of a hurricane that struck an unprepared Galveston, Texas, on September 8, 1900. The strength of the storm, together with the lack of adequate warning, caught the population by surprise and cost the lives of 6000 people in the city and at least 2000 more elsewhere (Figure 14).*

In the United States, early warning systems have greatly reduced the number of deaths caused by hurricanes. At the same time, however, an astronomical rise has occurred in the amount of property damage. The primary reason for this latter trend is the rapid population growth and accompanying development in coastal areas.

The Role of Satellites

Today many different tools provide data that are used to detect and track hurricanes. This information is used to develop forecasts and to issue watches and warnings. The greatest single advancement in tools used for observing tropical cyclones has been the development of meteorological satellites.

Because the tropical and subtropical regions that spawn hurricanes consist of enormous areas of open ocean, conventional observations are limited. The needs for meteorological data from these vast regions are now met primarily by satellites. Even before a storm begins to develop cyclonic flow and the spiraling cloud bands so typical of a hurricane, it can be detected and monitored by satellites.

The advent of weather satellites has largely solved the problem of detecting tropical storms and has significantly

---

*For a fascinating account of the Galveston storm, read *Isaac's Storm* by Erik Larson, New York: Crown Publishers, 1999.

(a)

(b)

FIGURE 14   Aftermath of the Galveston hurricane of 1900. Entire blocks were swept clean, while mountains of debris accumulated around the few remaining buildings. (AP Photos)

improved monitoring (see Box 3). However, satellites are remote sensors, and it is not unusual for wind-speed estimates to be off by tens of kilometers per hour and for storm-position estimates to have errors. It is still not possible to precisely determine detailed structural characteristics. A combination of observing systems is necessary to provide the data needed for accurate forecasts and warnings.

Aircraft Reconnaissance

Aircraft reconnaissance represents a second important source of information about hurricanes. Ever since the first experimental flights into hurricanes were made in the 1940s, the aircraft and the instruments employed have become quite sophisticated (Figure 15). When a hurricane is within range, specially instrumented aircraft can fly directly into a threatening storm and accurately measure details of its position and current state of development. Data transmission can be made directly from an aircraft in the midst of a storm to the forecast center where input from many sources is collected and analyzed.

Measurements from reconnaissance aircraft are limited because they cannot be taken until the hurricane is relatively close to shore. Moreover, measurements are not taken continuously or throughout the storm. Rather, the aircraft provides sample "snapshots" of small parts of the hurricane. Nevertheless, the data collected are critical in analyzing the current characteristics needed to forecast the future behavior of the storm.

A major contribution to hurricane forecasting and warning programs has been an improved understanding of the structure and characteristics of these storms. Although advance-

ments in remote sensing from satellites have been made, measurements from reconnaissance aircraft will be required for the foreseeable future to maintain the present level of accuracy for forecasts of potentially dangerous tropical storms.

FIGURE 15   In the Atlantic basin, most operational hurricane reconnaissance is carried out by the U.S. Air Force Weather Reconnaissance Squadron based at Keesler AFB, Mississippi, where they maintain a fleet of 10 C-130 aircraft. Pilots fly through the hurricane to its center, measuring all basic weather elements as well as providing an accurate location of the eye. The National Oceanic and Atmospheric Administration also flies aircraft into hurricanes mostly on research missions to aid scientists in better understanding these storms. The P3 Orion aircraft shown here and state-of-the-art high-altitude jet aircraft complement the reconnaissance function of the U.S. Air Force. (Photo by Rafael Perez/Reuters/Reuters Limited)

BOX 3 ▶ ATMOSPHERIC HAZARD

Examining Hurricane Katrina from Space

Satellites allow us to track the formation, movement, and growth of hurricanes. In addition, their specialized instruments provide data that can be transformed into images that allow scientists to analyze the internal structure and workings of these huge storms. The images and captions in this box provide a unique perspective of Hurricane Katrina, the most devastating storm to strike the United States in more than a century.

Figures B, C, and D, are from NASA's *Terra* satellite and are relatively "traditional" images that show Katrina in different stages of its development and dissipation.

Figure E is a color-enhanced infrared (IR) image from the *GOES-East* satellite. Cold cloud tops, and thus the most intense storms, are easily seen in this image of Hurricane Katrina taken a few hours before landfall. Color-enhanced imagery is a method meteorologists use to aid them with satellite interpretation. The colors enable them to easily and quickly see features that are of special interest.

FIGURE B The storm on August 25, 2005 at 12:30 PM EDT. At this time Katrina is a Category 1 hurricane. Because the storm was advancing slowly, just 10 kilometers (6 miles) per hour, heavy rainfall totals were expected. See Figure G to view the rainfall pattern. (NASA image)

FIGURE C This image shows Katrina at 1 PM EDT on Sunday, August 28, 2005, as a massive storm covering much of the Gulf of Mexico. After passing over Florida as a Category 1 hurricane, Katrina entered the Gulf and intensified into a Category 5 storm with winds of 257 kilometers (160 miles) per hour and even stronger gusts. Air pressure at the center of the storm measured 902 millibars. When Katrina came ashore the next day, it was a slightly less vigorous Category 4 storm. (NASA image)

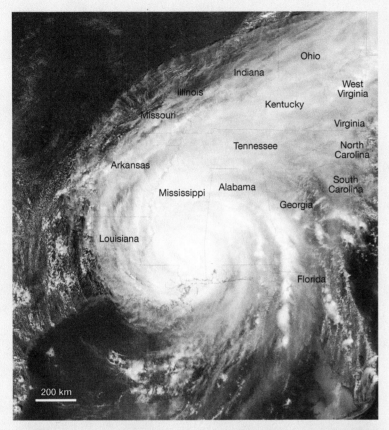

Ohio
Indiana
Illinois
West Virginia
Missouri
Kentucky
Virginia
Tennessee
North Carolina
Arkansas
South Carolina
Mississippi
Alabama
Georgia
Louisiana
Florida

200 km

FIGURE D In this image from 3:15 PM EDT on August 29, 2005, Katrina measured about 1260 kilometers (780 miles) across and is sprawled over all or part of 16 states. After coming ashore as a Category 4 storm, it was still a Category 1 after being over land for nearly 8 hours. (NASA image)

GOES-EAST AVNCOLOR IR CH. 4 - AUG 29 05 02:45 UTC

FIGURE E Color-enhanced infrared image from the *GOES-East* satellite of Hurricane Katrina several hours before making landfall on August 29, 2005. The most intense activity is associated with red and orange. (NOAA)

BOX 3 ▶ ATMOSPHERIC HAZARD (Continued)

FIGURE F NASA's *QuikSCAT* satellite was the source of data for this image of Hurricane Katrina on August 28, 2005. The image depicts relative wind speeds. The strongest winds, shown in shades of purple, circle a well-defined eye. The barbs show wind direction. (NASA image)

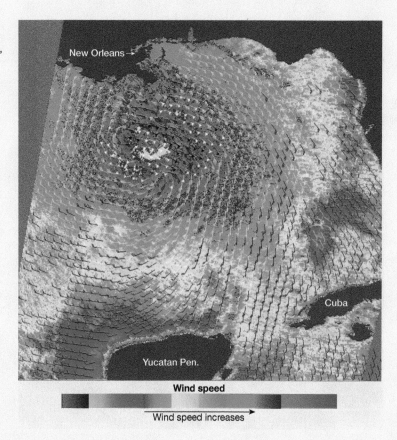

Wind speed

Wind speed increases

Figure F from NASA's *QuikSCAT* satellite is very different in appearance. It provides a detailed look at Katrina's surface winds shortly before the storm made landfall. This image depicts relative wind speeds rather than actual values. The satellite sends out high-frequency radio waves, some of which bounce off the ocean and return to the satellite. Rough, storm-tossed seas create a strong signal, whereas a smooth surface returns a weaker signal. In order to match wind speeds with the type of signal that returns to the satellite, scientists compare wind measurements taken by data buoys in the ocean to the strength of the signal received by the satellite. When there are too few data buoy measurements

to compare to the satellite data, exact wind speeds cannot be determined. Instead, the image provides a clear picture of relative wind speeds.

Figure G shows the *Multi-satellite Precipitation Analysis (MPA)* of the storm. This image, which also depicts the track of the storm, shows the overall pattern of rainfall. It was constructed from data collected over several days by the *Tropical Rainfall Measuring Mission (TRMM)* satellite and other satellites.

Figure H provides yet another satellite perspective. Seeing the pattern of rainfall in different parts of a hurricane is very useful to forecasters because it helps determine the strength of the storm. Scientists

have developed a way to process data from the Precipitation Radar (PR) aboard the TRMM satellite within 3 hours and display it in 3-D. Every time the satellite passes over a named tropical cyclone anywhere in the world, the PR instrument sends data to create a 3-D "snapshot" of the storm. Such an image provides information on how heavy the rain is falling in different parts of the storm, such as the eye wall versus the outer rain bands. It also gives a 3-D look at the cloud heights and "hot towers" inside the storm. Higher hot towers in the eye wall usually indicate a strengthening storm.

Storm track and rainfall values for Hurricane Katrina for the period August 23 to 31, 2005. Rainfall amounts are derived from satellite data. The highest totals (dark red) exceeded 30 centimeters (12 inches) over northwestern Cuba and the Florida Keys. Amounts over southern Florida (green to yellow) were 12–20 centimeters (5–8 inches). Rainfall along the Mississippi coast (yellow to orange) was between 15–23 centimeters (6–9 inches). After coming ashore, Katrina moved through Mississippi, western Tennessee, and Kentucky and into Ohio. Because the storm moved rapidly, rainfall totals (green to blue) in these areas were generally less than 13 centimeters (5 inches). (NASA image)

FIGURE H   Image from the Tropical Rainfall Measuring Mission (TRMM) satellite of Hurricane Katrina early on August 28, 2005. This cutaway view of the inner portion of the storm shows cloud height on one side and rainfall rates on the other. The tall rain columns provide a clue that the storm is strengthening. Two isolated towers (in red) are visible: one in an outer rain band and the other in the eye wall. The eye wall tower rises 16 kilometers (10 miles) above the ocean surface and is associated with an area of intense rainfall. Towers this tall near the core are often an indication the storm is intensifying. Katrina grew from a Category 3 to a Category 4 soon after this image was received. (NASA image)

FIGURE 16 Doppler radar image of Hurricane Charley over Charlotte Harbor, Florida, just after landfall on August 13, 2004. The range of coastal radar is about 320 kilometers (200 miles). (NOAA/National Weather Service)

Radar and Data Buoys

Radar is a third basic tool in the observation and study of hurricanes (Figure 16). When a hurricane nears the coast, it is monitored by land-based Doppler weather radar. These radars provide detailed information on hurricane wind fields, rainfall intensity, and storm movement. As a result, local NWS offices are able to provide short-term warnings for floods, tornadoes, and high winds for specific areas. Sophisticated mathematical calculations provide forecasters with important information derived from the radar data, such as estimates of rainfall amounts. A limitation of radar is that it cannot "see" farther than about 320 kilometers (200 miles) from the coast, and hurricane watches and warnings must be issued long before the storm comes into range.

VORTRAC—A New Hurricane Tracking Technique Rapidly intensifying storms can catch vulnerable coastal areas by surprise. In 2007 Hurricane Humberto struck near Port Arthur, Texas, after unexpectedly strengthening from a tropical depression to a hurricane in less than 19 hours. In 2004, parts of the southwest coast of Florida were caught off guard when Hurricane Charley's top winds increased from 175 to more than 230

kilometers (110 to 145 miles) per hour in just six hours as the storm approached land.

A new technique known as VORTRAC (*Vortex Objective Radar Tracking and Circulation*) was successfully tested in 2007 and put into use in 2008. It is intended to help improve short-term hurricane warnings by capturing sudden intensity changes in potentially dangerous hurricanes during the critical time when storms are nearing land.

Prior to the development of VORTRAC the only way to monitor the intensity of a landfalling hurricane was to rely on aircraft that dropped instrument packages (drop-windsondes) into the storm. This can only be done every hour or two, which means that a sudden drop in barometric pressure and the accompanying increase in winds could be difficult to detect in a timely manner.

VORTRAC uses that portion of the Doppler radar network that is along the Gulf and Atlantic coastline from Maine to Texas. Each unit can measure winds blowing toward or away from it, but until VORTRAC was established, no single radar could estimate a hurricane's rotational winds and central pressure. The technique uses a series of mathematical formulas that combine data from a single radar with knowledge of Atlantic hurricane structure in order to map the storm's rotational winds. VORTRAC also infers the barometric pressure in the eye of the hurricane, which is a reliable indicator of its strength (Figure 17). Each radar can

FIGURE 17 This graph displays the results of a test of the VORTRAC system on Hurricane Humberto, a storm that intensified rapidly as it approached the Texas/Louisiana coast on September 13, 2007. The VORTRAC estimates agreed closely with Humberto's actual central pressure as measured by reconnaissance planes just before landfall. VORTRAC also captured the storm's rapid intensification, indicating that the pressure began falling quickly near the end of a four-hour span when no aircraft data were available. (After M. Bell/National Center for Atmospheric Research)

sample conditions out to a distance of 190 kilometers (120 miles) and forecasters using VORTRAC can update the status of a storm about every six minutes.

Data Buoys Data buoys represent a fourth method of gathering data for the study of hurricanes. These remote, floating instrument packages are positioned in fixed locations all along the Gulf Coast and Atlantic Coast of the United States. When you examine the weather maps in Figure 4, you can see data buoy information plotted at several offshore stations. Ever since the early 1970s, data provided by these units have become a dependable and routine part of daily weather analysis as well as an important element of the hurricane warning system. The buoys represent the only means of making nearly continuous direct measurements of surface conditions over ocean areas.

Hurricane Watches and Warnings

Using input from the observational tools that were just described in conjunction with sophisticated computer models, meteorologists attempt to forecast the movements and intensity of a hurricane. The goal is to issue timely watches and warnings.

A **hurricane watch** is an announcement aimed at specific coastal areas that a hurricane poses a possible threat, generally within 36 hours. By contrast, a **hurricane warning** is issued when sustained winds of 119 kilometers (74 miles) per hour or higher are expected within a specified coastal area in 24 hours or less. A hurricane warning can remain in effect when dangerously high water or a combination of dangerously high water and exceptionally high waves continue, even though winds may be less than hurricane force.

Two factors are especially important in the watch-and-warning decision process. First, adequate lead time must be provided to protect life and, to a lesser degree, property.

Second, forecasters must attempt to keep overwarning at a minimum. This, however, can be a difficult task. Clearly, the decision to issue a warning represents a delicate balance between the need to protect the public on the one hand and the desire to minimize the degree of overwarning on the other.

Hurricane Forecasting*

Hurricane forecasts are a basic part of any warning program. There are several aspects that can be part of such a forecast. We certainly want to know where the storm is headed. The predicted path of a storm is called the *track forecast*. Of course, there is also interest in knowing the intensity (strength of the winds), probable rainfall amounts, and the likely size of the storm surge.

Track Forecasts The track forecast is probably the most basic information because accurate prediction of other storm characteristics is of little value if there is significant uncertainty as to where the storm is going. Accurate track forecasts are important because they can lead to timely evacuations from the surge zone where the greatest number of deaths usually occur. Fortunately, track forecasts have been steadily improving. During the span 2001–2005, forecast errors were roughly half of what they were in 1990. During the very active 2004 and 2005 Atlantic hurricane seasons, 12 to 72 hour track forecast accuracy was at or near record levels. Consequently, the length of official track forecasts issued by the National Hurricane Center was extended from three days to five days (Figure 18). Current five-day track forecasts are now as accurate as three-day forecasts were 15 years ago. Much of the progress is due to improved computer models and to a dramatic increase in the quantity of satellite data from over the oceans.

*Based on "Hurricane Forecasting in the United States: An Information Statement of the AMS," in *Bulletin of the American Meteorological Society*, Vol. 88, No. 6, June 2007, pp. 950–53.

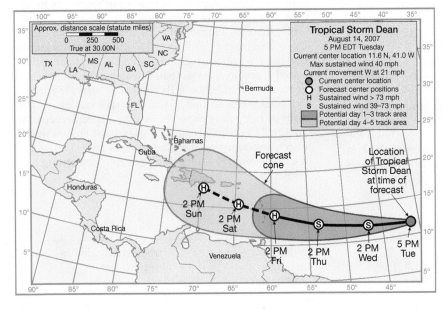

FIGURE 18 Five-day track forecast for Tropical Storm Dean issued at 5 PM EDT, Tuesday, August 14, 2007. When a hurricane track forecast is issued by the National Hurricane Center, it is termed a *forecast cone*. The cone represents the probable track of the center of the storm and is formed by enclosing the area swept out by a set of circles along the forecast track (at 12, 24, 36 hours, etc.). The size of each circle gets larger with time. Based on statistics from 2003–2007 the entire track of an Atlantic tropical cyclone can be expected to remain entirely within the cone roughly 60 to 70 percent of the time. (National Weather Service/National Hurricane Center)

Despite improvements in accuracy, forecast uncertainty still requires that hurricane warnings be issued for relatively large coastal areas. During the span 2000–2005, the average length of coastline under a hurricane warning in the United States was 510 kilometers (316 miles). This represents a significant improvement over the preceding decade when the average was 730 kilometers (452 miles). Nevertheless, only about one-quarter of an average warning area experiences hurricane conditions.

Forecasting Other Characteristics In contrast to the improvements in track forecasts, errors in forecasts of hurricane intensity (wind speeds) have not changed significantly in 30 years. Accurate predictions of rainfall as hurricanes make landfall also remains elusive. However, accurate predictions of impending storm surge are possible when good information regarding the storm's track and surface wind structure are known and reliable data regarding coastal and offshore (underwater) topography are available.

Chapter Summary

- The vast majority of hurricane deaths and damage are caused by relatively infrequent, yet powerful storms.
- Most hurricanes form between the latitudes of 5° and 20° over all tropical oceans except the South Atlantic and eastern South Pacific. The North Pacific has the greatest number of storms, averaging 20 per year. In the western Pacific, hurricanes are called *typhoons*, and in the Indian Ocean, they are referred to as *cyclones*.
- A steep pressure gradient generates the rapid, inward spiraling winds of a hurricane. As the warm, moist air approaches the core of the storm, it turns upward and ascends in a ring of cumulonimbus towers and forms a doughnut-shaped wall called the *eye wall*. At the very center of the storm, called the *eye*, the air gradually descends, precipitation ceases, and winds subside.
- A hurricane is a heat engine fueled by the latent heat liberated when huge quantities of water vapor condense. They develop most often in late summer when ocean waters have reached temperatures of 27°C (80°F) or higher and are thus able to provide the necessary heat and moisture to the air. The initial stage of a tropical storm's life cycle, called a *tropical disturbance*, is a disorganized array of clouds that exhibits a weak pressure gradient and little or no rotation. Tropical disturbances that produce many of the strongest hurricanes that enter the western North Atlantic and threaten North America often begin as large undulations or ripples in the trade winds known as *easterly waves*.
- Each year, only a few tropical disturbances develop into full-fledged hurricanes (storms that require minimum wind speeds of 119 kilometers per hour to be so-termed.) When a cyclone's strongest winds do not exceed 61 kilometers per hour, it is called a *tropical depression*. When winds are between 61 and 119 kilometers per hour, the cyclone is termed a *tropical storm*. Hurricanes diminish in intensity whenever they (1) move over cool ocean waters that cannot supply warm, moist tropical air, (2) move onto land, or (3) reach a location where large-scale flow aloft is unfavorable.
- Although damages caused by a hurricane depend on several factors, including the size and population density of the area affected and the nearshore ocean bottom configuration, the most significant factor is the strength of the storm itself. The *Saffir–Simpson scale* ranks the relative intensities of hurricanes. A 5 on the scale represents the strongest storm possible, and a 1 is the least severe. Damage caused by hurricanes can be divided into three categories: (1) *storm surge*, which is most intense on the right side of the eye where winds are blowing toward the shore, occurs when a dome of water sweeps across the coast near the point where the eye makes landfall, (2) *wind damage*, and (3) *inland freshwater flooding*, which is caused by torrential rains that accompany most hurricanes.
- North Atlantic hurricanes develop in the trade winds, which generally move these storms from east to west. Today, because of early warning systems that help detect and track hurricanes, the number of deaths associated with these violent storms have been greatly reduced. Because the tropical and subtropical regions that spawn hurricanes consist of enormous areas of open oceans, meteorological data from these vast regions are provided primarily by *satellites*. Other important sources of hurricane information are *aircraft reconnaissance*, *radar*, and remote, floating instrument platforms called *data buoys*. Using data from these observational tools, meteorologists can issue an announcement, called a *hurricane watch*, aimed at specific coastal areas threatened by a hurricane, generally within 36 hours. By contrast, a *hurricane warning* is issued when sustained winds of 119 kilometers per hour or higher are expected within a specified coastal area in 24 hours or less. Two important factors in the watch and warning decision process are (1) adequate lead time and (2) attempting to keep overwarning to a minimum.

Vocabulary Review

easterly wave	hurricane	Saffir–Simpson scale	tropical disturbance
eye	hurricane warning	storm surge	tropical storm
eye wall	hurricane watch	tropical depression	

Review Questions

1. Why might people in some parts of the world welcome the arrival of the hurricane season?

2. When a parcel of air approaches the center of a hurricane, how does its speed change? What law explains this change? (See Box 1.)

3. Which of these statements about the eye of a hurricane are true and which are false?
   a. It is typically the warmest part of the storm.
   b. It is usually characterized by clear, blue skies.
   c. It is in the eye that winds are strongest.

4. During what time of year do most of the hurricanes that affect North America form? Why is hurricane formation favored at this time?

5. Tropical storms that form near the equator do not acquire a rotary motion as cyclones of higher latitudes do. Why?

6. What are streamlines? How do streamlines indicate an easterly wave in the North Atlantic?

7. List two factors that inhibit the strengthening of tropical disturbances.

8. Which has the stronger winds, a tropical storm or a tropical depression?

9. Why does the intensity of a hurricane diminish rapidly when it moves onto land?

10. What is the purpose of the Saffir–Simpson scale?

11. Hurricane damage can be divided into three broad categories. Name them. Which one of the categories is responsible for the greatest percentage of hurricane-related deaths?

12. Great damage and significant loss of life can take place a day or more after a hurricane has moved ashore and weakened. When this occurs, what is the likely cause?

13. In 1992 Hurricane Andrew was classified as a Category 4 storm. Ten years later its intensity was officially changed to Category 5 by the National Hurricane Center. Why was the storm reclassified?

14. List four tools that provide data used to track hurricanes and develop forecasts.

15. A hurricane has slower wind speeds than a tornado, but a hurricane inflicts more total damage. How might this be explained?

16. Briefly describe the potential problem of "overwarning" that is related to the issuing of hurricane warnings.

17. Although observational tools and hurricane forecasts continue to improve, the potential for loss of life due to hurricanes is growing. Explain this apparent contradiction.

Problems

The questions that follow refer to the weather maps of Hurricane Fran in Figure 4.

1. On which of the two days were Fran's wind speeds probably highest? How were you able to determine this?

2. a. How far did the center of the hurricane move during the 24-hour period represented by these maps?
   b. At what rate did the storm move during this 24-hour span? Express your answers in miles per hour.

3. A middle-latitude cyclone has an east–west diameter of approximately 1200 miles (when the 1008-mb isobar is used to define the outer boundary of the low). Measure the diameter (north–south) of Hurricane Fran on September 5. Use the 1008-mb isobar to represent the outer edge of the storm. How does this figure compare to the middle-latitude cyclone?

4. Determine the pressure gradient for Hurricane Fran on September 5. Measure from the 1008-mb isobar at Charleston, to the center of the storm. Express your answer in millibars per 100 miles.

Atmospheric Science Online

The Atmosphere 11e website uses the resources and flexibility of the Internet to aid in your study of the topics in this chapter. Written and developed by meteorology instructors, this site will help improve your understanding of meteorology. Visit **www.mygeoscience.com** in order to:

- **Review** key chapter concepts

- **Read** with links to the eBook and to chapter-specific web resources

- **Visualize** and comprehend challenging topics using learning activities in *GEODe: Atmosphere*

- **Test yourself** with online quizzes

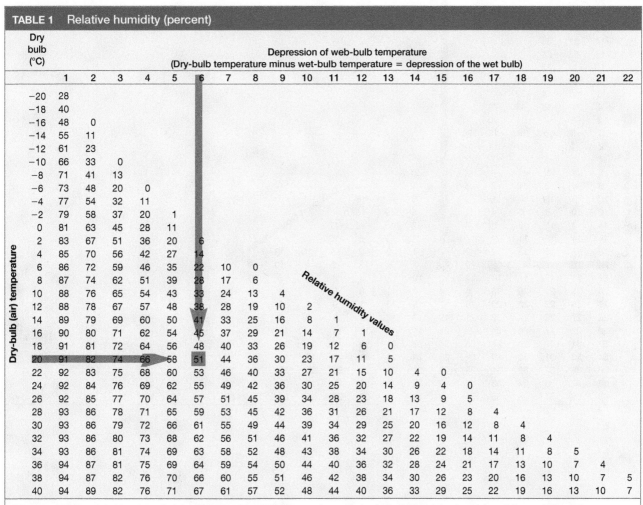

TABLE 1   Relative humidity (percent)

Dry bulb (°C)	Depression of web-bulb temperature (Dry-bulb temperature minus wet-bulb temperature = depression of the wet bulb)																					
	1	2	3	4	5	6	7	8	9	10	11	12	13	14	15	16	17	18	19	20	21	22
−20	28																					
−18	40																					
−16	48	0																				
−14	55	11																				
−12	61	23																				
−10	66	33	0																			
−8	71	41	13																			
−6	73	48	20	0																		
−4	77	54	32	11																		
−2	79	58	37	20	1																	
0	81	63	45	28	11																	
2	83	67	51	36	20	6																
4	85	70	56	42	27	14																
6	86	72	59	46	35	22	10	0														
8	87	74	62	51	39	28	17	6														
10	88	76	65	54	43	33	24	13	4													
12	88	78	67	57	48	38	28	19	10	2												
14	89	79	69	60	50	41	33	25	16	8	1											
16	90	80	71	62	54	45	37	29	21	14	7	1										
18	91	81	72	64	56	48	40	33	26	19	12	6	0									
20	91	82	74	66	58	51	44	36	30	23	17	11	5									
22	92	83	75	68	60	53	46	40	33	27	21	15	10	4	0							
24	92	84	76	69	62	55	49	42	36	30	25	20	14	9	4	0						
26	92	85	77	70	64	57	51	45	39	34	28	23	18	13	9	5						
28	93	86	78	71	65	59	53	45	42	36	31	26	21	17	12	8	4					
30	93	86	79	72	66	61	55	49	44	39	34	29	25	20	16	12	8	4				
32	93	86	80	73	68	62	56	51	46	41	36	32	27	22	19	14	11	8	4			
34	93	86	81	74	69	63	58	52	48	43	38	34	30	26	22	18	14	11	8	5		
36	94	87	81	75	69	64	59	54	50	44	40	36	32	28	24	21	17	13	10	7	4	
38	94	87	82	76	70	66	60	55	51	46	42	38	34	30	26	23	20	16	13	10	7	5
40	94	89	82	76	71	67	61	57	52	48	44	40	36	33	29	25	22	19	16	13	10	7

*To determine the relative humidity, find the air (dry-bulb) temperature on the vertical axis (far left) and the depression of the wet bulb on the horizontal axis (top). Where the two meet, the relative humidity is found. For example, when the dry-bulb temperature is 20°C and a wet-bulb temperature is 14°C, then the depression of the wet-bulb is 6°C (20°C − 14°C). From Table 1, the relative humidity is 51 percent and from Table 2, the dew point is 10°C.

From Appendix C of *The Atmosphere: An Introduction to Meteorology*, Eleventh Edition, Frederick K. Lutgens, Edward J. Tarbuck, Dennis Tasa. Copyright © 2010 by Pearson Education, Inc. Published by Pearson Prentice Hall. All rights reserved.

TABLE C–2 Dew-point temperature (°C)*

Dry bulb (°C)

Dry-bulb temperature minus wet-bulb temperature = depression of the wet bulb

Dry-bulb (air) temperature

Dry bulb	1	2	3	4	5	6	7	8	9	10	11	12	13	14	15	16	17	18	19	20	21	22
−20	−33																					
−18	−28																					
−16	−24																					
−14	−21	−36																				
−12	−18	−28																				
−10	−14	−22																				
−8	−12	−18	−29																			
−6	−10	−14	−22																			
−4	−7	−12	−17	−29																		
−2	−5	−8	−13	−20																		
0	−3	−6	−9	−15	−24																	
2	−1	−3	−6	−11	−17																	
4	1	−1	−4	−7	−11	−19																
6	4	1	−1	−4	−7	−13	−21															
8	6	3	1	−2	−5	−9	−14															
10	8	6	4	1	−2	−5	−9	−14	−18													
12	10	8	6	4	1	−2	−5	−9	−16													
14	12	11	9	6	4	1	−2	−5	−10	−17												
16	14	13	11	9	7	4	1	−1	−6	−10	−17											
18	16	15	13	11	9	7	4	2	−2	−5	−10	−19										
20	19	17	15	14	12	10	7	4	2	−2	−5	−10	−19									
22	21	19	17	16	14	12	10	8	5	3	−1	−5	−10	−19								
24	23	21	20	18	16	14	12	10	8	6	2	−1	−5	−10	−18							
26	25	23	22	20	18	17	15	13	11	9	6	3	0	−4	−9	−18						
28	27	25	24	22	21	19	17	16	14	11	9	7	4	1	−3	−9	−16					
30	29	27	26	24	23	21	19	18	16	14	12	10	8	5	1	−2	−8	−15				
32	31	29	28	27	25	24	22	21	19	17	15	13	11	8	5	2	−2	−7	−14			
34	33	31	30	29	27	26	24	23	21	20	18	16	14	12	9	6	3	−1	−5	−12	−29	
36	35	33	32	31	29	28	27	25	24	22	20	19	17	15	13	10	7	4	0	−4	−10	
38	37	35	34	33	32	30	29	28	26	25	23	21	19	17	15	13	11	8	5	1	−3	−9
40	39	37	36	35	34	32	31	30	28	27	25	24	22	20	18	16	14	12	9	6	2	−2

Dew point temperatures

Index

359